HISTORIC VITRY-LE-FRANÇOIS, ON THE MARNE

PREFATORY NOTE

LITERARY projects may be put in two classes. Some
are like steamers that go in a regulated course
direct to their destinations, while others tack here
and there like sailing ships, governed by a zigzag progress.

The subject of bridges belongs to this latter class.
For five-and-twenty years I have tried to order it into
a methodised hobby. As well try to teach a hive of
honey-bees never to visit certain flowers in a garden, and

v

never to fly beyond certain pathways and hedges. Yet
a writer cannot help rebelling when his chosen theme
declines to play in the game of authorship, and deviates
from many careful plans which are made for its benefit.
Every chapter in this book has been rewritten eight or
ten times, yet my sailing ship has not become an Atlantic
liner.

My wish for a long time was to show the evolution
of bridges in about seven hundred photographic illustrations, with eight lines of text under each print; and in
preparation for this work I collected materials, and received
invaluable help from other pontists, particularly from
Mr. Frank Brangwyn, Mr. H. T. Crofton, Mr. C. S. Sargisson, Mr. Edgar Wigram, the Rev. O. M. Jackson, and
the Church Missionary Society. Pontist after pontist sent
me notes, photographs, sketches; and then Frank Brangwyn
suggested that we should work in collaboration. Here
was luck indeed! His pictures and drawings would be
the book of art; and the rambling subject, if it passed
over mere technique into the human drama, ought to interest
the general reader who does generally read. For bridges
have represented types of society, every change in their
development having been brought about by changes in
social needs.

One thing more than any other is attractive to a pontist:
it is the varied strife that bridges and roads have circulated,
not only in military campaigns, but in the thronged
struggle for existence—the one incessant war in the affairs

of men. A routine of idle sentiment prattles about an illusion named Peace, yet strife everywhere remains the historian of life, every effort to do and to live claiming a battle-toll of killed and wounded and maimed. Even sleep, the nearest kinswoman of peace, is united to the law of battle by dreams that torture. A pontist, then, when studying the strife that roads and bridges have distributed, must clear from his mind the fanciful ideas that pacifism has invented; he is an adventurer in history, not an idler in a world of visions. To-day, above all, he is called upon to see the truth, because Europe, driven by the rival motive-powers of hostile ideals, has passed from industrial strikes and contests into other phases of necessary warfare. Once more differing civilizations will have their worth tested to the full on stricken fields; and once more roads and bridges will dominate the military tactics and strategy.

This great War broke out when my last chapter was nearly finished, and its early events illustrate and confirm the main arguments which I have tried to make as clear as possible, so that no person may think of bridges apart from their historic service to mankind. During many centuries, for example, all strategical bridges were fortified; then a gradual decline began, and it culminated in the defenceless modern bridge that sappers blow up in a few minutes. Bridge-builders everywhere have much good sense to regain from the science of national defence, a very difficult science to-day, for many of its methods are being rendered obsolete by airships and aeroplanes. So a book on historic bridges could not be published at a time more opportune than the present moment.

*   *   *   *   *   *   *

Several collectors have lent pictures, and their kind aid is acknowledged in the table of illustrations.

W. S. S.

November 11th, 1914.

CONTENTS

CHAPTER THE FIRST

CHAPTER THE SECOND

CHAPTER THE THIRD

CHAPTER THE FOURTH

CHAPTER THE FIFTH

CONTENTS

APPENDIX I

APPENDIX II

LIST OF COLOUR PLATES

xi

LIST OF BLACK AND WHITE ILLUSTRATIONS

A BOOK OF BRIDGES

BRIDGE OF BOATS AT COLOGNE

CHAPTER THE FIRST

ON THE STUDY OF BRIDGES AND ROADS

B

I

GENERAL VIEWS

A PONTIST, or devotee of bridges, ought to be envied and pitied; his work is marvellously attractive, but he cannot hope to learn even a twentieth part of the discoverable history which has circulated along highways. Indeed, the history goes back to a time that preceded the descent of man; a primal time when every bridge was made by Nature, and when footpaths and tracks were the runs and spoor of wild animals, many of which were huge enough to plough their way through deep jungles and to trample wide paths through the undergrowth of virgin forests. There were eight or nine sorts of natural bridge (p. 113), and they were all useful to the many quadrupeds that travelled far in their search for prey and forage. To meditate on this fact is to visualise many probable happenings; vivid pictures live before the mind's eye, and in one I see how a full-grown Iguanodon, after gorging all day in a ravaged weald, was overcome by the sleep of glutted hunger as he tried to cross a big fallen tree that bridged a chasm near by his lair under a rock-shelter; and a flock of little bright birds came and settled on the seventy feet of body and tail, just to pick up vermin. Why not? Life everywhere has fed on lives; something has died, and

3

suffered a resurrection of vitality, whenever appeased hunger has renewed the health of an organism; and this picture of an edacious Iguanodon and his bird friends attracts me for two reasons: it reminds me that bridges throughout their history have circulated strife, and it represents the perpetual law of battle that rules creatively over all living creatures, like foul manure over gardens and harvest fields.

A pontist, then, must try to see clearly, under a form of visual conception, what part his subject played in the earliest war of organic life, when natural bridges aided the first animals not only to hunt over great territories, but to migrate from their first homes into lands very far away. In the second chapter we shall try to feel the inspiring pressure of events which must have acted during the descent of man on a brain remarkable for its imitative faculties. Perhaps we can get into imaginative touch with our earliest ancestors; perhaps we can find in ourselves a vestige of their aboriginal nature; and then we shall know, by a sympathy which we shall not question, how each natural bridge helped them in their wanderings, and became a model to be copied, and adapted, and improved.

Such is the beginning of our enviable studies, but their end is never reached. Not even the long days and years of Hilpa and Shalum, in Addison, where antediluvian seconds endure about as long as our trivial minutes, would be enough for a complete study of bridges and roads, viewed as inestimable servants to the commonweal of mankind. A complete study would follow their evolution through eight world-wide subjects : architecture, civil engineering, antiquarian research, the development of trade and commerce from primitive barter, social wayfaring, war and its red tragedies, the longevity of barbaric customs, usages, traditions, and the ups and downs of fortune in the slow fever called progress, whose clinical thermometer has been tribal and national enterprise, and whose gradual effects on the temperature of bodies civil have produced many withering crises fatal to civilizations.

These eight subjects are vastly intricate as well as world-wide. In scope they are infinite, if we compare their magnitude with the brief seasons of our perishable days. Let us then ask ourselves a question : How much may we expect to learn about bridges and roads, the distributive agents of all human aims and ambitions ? Suppose we live to be threescore years and ten, and suppose we work gladly for eight hours a day from the age of fifteen to that of seventy ; encouraged by perfect health, and so delighted with our work that we rescue Sunday from a sabbatarian inertia, and lose no time at all by being drudges to the holiday mania. For a pontist never need be idle ; not only has he a thousand problems to reconsider, but in all his walks and rides he is a wayfarer with his hobby. When he feels cocksure he can visit a detestable railway bridge and drink the wormwood of pessimism ; and when for a whole week he has tried in vain to follow a devious fact through all its golf-ball antics from bunker to bunker, let him go to a classic bridge such as the Puente Trajan over the Tagus at Alcántara; or let him be as a delighted pupil to Turner's Walton Bridges or to Brangwyn's magnificent vision of the Pont St. Bénezét at Avignon.

From time to time, also, after paying his rates and taxes, a pontist should recall to memory the rare great "finds" which his long research has unburied. To enjoy a "find" properly is to feel sure that one has made a gallant entry into El Dorado. Never shall I forget the elation that came to me when at the same moment I came upon two wondrous facts: first, that Nature had created lofty arched bridges, like the Rock Bridge in Virginia and the Pont d'Arc over the Ardèche* in France; next, that the earliest archways in handicraft were copied from Nature's models, and copied with a plodding mimicry, for they were built not with converging archstones, but with courses of stone laid horizontally, just as Nature in stratified rocks had put one flat layer upon another (p. 155). To discover facts of this kind is a joy that keeps the heart youthful. Study is not a friend to the Income Tax, but it puts trouble out of mind, a true Nepenthe. Even aged scientists at the Pasteur Institute grow young and merry when they isolate a virulent microbe which for a long time has baffled their curiosity.

* The Pont d'Arc at Ardèche, over the river Ardèche, has a total height of sixty-six metres. From water-level to the crown of the arch is a flight of thirty-four metres; and in a span of fifty-nine metres this great natural bridge puts a huge vault over the river. As to the shape of the arch, it is pointed in a rather waved outline, and quite possibly it suggested the pointed arch to French bridge-builders long before the introduction of "ogivale" arches from the East (p. 88).

Yes, research ought to be very popular; in its companion-ship any person of sense may learn gladly as an "old boy" from his fifteenth year to the seventieth, working daily for eight thorough hours.

How many hours in all would be given to study and thought? In fifty-five years there are twenty thousand and seventy-five days; these we multiply by eight and behold! we have been sedulously youthful for 160,600 hours. Here is a record of industry; it may be unexampled until centenarians become as frequent as M. Metchnikoff wants them to be; and yet, after all, is it a great record? Great it may be in its relation to human weakness, but it means only a trivial apprenticeship to any vocation that lures the mind with illimitable open fields. Our happy toil is nothing more than a gleaner, but it should keep us from being prigs—little students overfed on a little knowledge and too foolish to feel ignorant. What Sir Clifford Allbutt has told the public about the immaturity of modern science is true also of the study of bridges and roads; here, too, knowledge is often hollow while ignorance has a solid weight, even among men who are not content with current formulas. "In every direction we seem to travel but a very short way before we are brought to a stop; our eyes are opened to see that our path is beset with doubts, and that even our best-made knowledge comes but too soon to an end. In every chapter arises problem after problem to beckon us on to farther investigation; yet this way and that we are so baffled by darkness and ignorance that to choose one of these problems for attack, one which is likely to repay his labour, is often beyond the scope of a junior candidate."*

Not that a young man should be very humble in his choice of a problem, for it is with students as with empire makers, who would do very little if a bold indiscretion were unfruitful. Let us have faith in the sunburnt cockiness of extreme youth. When it hunts the far horizon as if mirages of self-deception were the butterflies of ambition, easy to catch and easy to preserve, it is guided by the genius of research; and certainly it has done far more for the world than will ever be done by a reasoning caution that looks too far ahead.

About five-and-twenty years ago, when I began in my leisure time to be a pontist, a good old slippered antiquary gave me some hints on what he called "a discreet fervour in the study of bridges." I was to choose an English county, perhaps Derbyshire, and for eight or nine years I was to live all day long with the bridges, getting them photographed from many points of view, and recovering bits of their stories from dusty old records and forgotten muniment chests. Then a clay-cold book in two volumes was to be written, with a frigid zeal for the accuracy of minute data, and with enough glacial footnotes on every page to strike terror into that general reader who does generally read. No thought at all was to be given to the

* "Notes on the Composition of Scientific Papers," T. Clifford Allbutt, London, 1904, p, 3.

RAILWAY BRIDGE AT ALBI IN FRANCE

public, whose vulgar mind had neglected the many antiquaries who had told the historic truth unflinchingly, with a desperate effort to be impartial, unemotional, and yet effective also, like icebergs. I told my adviser that his ideals were those of a studious millionaire. He could afford to write without heart and to be pleased with a bad circulation; could afford also to forget that old English bridges, though at times as charmingly rustic as the Robin Hood Ballads, were not great masterpieces of art, like a good many old bridges on the Continent. If I invited readers to dine with me on Brazil nuts, unaided by nut-crackers, how in the world could I expect to receive company? But argument was useless. The antiquary had two homes—himself and the past, and in both he lived as a rapt dreamer. I see him still, a lean and dusty figure, unkempt, unwashed, for he "hated immersion" like Dr. Johnson. His favourite aim—and he never realised it—was to put a spade tenderly against a human skull buried in Pliocene deposits. "I would sooner do that," he declared one evening, "than be married to all the prettiest women in England—girls, not widows, of course." Courage was not his forte—except in one pugnacious habit which he shared with most antiquaries: not only did he love facts with a zeal that was always ready to defend them, but he regarded every fact as a big truth.

The old man would say to me, for instance, "Hunt in the Middle Ages for common but shining truths about roads and bridges. Ah yes! There's the fact that many

bridges were property owners; their landed estates were
sometimes inconsiderable, to be sure, like the noble parks
of Lilliput; but each estate, whether large or small, was a
great truth in the history of bridges. And I like to remember the good folk who in their wills bequeathed money
to their favourite bridges, like Count Neville, who in 1440
left twenty pounds to 'Ulshawe Bridge,' near Middleham.
Now and then the testator was a skinflint, like John
Danby, who in 1444 left in his will a beggarly six and
eightpence to 'Warleby Bridge.' Yes, and he was rash
enough to die unrepentant. Another man, a notable merchant in his day, Roger Thornton, of Newcastle, was
clever enough to save himself from oblivion, a merchant's
destiny, by leaving a hundred marks to the Tyne Bridge in
his native town—a bridge, by the way, that needed much
renovation. But Thornton in his charity struck a hard
bargain: the hundred marks would not be paid unless the
'mair and ye comyns' released the testator from certain
actions at law! Thornton died in 1429; and to show you
that the beautiful truth which I am illustrating was not
then historically juvenile, I will mention an earlier fact
from the life of a Newcastle citizen, John Cooke by name,
who in 1379 bequeathed twenty marks to the fortified
bridge at Warkworth."

The old man gossiped quaintly about his "truths," but
when he wrote about them he was legal in profuse entangle-
ments. Then it seemed to him that truth could not be protected by too many fortifications. Had he looked upon

facts as facts, mere things which had happened and which had no future, his antiquarian knowledge would have been less arid. But he belonged to a school of pedants—the same school which either kills antiquarian magazines or enables them to live obscurely on unpaid contributions. That a man's lifework should be futile to the public, a mere cemetery where facts lie buried like fossils in a rock, is pitiful; yet antiquaries are very proud of their barren labour. Scarcely one of them understands, that a fact, however entertaining, has no value to thought unless it is a useful item in a mass of corroborative evidence; and even then it can be nothing more than a fact, a thing to illustrate the perpetual action of an absolute truth, or the increasing worth of a given hypothesis, or the general belief in a given theory. Two or three facts that confirm each other justify a guess, a random " shot," or a vague suspicion; an important collection of such facts, if it continues to grow, gives validity to a hypothesis; and when from many sources as various as they are many new facts are added year after year to the collection, until at last the cumulative evidence holds the field with the best judges, then we know that the hypothesis has been developed into a theory, the highest form of mobile knowledge in the realms of Thought. But a theory is not absolute truth, of course; it is a harbour where Knowledge rests while Thought is on the high seas, a Columbus, searching for new worlds.

From a guess to a theory; this, then, is the architecture of constructive growth that research and revision build with facts; and if we as pontists wish to think clearly and humanely, we must use facts as a means to a worthy end, as architects employ their materials. One by one facts are to us what a few slates and tiles are to a builder, but Thought collects them, and then with care and inspiration she builds with them as she builds with stones and bricks and timber. In her work, moreover, there is nothing little when she does little things admirably; but when her devotees go away from her and parade guesswork as theory and fact as truth, we should ask them whether brick-kilns are houses and stone quarries cathedrals. To-day, unhappily, most people exalt facts into truths, and very often the great word "theory" is a journalistic term for any supposition that is loose or wayward or foolish. Thus, "Mrs. Jones has a mere theory that her husband is hard at work when he remains in town after office hours."

From the life of bridges we may draw a great many conjectures, suppositions, speculations, suggestions, fancies, ideas; and here and there we find some attractive hypotheses, notably those that concern the introduction of pointed arches into French bridges, and of ribbed arches into English bridges. Are there any truths, any useful and necessary things that repeat and confirm themselves age after age? Yes. There are some technical truths that belong for all time to the mechanics of bridge building; the world can employ them for ever, and always with the same good results, if engineers and architects work competently. There is also a great social truth in the life of bridges and roads ; namely, that types of society are as old as their systems of circulation, just as women and men are as old as their arteries. So the condition of a body social can be judged accurately if we examine with care its landways and waterways. In Spain, for example, where the genius of modernity is inactive, and where fine bridges represent many dead social states, Roman, Moorish, Mediæval, and Renaissance, the past reigns over the highways, sometimes as an inspiration, as in the great and vast bridge at Ronda, but usually as a mournful historian. Even in those parts of Spain where trade endeavours to be modern, workmen have time enough to be honest craftsmen ; their metal bridges are not uncouth, and their stone bridges are charmed with hints taken from classic models. They do not " progress," for they keep far off from that spirit of trade which regards the lies of advertising as proofs of a pushful honour. From a modern standpoint, then, Spain does not live except as a dim reflexion of her long ago.

A pontist has few theories to consider, only two, indeed, and these are sisters. Let me introduce you to them.

A BROKEN WAR-BRIDGE OF THE XIII CENTURY, AT NARNI IN ITALY; REPAIRED
WITH WOOD

II

STRIFE AND HISTORIC BRIDGES

THE first theory sets thought astir on the necessity
of having landways and waterways which in all
respects are fitted to distribute the many func-
tional activities of military and civil life.   It is not enough
that a complex type of society should have many intricate
systems of circulation for its multiform traffic.   The weak-
est points in each system ought to be regarded as danger

14

zones in the strategy of national defence, so it is a duty to protect them from attack, and the protection should be as complete as the military arts can make it, age after age. Now the most vulnerable points in a system of landways are the long bridges by which roads and railways are conducted across wide chasms, and deep valleys, and perilous waterways. Yet in England, and in other countries also, neither roads nor railways are defended; indeed, modern bridges are not only unfortified, but as sensitive to bombs as elephants are to large bullets. Why has the world forgotten that a powerful nation whose bridges were cut would be like a giant whose arteries were severed? As the suffragettes burnt down Yarmouth pier, so a conspiracy of civil disorder, acting in accordance with a well-formed plan, could in a night, with a few sappers, cripple a vast railway, by blowing up the main strategic bridges. I am giving a chapter to this urgent subject, most engineers having evaded with equal zest the charm of beauty and the security of our food supplies. At a time when the nations overarm themselves for war, tradesmen and engineers have erected ugly bridges for an imagined peace; but now that the art of flying threatens civilization from overhead and from all around, like a new Satan, the public attitude to highways cannot remain lethargic. Willingly or unwillingly, we must recall and renew those principles of defensive war with the help of which bridges were safeguarded by the Romans and also in the Middle Ages. Frank Brangwyn has painted many aged fortified bridges, making a most varied selection; and in each of these historic pictures he illustrates the attitude of old times to the theory of pontine defence.

The apathy of the public has been unintelligent, but not unintelligible, because bridges and roads are so ordinary, so very trite, that we who use them every day do not think of their supreme influence on the nation's health and safety. They belong to that realm of custom where truths fall asleep in truisms and facts in platitudes. To understand a thing that seems obvious, or "inevitable," is among the problems that genius alone can solve in a complete way. Dr. Johnson believed that men and women could marry ugliness without being in the least intrepid, because custom would soon teach them not to know the difference between good looks and bad. As custom dulls our minds even in family life, where affection is most watchful, we cannot be surprised that common roads and bridges are too evident to be seen intelligently.

Very few persons love a bridge until it is gone, or until it has been put out of action by Napoleon's "whiff of gunpowder." Then a victorious army may be brought to a standstill, like Wellington's, in Spain, when the retreating French blew up an arch of the colossal Roman bridge at Alcántara, so that for some long days the unfordable Tagus might protect their rearguard. It was no easy task to repair the bridge with a netting of ropes that carried planks; and when the British army crossed the gap on this makeshift footway, Wellington knew that the Devil was not the only archfiend in human affairs.

PONT VALENTRÉ AT CAHORS IN FRANCE: THE FORTIFIED
GATES AND TOWERS. SEE ALSO THE SECOND PICTURE

Yes, believe me, it is worth while to think of the highways and byways. Try to imagine, for instance, what it has cost in suffering and in death to make fit for use all the traffic arteries and veins that nourish and sustain life in the bodies civil of the world. How long would it take to explore the myriads of rambling footpaths? Could this work be done in two hundred years by a thousand Stanleys? How many lives have been lost in making roads through forests and fens and over mountains? in the construction of railways? in the building of bridges? in the slow cutting of canals? The Suez Canal was a long campaign of stricken fields in the war of trade enterprise;* and the Panama Canal has reaped lives as quickly as minor battles reap them. If we could see in a form of visual conception all the sacrifice of life that civilizations have offered to progress on the historic landways and waterways, how terrified we should be! Even the hospitals and sick-beds of humanity have not had a more scaring pathos than that which has accompanied the more peaceable enterprises of mankind.

This reflexion brings us to the second theory that has a home in the life of bridges and roads. Other homes it has also, a vast number of them, for this theory belongs to the law of battle, the universal law of strife. In so far as the

* The earliest canal in history is the one that Necho II began in 610 B.C., to connect the Arabian Gulf with the Mediterranean Sea; and Herodotus relates that the work went on for a year and was then abandoned, after costing the lives of 120,000 men. Necho was uninspired by the spirit of industrialism which would have finished the work, while praising the beauty of peace.

lower organisms are concerned, this law seems to be as permanent as the sun ; we have no reason to suppose that its rule will ever be relaxed among birds, beasts, fishes, insects, or among other forms of life, such as competitive

A WAR-BRIDGE OF THE XIV CENTURY AT ORTHEZ IN FRANCE

trees in a wood; but mankind is an eternal mystery, and none can say into what civilization of symphonic harmony the human race may be evolved by gradual improvements in the crowded struggle for existence.   A hundred thousand years hence the competitions of human life may be like harmonious rivalries between notes in music, or like the wondrous orchestration that unites into a symphony of benign health all the communities of cells in a sound body. "All for Each, Each for All" is the social rule that Nature administers in her cellular civilizations; and she punishes with disease and death the bodies that rebel against her rule by developing harmful egotisms. Yet mankind has stereotyped a very different social rule, "Each for All, yet Each for Himself"; and what right have we to believe that this egotism, so long inherited, and continuously active, can change its nature gradually, till at last it will be as philharmonic as the cellular commonwealths forming a strong human body? At present this appears to be very improbable, but impossible we dare not call it, since every type of society is free to improve its own lot. So the law of strife in human affairs appeals to us not as a truth destined to last till doomsday, like the strife of carnivorous hunger, but as a theory which human life has not yet contradicted, but which in course of time may be tempered into a social art—a competitive harmony favourable to everybody. Yet even then, no doubt, inequalities of mind will be active in accordance with Nature's law of infinite variation.

Meanwhile, however, we have to accept history as mankind has made it. Strife has reigned everywhere; even the test of efficiency has been—not the survival of the finest natures, but—the survival of the least unfitted for a long battle against bad environments. Very often the delicate have the best characters and the most alert brains; and in times past the delicate died from hardships by myriads.

Consider also the innumerable wars ; slaughter and success have tried to go hand-in-hand together as boon companions. Every road through history is a changing procession of armies ; every ancient bridge has a long story of battles. Indeed, bridges and roads have circulated all the many phases of strife that men have employed in civil rivalries, in mercantile competitions, in generative migrations, in roadside adventures with footpads and cut-throats, in fateful invasions, and in those missionary conquests which have given to religions their rival empires.

No one knows how many invasions were broken up by the forests and fens of England before the Romans came with their colonising methods, and linked their scattered camps together by means of paved highways, great roads destined to be used for many centuries, and by many raids and armies. The earliest prehistoric tribes came along a bridge of land by which England was united to France ; they found in their course some of the nature-made bridges (p. 114), and the spoor and tracks of formidable animals, such as the mastodon and the mammoth. Much later invasions, also prehistoric, must have come over the sea in boats, for the bridge of land had the history of most bridges, the water swallowed it up ; but every boat may be regarded as a floating bridge which is moved from place to place, so that a pontist when he studies the sea-borne invasions keeps in touch with his favourite subject. On their arrival in England the later prehistoric colonists found that most of the nature-made bridges had been copied, and that a great many footpaths and tracks rambled from settlements to watering-places and through the forests where huntsmen risked their lives in a sport of habit.

The men of the Bronze Period were supplanted in Europe by a race more powerful, whose clenched fists needed larger sword-handles; it was a race of manly and swaggering nomads, strong and fierce; and yet, as Darwin believed, their success in the war of life may have been aided still more by their superiority in the arts. Can we fix a date for the introduction of bronze into the British Isles? Here is a matter of opinion; but, according to Sir John Evans, the most likely date is separated from the Christian era by about 1400 years, perhaps 200 years less. Iron belongs to a much later time. Probably, in the fourth century B.C., it was known as a metal in South Britain; and about a century later it began to supersede bronze in the manufacture of cutting implements.*

Then, as now, England waited for great discoveries to be imported. Many British tribes were hermits of convention, willing drudges to a routine of fixed habits and customs. For example, the highest form of prehistoric bridge-building, the lake-village, came to England not earlier than the Bronze Age, and we shall see (p. 137) that a lake-village, with its late Celtic handicrafts, existed at Glastonbury when in its neighbourhood the Romans were at work. But I do not wish to imply that no British tribe had any alertness.

* "Archæology and False Antiquities," by Robert Munro, M.A., M.D., LL.D., F.R.S.E., F.S.A.SCOT., page 12.

As Cæsar found out to his cost, there were Britons with an enterprising conservatism, whose war-chariots were managed with a skilful bravery. This wheeled traffic postulates a good road here and there, with bridges over some deep rivers; and to this supposition two facts must be added: the war-chariots were small, and their wheels were primitive, so in a wet climate they would have been useless on unmended tracks. Let us infer, then, that the Roman conquest of England was aided by some British landways which were genuine roads, valued for their service and kept in repair. Is not this implied also by the circulation of Druidism from its venerated heart in Anglesey? There is no evidence better than that of a just inference from known events, for events cannot lie, whereas the eye-witness *can*, and very often he *does*.

Again, to think of the aggression which has travelled along roads and over bridges, is to think also of the five phases through which civilization has evolved many times. During the first phase a new home is won by invasion; and during the second phase the new home is extended by invasions, and efforts are made to co-ordinate the separated parts by improving their intercommunications. Then civil and economic competitions not only multiply, but become too active in the body social; wealth breeds wealth, and poverty, poverty. So the classes grow discordant, and put too much strain on each other, just as diseased lungs poison the strongest heart, or as virile hearts rupture weak arteries. Here is the fourth phase; it means a gradual disintegration brought about partly by the economic war, partly by a relaxing faith in stern duties and in patriotism. Amusement becomes a passion, even a mania, and discontent seethes under the fool-fury of the merry-making. Then comes the gradual break-up or downfall, which may be hastened by invasions from a younger and more militant country. Each phase may be a long development, sometimes delayed by events, and sometimes hurried ; and the final phase may be postponed for a long time when the strife of poverty is relieved by constant emigration. Human gunpowder does not explode if it is shipped to a happier country where a day's work brings comfort enough for three days. But the main point is this : that civilizations have travelled always in the same direction and ended always in a break-up, just as great rivers have flowed always toward their destiny in the sea, though all have changed their beds many times and widened their valleys.

When we meditate on the part played by bridges and roads in the rise and fall of ambitious nations, we should choose a fit environment, such as a Roman bridge crippled by three forms of war : floods, winds, and human strife. France has three or four Roman bridges of this kind, but let us take an Italian example. Brangwyn has chosen the Ponte Rotto, at Rome, and the great ruins of the bridge at Narni. It was Augustus Cæsar who erected Narni Bridge, in order to join two hills together across the valley of the Nera, on the Flaminian Way, in the Sabine country. There were four arches of white marble, and the finest one

had a span of 142 feet. The others varied much in breadth.*
The Romans plumbed the river and chose the best natural
foundations for their piers; stability was more to them

RUINS OF THE GREAT ROMAN BRIDGE OVER THE NERA AT NARNI, ITALY

than a sequence of uniform arches. At the present time
only one arch remains; but under its great vault, as you

* Some authors give various measurements. Legrand says that the biggest arch
had a span of thirty-four metres, and that its greatest height, when intact, was thirty-
two metres. I cannot do better than refer you to Choisy's "Art de bâtir chez les
Romains," Paris, 1874. Several ancient writers—Claudian, Procopius, and Martial—
guide Sir William Smith in his remarks on Narni Bridge, but he makes a mistake
when he speaks of "three" arches.

stand on the left bank, you will feel alone with the pity and terror that history brings to those who see past events as clearly as painters behold their concepts.

Under this arch at Narni many types of society have passed, with their customs, religions, fears, hopes, ambitions, predatory trades and pillaging armies ; have passed one after the other, and vanished. *Tempus edax* devoured them ; and now they are studied in relics of their arts and crafts, their mute historians. What permanent social good did they do? Ought we to be as forgetful of them as they were of their buried generations? Do they merit any praise at all? They were proud, of course, and looked upon change as abiding progress, yet the more they altered the more their egotism was the same thing, either intensified and developed, or slackened and degraded ; for the ruling motive powers of their life were but variations of the aboriginal war between the enfeebled and the strengthened. The social rule tried to prove that " Each for All, yet Each for Himself," was the only sane doctrine for men to be guided by in their civil competitions. Everybody had to do much for the commonweal, but yet he was taught to believe that astuteness, even more than upright ability, would enable him to gain control over a number of slaves, or serfs, or servants, whose lot would be what he thought fit to make it. This habitual struggle for Dominion over others was a friend to the fortunate classes only : it bred microbes in the body social and produced fever and disruption. Is it surprising that civilizations withered away?

Their autopsies have a horrible sameness; but from their mute historians—their books, pictures, sculpture, potteries, bridges, roads, and other relics of a lasting communism— we learn to have faith in useful work done thoroughly. In all that endures there is some altruism. Who would care a fig for ancient Greece if all her mute historians had perished with her incompetent social order?

The Middle Ages exist for us, not in records of their freebooting social aims, but in the work done by a few men of genius and their pupils and assistants. More than one mediæval century is represented by a few churches, a few castles, a few bridges, a few books, a damaged house here and there, and some weapons, tools, and furniture. All else in the story of its life is tragic and sinister, a wild pilgrimage whose shrines are battlefields and whose ranks are visited periodically by the plague.

Again, what are we as pontists to say about the fallen master of many Christian periods, the Roman genius, whose architecture and road-making were copied? The Roman baths were not copied, of course, for a clean body was not regarded as sacred in a Christian way; but the Roman bridges, roads, aqueducts, were favourite models for imitation. Many a ruler, from Charlemagne to the Moorish zealots in Spain, not only valued their service, but restored them carefully. Mediæval architects invented very little in bridge-building; their first work tried to recover the lost Roman art; and then, little by little, they added some ideas to their acquired knowledge. Here and there they equalled the

Romans, as in the great bridges at Montauban and Cahors, which Brangwyn has painted with a vigorous enjoyment; but in most of their efforts the design was either too rustic or too lubberly, so ponderous was the technical inspiration. Far too often their ideal of strength was a mere man-at-arms, brave but underbred. Rivers were obstructed by immense piers, for instance, by which spates were turned into dangerous inundations; and footways along bridges were so narrow that safety recesses for pedestrians had to be built out from the parapets into the piers. Even in exceptions to this rule of ungainliness, as in much Spanish workmanship, architects were overapt to make the use of bridges a tiring penance that wayfarers could not avoid. Thus the bridge over the Sella at Cángas de Onis has a lofty footway shaped like a gable; to-day it is little used, for the climbing exercise that it offers to everybody is put out of vogue by a modern bridge, its neighbour and rival. In brief, many gabled bridges in Spain* were made narrow enough to be useless to wheeled traffic and friendly to pack mules; friendly in a mediæval manner, for a seasoning of peril was added to their inconvenience. Most of them are without parapets; and when their rivers flood into roaring spates, and across their giddy pathways a gale sweeps

---

* See "Northern Spain," by Edgar Wigram, an excellent book. The gable-shaped bridges are mostly of mediæval date. Some fine examples: at Martorell (partly Roman), at Puente la Reina, and across the Gallego river between Jaca and Huesca. To-day these are seldom used because of their steep pitch and of their narrowness. The great one at Orense, over the Miño, is still in daily use.

eagerly, an Alpinist can enjoy a mad crossing, after dark, between dinner and bedtime.

Frank Brangwyn has drawn for us, with as much fidelity as vigour, one of the finest gable bridges, the Puente de San Juan de las Abadesas at Gerona. This bridge has a great historic interest. The Moors left in Spain a peculiar grace of style which native architects often united to their own qualities—a haughty distinction and a lofty ambition. Consider the immense nave in Gerona Cathedral, a glorious pointed arch not less than seventy-three feet from side to side, almost double the width of Westminster nave. It belongs to the fifteenth century, yet in the magic of its youthful hope it proves that its architect, Guillermo Boffiy, was a child of the thirteenth. And the great central arch of the Gerona bridge has in it some of the soaring courage that transcends all expectation in the cathedral nave.*

Yet this gabled bridge, though very spacious and attractive, has less charm than its rival at Orense, in Gallicia, a noble monument 1319 feet long, built in 1230 by Bishop

---

* Gable bridges are uncommon in Great Britain, but a fine example crosses the river Taff not far from Cardiff. It is called the Pont-y-Prydd. Between its abutments the great arch measures 140 feet, and the footway is so very steep that laths of wood used to be fastened across it to keep horses from falling. Before industrialism murdered a beautiful countryside the Pont-y-Prydd was a rainbow of stone that shone all the year round. We owe this bridge to a self-educated country mason, William Edwards by name, who in 1750 brought his work to completion, after suffering defeat in two previous efforts. My photograph of the Pont-y-Prydd is disgraced by a very hideous commercial bridge that progress has put quite close to the Welsh masterpiece, but, happily, there are many old engravings and pictures that do full justice to William Edwards. Richard Wilson painted the Pont-y-Prydd—an excellent recommendation to a fine piece of handicraft.

Lorenzo, and repaired in 1449 by Bishop Pedro de Silva. The six arches differ in size, yet their combination is symmetrical; four are gracefully pointed, and the finest one

PUENTE DE SAN JUAN DE LAS ABADESAS AT GERONA, SPAIN

rises above the Miño to a height of a hundred and thirty-five feet, and its brave span, a hundred and fifty-six feet from pier to pier, is the widest of any in Spain.*

It is commonly supposed that gable bridges were

* Mr. Wigram, in his finely illustrated book on Northern Spain, reminds us that the Puente Mayor at Orense played a various part in the Peninsula War. It was the pivot of the French operations when Soult led his troops from Coruña to renew the subjugation of Portugal. At first all went well, but "within two months his army was reeling back from Oporto, without hospital, baggage, or artillery, in a worse plight even than Moore's. He had wrestled his first fall with the great antagonist who was destined to beat him from the Douro to Toulouse."

invented by the genius of Gothic architecture. Yet Marco Polo found them in China,* and the Roman bridge of two arches at Alcantarilla is hog-backed. Usually the Romans liked a flat road over a river, though it was easier and less expensive to build a steep bridge from low embankments. But the bridge at Alcantarilla, about twenty miles below Seville, is quite steep enough to be the forerunner of all the gable bridges erected in Spain.†

There is little in stone bridge building that the Romans did not discover. To this day their aqueducts and bridges are models of thoroughness, and apologise nobly for a civilization that rambled through wonderful achievements into a gradual suicide. While arenas for barbaric sports were being built at a great expense, and while most of the Roman roads circulated war, did many persons guess that their imperial genius in handicraft would outlive their statesmanship by hundreds of years? Who knows why Rome very often squandered her energy on the least fruitful phases of strife, neglecting those benign phases out of which intellectual vigour ought to have come, age after age, in a continuous zeal for research, and revision, and improvement? She neglected science, for instance, and her bad example was followed by the mediæval Church. Not a mind had any inkling of the fact that the brightest hopes for mankind would emerge from science, like medicinal plants from dry seeds. Innumerable millions died from

* See Appendix I.
† See Appendix II for a description of this Roman bridge.

ignorance because Pasteur and Lister were not evolved until the races of man were perhaps a million years old. In the creeping progress of humanity the dead have been mocked by every good discovery; there has been nothing so cruel as a healing success, for it has ever been too late by thousands of years.

To visualise this truth in the strife of man is a great trial to any mind; but yet it is the one thing that a pontist cannot evade without being disloyal to his honour as a student, since he knows that strife has ruled over the tremendous drama which has had for its theatres the highways and byways, and for its actors the races of man, continuously at odds with one another. If this truth had to be deleted from the drama, then I, for one, would not be a student of roads and bridges. As well read the Greek tragedians after deleting all the passions that make for contests and crises.

So let us try to get nearer and nearer to strife, the most active genius in the life of our subject. Why has it set tribe against tribe, nation against nation, class against class, tradesman against tradesman, intellect against intellect? Must we clear from our minds all the shibboleths of modern idealism? and feel pity for the supergood when they chatter to us about their isles of dreams, their unsubstantial fairy places, where "cosmic conscience" reigns with "the universal brotherhood of man," and where "everlasting peace" promises never to be effete and sterile? When a Wellington of Finance erects a Peace Palace, at The

Hague or elsewhere, are we to be glad that the pomp of irony did not leave the world when Gibbon died? Should we gain anything at all if we were bold enough to condemn the whole past life of the human race? Ought we to pass with Carlyle from democratic hopes into hero worship, and thence into a hot-brained conviction that faith in mankind is impossible? Are we to suppose that man has transformed into instincts the worst habits he has acquired, so that his ultimate destiny upon earth will be determined by his attitude to these instincts? Will he obey them or will he try to conquer them?

Again, is there a glint of hope in the hysterical words that came to Charles Dickens when he wrote as follows, after a visit to Chillon?—"Good God, the greatest mystery in all the earth, to me, is how or why the world was tolerated by its Creator through the good old times, and wasn't dashed to fragments." You see, Dickens understood the terror of strife, but he made no effort to be calm with Darwin, who knew that the evolution of man could not have happened if nascent humanity had been unfit to endure the sufferings of its daily contests both against Nature's violence and against a terrible fauna. Thus a pitiless character was thrust upon primitive man by the environment in which unlimited strife worked his development; and what the ages have evolved only a long future can amend in another evolution. What Dickens called unpardonable cruelty was to the distant past what strikes are to our own time, a weapon, a phase of war, approved by

A GREAT SPANISH BRIDGE, THE ALCÁNTARA AT TOLEDO. MAINLY THE WORK OF ARCHBISHOP TENORIO, A.D. 1380; FORTIFIED BY ANDRES MAN-RIQUE, A.D. 1484. ON THIS SITE A ROMAN BRIDGE WAS DESTROYED IN A.D. 871

public opinion ; and let us remember also that the cruelties which a hard life has bred, and turned into customs, have not shown an egotism fiercer than that primal necessity which has compelled life among the species to feed on lives. Dickens himself, while writing his condemnation of the past, was nourished by the death of many living things ; was in himself a mysterious alembic that transmuted food, slain life, into benign health and action. Had he been logical in his feelings toward strife he would have had mercy on those forms of life that feed mankind ; in other words, he would have died of hunger rather than be cruel ; but, naturally, the manifestations of strife hateful to him were those that happened to be far off from his needs and sympathies. Yet he ought to have seen in the national efforts of his time that strife, though easy to rebel against, is woefully difficult to improve, since even kindness of heart when shown in promiscuous charities may unseat from their thrones in the public mind many good racial qualities, doing as much harm as ever was done by mediæval brutality.

"Let me think" should be everybody's motto ; nothing less than arduous thinking can save us from the cant and the sentimentalism which at the present time enfeebles England.* Let me give you an example. Yesterday I was

---

* This was written several months before the outbreak of the Great War, which England had invited by allowing her peace-fanatics to bill and coo in her foreign politics. Instead of reading the arrogant books on blood-lust that nourished the well-advertised aims of Germany, England played the fool with epicene triflers of all sorts and conditions, and turned her back on Lord Roberts, her truthful statesman. She

D

talking to a friend about the mediæval battle-bridge. Putting before him Frank Brangwyn's excellent sketch in watercolour of Parthenay Bridge, I said : "This fortified gateway belongs to the thirteenth century, and through its machicolations red-hot stones and boiling oil were poured down many times upon the head and shoulders of an attack.   The

babbled about peace until she received from the Prussian junkerdom proposals so abominable that they brought her to the fighting point of honour ; and then she cried out for a million new soldiers.   Yet British statesmen, even then, paid many compliments to their bad old habit of ingenuous pacifism.   No political dove wanted the world to believe that there had been anything of the eagle in his attitude to German war-culture.   As if this truism could be a consolation to heroic little Belgium, the Jeanne d'Arc of nations, whose safety England had guaranteed, and whose experiences in the hell of Teutonic savagery had left her scorched, mutilated, yet unconquered. Can anyone explain why the word "peace" has been hypnotic to Anglo-Celtic minds ? Every phase of human enterprise must be a phase of war, because it claims a battle-toll of killed and wounded and maimed.   Poverty alone is such a terrible phase of permanent war that pacifists ought to devote all their energy to its gradual betterment. Even the accidents of civilization—street and railway accidents, colliery explosions, sea tragedies, and so forth—equal in a century the casualties on stricken fields.   If only our sentimentalists would try to think ! Then they would learn that the occasional strife between armies never destroys in a century as many lives as the multiform continuous strife called peace.   And we may be certain that all the human war of the future will not belong to "peace" alone.   The birth of many a new era will be aided by the fierce midwifery of military and naval warfare. To-day is the 26th of September, 1914, and England in two months has nearly outgrown the routine claptrap of her effete idealism.   To-day she is eager to bear any amount of self-sacrifice ; two months ago her peace-mania was a crime against the Empire and against her treaty obligations to Belgium.   She had no faith in National Service till Germany had passed from arrogant warnings to barbaric aggressions.   Agadir was not enough to put common sense into her dreamful solicitude about international "peace." "Peace" in her home affairs she never tried to get ; she wanted peace to conquer the nations, not to cure industrial conflicts and the Irish Question.   What a comic tragedy !   And let us remember that our peace-fanatics, though silent to-day, are not dead.   Their influence will become active again after the overthrow of Germany.   New mischief will flow from their sentimentalism.   To lose the flower of British youth, while keeping our peace-fanatics : here indeed is a sinister fact.

gateway was built between 1202 and 1226, not without help from English money, for the Josselin-Larchêveques of Parthenay were allies of the Anjou Plantagenets, who gave us English kings; but a few years later our English troops were driven from Parthenay by Louis IX, called St. Louis. Can't you imagine the assault? Would you care to rush that gateway in a thirteenth-century manner?"

My friend, a Quaker, was scandalised. "Rush the gateway?" he cried. "Red-hot stones and boiling oil! What imbecile savagery! Thank goodness, we are not savages now; life has improved wonderfully. To-day most men of sense fear war, and those who don't fear it scorn it for moral reasons."

"Are you sure?" I asked. "Do you really believe that the history of this old war-bridge is more strifeful than the industrialism of to-day? Is it an act of peace when a trust 'corners' some article of food, or when a limited liability concern kills all competition from little neighbours, whose wives and families can't get rid of hunger because business has failed? Those who attacked the bridge at Parthenay were armour-clad, while those who suffer in trade wars from the greed of co-operative egotisms have usually no self-defence, as their capital is small. Don't you see, then, that from machicolated towers to millionaire tradesmen is but an evolution in social strife? Chivalry did try to put some generous feeling into mediæval warfare; and how much feeling of chivalry do you expect to find in the battles of industry? Are the strategic victories of finance more

humane than were the politics of the Black Prince? Do
they harm the defeated less, or more? And can you explain, old chap, why it is that Quakers, Jews, Hindus,
though they fight for money with an astuteness that
never flinches, prattle about peace after office hours?
Their ideal of peace includes all warfare except that which
employs battleships and big battalions. Myself, I would
sooner lead an attack against the Porte St. Jacques on
Parthenay Bridge than be opposed in trade by a wealthy
firm of shrewd Quakers, whose great skill in the combats
of trade would soon ruin me. I shouldn't have a chance of
doing credit to myself in a dangerous adventure."

There is nothing more odious than the modern cant
about peace. But a pontist soon learns that strife of every
sort is a phase of war. Indeed, whether roads and bridges
aid a pilgrimage of the sick, or an army of Crusaders, or a
primitive migration, or the ramblings of charity, or the
enterprise of monasteries; whether they help a mediæval
pope at Avignon to thwart the land-hunger of a French
king, or enable modern life to turn industrialism into a
world-wide Armageddon whose scouts are lying advertise-
ments; whatever they do or have done their history brings
us in touch with the same human motive, a desire to win
victories. James Martineau went so far as to picture the
strife as absolutely barbaric. He said: "The battle for
existence rages through all time and in every field; and its
rule is to give no quarter—to despatch the maimed, to over-
take the halt, to trip up the blind, and drive the fugitive

A WAR-BRIDGE OF THE MIDDLE
AGES AT PARTHENAY IN FRANCE

host over the precipice into the sea." Tennyson also went too far when he wrote about strife; too far, because he did no more than skim along the surface of a primordial truth, by which man's history has been made a part of Nature's. From Tennyson we gain no help at all; he tells us merely "that hope of answer or redress" must come from "behind the veil." In his opinion Nature cares for nothing, so careless is she of the single life, and so ready to let a thousand types go. Yet her realms teem with miracles of contentious life, and I cannot think of any great extinct species that I should care very much to meet in a country walk. I do not wish to hob-nob with the Iguanodon, for instance. When John Stuart Mill complains that "nearly all the things which men are hanged or imprisoned for doing to one another are Nature's everyday performances," he forgets the far-reaching harm that men can do within the tolerance of "Old Father Antic, the Law"; and, besides this, he forgets to explain how a world of organisms ruled by hunger and thirst and passion, and dependent on innumerably various climates, could be other than Providence has decreed.

To talk as Mill did is to imply that Nature sins against us, and against herself, when she allows any species to grow completely unfit for the gift of life. Yet her aim is to protect life from the suicidal fertility of lives, so that the whole economy of Nature demands death in the highest interests of the future. When we die we do an act of charity to our children and grandchildren; for if each of us lived to be active at ninety, the world would need a much smaller

population of young people. It is our frail tenure of life
that renders a high birthrate necessary; and progress gains
more from the enterprise of vigorous youth than from the
too cautious knowledge of old age. So I do not understand the pother raised by Mill and others over the benign
discipline of death that Nature wields as a servant of the
Eternal.

Believe me, a pontist can never solve even one problem
in the law of battle if he lets himself be scared into a re-
volt against natural forces; scared by the incessant tragedy
that each day's little trip along the highways of history
brings in a challenging manner before his mind's eye. He
must try to protect himself with humour and irony and
scorn, as Thackeray tried to save himself from a feminine
heart. The main point is that he should learn to live outside himself; then self-pity will not be his troublesome
guide through the labyrinths of strife.

Cardinal Newman asks us to believe that human life has
been terrible—" a vision to dizzy and appal "—because mankind has been punished by God for some aboriginal sin
too abominable for mercy and forgiveness. This doctrine
is completely dark and horrible. If it were illumined on
one side only, like the moon, it would invite the companion-
ship of thought, but it gives no light whatever. Indeed,
it implies that no civilization has been free to improve its
own lot and to get progressive reason from the large brain
of man. To blame God for our own follies—to say that
our social acts are wild and foolish because we are being

punished by Heaven for a sin of ignorance committed by man in the babyhood of the human race—what is this but a charge of illimitable cruelty against the Creator? Besides, we learn from the much nobler doctrine of evolution that human nature, despite all her wilful fondness for wrong actions, has crept up and up from a very low beginning, in an ascent continually wonderful, though infinitely slow and tragical. The accumulated progress excites in me as much awe as I should feel in the presence of a resurrection from the dead. Indeed, what is evolution but a vast drama of resurrections, by means of which base forms of life have become gradually better? Can anyone suppose that Milton, had he been a contemporary of Darwin, would have turned from the endless hopes that evolution ought to inspire, just to dally with fallen angels and with an errant couple in the Garden of Disobedience? And can we suppose that Newman would have written his famous page on the doctrine of original sin, had he not turned his back on modern thought and knowledge?

Amid the doubts and difficulties that trouble this meditation on strife, just a few things are bright and clear-eyed, like illumined windows which on dark nights cause jaded tramps to feel less their lone wayfaring ; and these things I have watched for years in the life of bridges, where their activity never ceases. It is clear enough, for instance, that custom and convention have acted as narcotics on the mind, sending reason to sleep. This explains why human strife has never turned to the best use the great opportunities that each generation has inherited. To custom and convention, mankind has owed the social rule which has sown the seed of death in every civilization; the rule of illogic and discord, "Each for All, yet Each for Himself." Let us see this rule in operation on the highways, taking care to note how it has inflamed egotism and deadened both the sense of honour and the spirit of citizenship.

The just and beautiful principle that every man lives by his mother the State, and that he must do good for the benefit of the commonweal, was enforced upon mediæval landowners by the *trinoda necessitas*, or triple obligation, which among other duties made the upkeep of roads and bridges a general charge on all owners of the English soil. Not even the religious houses were exempted, though the State favoured them in other ways. But the second principle of the social rule—"Each for Himself"—interfered constantly with the first principle, bringing trouble after trouble into the administration of the highways, as into all other useful and necessary things. Landowners transferred their duties to their tenants, and very often the tenants made negligence a habit, until at last the Law and the Church became equally active for the people's benefit. Again and again bishops offered "forty days' indulgence to all who would draw from the treasure that God had given them valuable and charitable aid towards the building and repair" of a poor bridge ruined by neglect, or of some quagmire which had been a decent road.* It happened in the year 1318 that

* See "English Wayfaring Life in the Middle Ages." J. J. Jusserand. The chapter on roads and bridges.

the Law pottered into action because a timber bridge at Old Shoreham, in Sussex, had been scandalously ill-used by those who were responsible for its upkeep. Half of it had fallen into the river. Year after year an evident crime against the State had gone on publicly, yet no one had taken steps to make the dangerous condition of the bridge a subject for legal enquiry and punishment. The village grumbled, of course, but grumblers have never had any initiative of their own ; unless a man of action has come to be their conscience and their leader, they have done nothing. Their energy has evaporated in talk, like steam from a boiling pan. It was not until the bridge had fallen that the village hummed intelligently like a hive of bees, and set itself to work. What could be done then? Who was the landowner? No less a person than the Archbishop of Canterbury. Are we then to believe that in 1318 a Primate of England scamped his public duty? Was his attitude to a timber bridge inferior to that of the high priests of ancient Rome, who called themselves *pontifices* because they built and repaired the Pons Sublicius, a bridge of stakes at the foot of Mount Aventine?* The sheriff and his officers had a different question to consider ; they would wish to know whether the Archbishop had been an astute man of the world, whether he had made his tenants responsible to the *trinoda necessitas*. If not, then he and the Law were in a fix, and peasants over their ale would guffaw with malice. But enquiries proved that his Grace

* There has been much controversy over the position of the Pons Sublicius. (See p. 140.)

was a canny landlord; the tenants alone ought to have mended the bridge; and so the Law was free to act with a vigour that common folk knew too well.

Its agent was the bailiff, good Simon Porter, and Porter set out at once to collect money from the tenants. If any tenant either declined to pay his share or was unable to pay it, then the bailiff put his hand on some marketable property, perhaps a few sheep, or a cow, or "a gaggle of geese." The necessary thing was to take enough; never an easy thing to do in the country, as no one cared to pay a fair price for escheated live stock. The peasant has ever been at heart a pawnbroker. But Simon Porter had no reason to look upon his troublesome work as a high office of trust important enough to keep his name alive for six hundred years. It was when he met Hamo de Morston, a truculent fellow, that Simon entered into history. Hamo de Morston was a logical egoist, he fought for his own hand only, trying to use the State at a trivial cost to himself; but now this amusement, after prospering for years, brought him suddenly face to face with legal pains and penalties—a thing most irritating to a bad temper. So Hamo refused to pay; and his fury was terrific when Porter confiscated a horse. Even then he was not defeated, for he set lawyer against lawyer, and one day a petition was sent by him to King Edward II. The rascal was a good fighter, but his appeal to the supreme authority failed; the bailiff's action was approved, and Hamo had costs to pay.

As for the bridge, it was repaired, and repaired very well. Twenty years ago it was in use, a shaggy and venerable structure, not yet crippled by old age. Then certain highwaymen, popularly known as road officials, visited Old Shoreham, and there they tried to prove that a bridge admired by landscape painters was unfit for a commercial time. The poor bridge! At this moment it has no charm at all; not only is it dull, it is neat in a shabby way—a discord in good surroundings, like bankruptcy at a wedding breakfast. So we pass from Hamo de Morston to our own roadway officials, and find ourselves in the presence of a public bridge injured by public servants. To Hamo we can give a little sympathy, he fought for his creed of self and paid costs, whereas highway boards have never been fined for spoiling old bridges. Perhaps they do not hate venerable architecture, but they belong to a system of public service that is ill-equipped for its work, receiving neither criticism from the newspaper press nor supervision from county committees of independent architects.

That the State has been wronged by these public servants is known to all artists and antiquarians; also the fact is advertised by the great many hideous railway bridges that demean towns and blemish the country. In this matter, as in others, the State must defend her own just rights, so as to get by compulsion what a free egotism has declined to give—efficiency and good taste. It is possible that England has not suffered a great deal more than the Continent; for even in France, despite the excellent administration of the *Ponts et Chaussées*, crimes against noble bridges have been committed, as when the second ancient bridge at Cahors was lost in a storm of local party politics. But England happens to be poor in great old bridges, whereas the Continent is rich; we cannot afford to lose even the modest little ballads of arched stone which have resisted floods for many generations, while working as necessary drudges in the making of England. Trivial they are when compared with the bridges of Isfahan or with many of those in France and Spain, but yet they are hallowed by time, and they mimic the gentle rusticity of English landscapes. It is a crime to spoil them, because modern bridges for heavy traffic can be built at a lesser cost near by the little mute historians.

To the Scotch, on the other hand, many a fine old brig is a Burns of the highways; and this sentiment for history and for sylvan poetry has kept from the cruel hands of industrialism some very attractive single-arched bridges, and some long bridges also, notably the rhythmical Brig of Stirling, which Brangwyn has chosen as an example of quiet good taste in mediæval civic architecture. The Brig of Stirling is a Scotch citizen of the dour old school, but warmed with an undercurrent of that kindly emotion which even the canniest Scot is glad to show off when he is away from business. I am inclined to think that not even a militant suffragette would have folly enough to attack the Scotch brigs; she would be fascinated by their names, and this would keep her out of mischief. Such a name as the Brig

o' Doon is music combined with a racial vigour. No weak
people would have invented it, and no dull people could
have retained such a poetic name.

The Irish also are fond of bridges, like the true unspoiled Welsh. As late as a century ago Irish peasants

THE OLD WAR-BRIDGE OF STIRLING

were pious in their attitude to any bridge that crossed a
dangerous river; they saluted it reverently because of its
friendliness to poor wayfarers, and because good thoughts
come from simple hearts. As for the Welsh, thanks partly
to their Celtic blood and partly to the waywardness of their
rivers, they have been known as pontists for a very long

time. In the romantic hills their bridges seem to belong to Nature herself, so lovingly have they been united to the spirit of ancestral landscapes ; whereas the industrial parts of Wales make the bridges of trade into vile objects, as if beauty has no right to a home where money is earned out of coal mines, and ironworks, and the debilitating factory system. Far too often the industrial bridge every- where is like an ill-used highway uniting the purgatory of a seared district to some hell or other invented by poets or by priests. There are many such bridges in the Staffordshire Black Country, and in the scarred Potteries, where an ebon meanness lives with jerry-builders, and where puny drab children take from the present generation the youth that endures. What would a Dante think in the stricken fields of industrialism ? And why is it that only a person here and there, after compelling himself to leave the atmosphere of custom, sees our industrial war clearly, and views it in its relation to the body social ?

The truth is that our creed of self has become instinc- tive ; we cannot without an effort live for an hour outside our personal interests ; and thus the beautiful principle " Each for All " has to be kept alive by a host of active laws that encircle us with compulsion. Where there is no compulsion we are governed by our preferences. If we like bridges, for instance, we try to protect them from ill- usage ; but if they are indifferent to us we care not a straw when engineers add half a dozen uncouth viaducts to the many other misdeeds which they have thrust upon the

State. Instead of regarding all bad public work as a sin against the commonweal, we let ourselves be ruled by the creed of self even in our best efforts to serve the State properly.

Is our egotism better or worse than that of the Middle Ages? This seems to be a matter of opinion. Thorold Rogers believed that mediævalism in a good many respects was kinder than our industrialism; and the late Russel Wallace regarded "our social environment as a whole, in relation to our possibilities and our claims," as "the worst that the world has ever seen." On the other hand, a great scientist from his laboratory has told us that "the sun rises on a better world every morning." Gracious! If the sun could speak to us about his complete knowledge of mankind, if he did not obey the law of silence that rules over the greatest motive-powers and creative agents, our conjectures would be less wayward, for sunrays would whisper into our ears the story of the most evil civilization in the whole strife of mankind. In this matter the sun would be authoritative; but how can we poor mortals expect to see the whole past truly when we are half blind to the significance of our own social life? Besides, it is enough for us to see how one civilization has differed from another, and how in many respects all human life has been like the sky, always the same elementally, but never quite the same in colour and form, and in the effects of strife.

A pontist, as he journeys through present-day England, sees very clearly the difference between our commercial

time and the past; for industrialism is plainly out of joint
with that which is normal in organic growth, and its workmen are conscious of the unstable energy bred and frittered
away by hurry and speed-worship. Consider those dread
"hives of industry" where trade bridges are makeshifts,
and where the jerry-built villa or cottage is repeated thousands of times, and always in mean streets. Do they not
bear witness to the feeling of insecurity from which our
age suffers? I shall be told that many things are very well
made, as in the case of battleships, motor-cars, engines,
steamships, guns, rifles, artillery, surgical instruments, expensive clothes, implements for games, and gigantic metal
bridges; but in this good craftsmanship, tradesmen are
thorough because they dare not be slipshod; they fear to
turn out work that would endanger human life, and business would fail if they angered the specialists of luxury
and of sport. Where they are free from restraint, as in
work for ordinary households, tradesmen manufacture
trash and prosper. In fact, the quicksands of cheapness
are to most people in England what cheese in a trap is to
mice, or what seasonable bait is to fish. So widespread is
the feeling of insecurity that the poorer classes do not think
it worth while to buy enduring goods and chattels. Instead
of practising a thrift that would hand on furniture to their
grandchildren, they say, "Never mind; perhaps these things
may last our time." And this dull pessimism in the creed
of self is the most wretched phase of strife that a pontist
has to connect with the circulation of trade enterprise.

CANNON STREET RAILWAY BRIDGE, LONDON

Even the prehistoric tribes wanted to be remembered by their posterity, so they built enduring barrows or set up cromlechs to their ancestor-worship, this being their spiritual bond between past and present and future. In the Middle Ages also, though disease and filth and bloodshed made life as uncertain as a game of chance, the social egotism that built and purchased for itself had faith in the future, and claimed and got full value for its money. In fact, from nearly all specimens of mediæval handicraft we may learn why the peoples of Europe survived terrible crises and bred men of genius to represent them for ever. In each race, and particularly in ours, there was a wonderful endurance, certainly based on the creed of self, but admirable all the same, like the tough elasticity of yew timber. The ruling egotism was honest in nearly all its private work, but when it was expected to be equally thorough as a public servant, then a habit of dishonesty appeared in handicrafts, sometimes to be followed by new laws or by threatening proclamations. Again and again the conscription of the archery laws was imperilled by bowyers and fletchers and merchants, who formed "rings" and flooded the markets with nefarious work to be sold at high prices. Certain bridges, also, and notably the one at Berwick-on-Tweed, fell so often that the supervision of town authorities must have been exceedingly lax. On this point, M. Jusserand says :—"London Bridge itself, so rich, so useful, so admired, had frequent need of reparation, and this was never done until danger was imminent, or even till catas-

E

trophe had happened. Henry III granted the farm of the
bridge revenues to his 'beloved wife,' who neglected to
maintain the bridge, appropriating to herself without
scruple the rents of the building; none the less did the
king renew his patent at the expiration of the term, that
the queen might benefit 'from a richer favour.' The out-
come of these favours was not long to wait; soon it was
found that the bridge was in ruins, and to restore it the
ordinary resources were not enough; it was necessary to
send collectors throughout the country to gather offerings
from those willing to give. Edward I begged his people
to hasten (January, 1281), the bridge would give way if
they did not send prompt assistance; and he ordered the
archbishops, bishops, all the clergy, to let his collectors
address the people with 'pious exhortations' that the sub-
sidies should be given without delay. But the money thus
urgently needed arrived too late; the catastrophe had
already happened, a 'sudden ruin' befell the bridge, and to
repair this misfortune the king established a special tax
upon the passengers, merchandise and boats (February 4,
1282), which tax was enacted again and a new tariff put into
force on May 7, 1306. . . ."

What were the citizens doing while Henry III and his
dear wife ruined the bridge by confiscating her revenues?
Did they believe that everybody's affair was nobody's
business, and that they would be asked to mend the bridge
if they drew attention to her condition? As to Edward I,
he kept his hand away from his own pocket, and personated

charity that for ever begs. " Each for Himself " was a policy that suited Edward ; and his orders to the clergy proved that he knew it to be a policy which his loyal subjects followed as a habit. Hence the " pious exhortations," with indulgences also, we may rest assured. The whole story is pitifully ironic. London had no other bridge over the Thames, yet the people looked on while a king and his wife played the part of bridge wreckers. Some protest there must have been, for London Bridge—a great street of timber houses—was more populous than many a village ; and the tenants, like other Englishmen of those days, had no wish to be plunged into cold water. According to Stow's " Annals," five arches fell, so many houses also were lost, perhaps with their inmates.

M. Jusserand believes that during the Middle Ages our English highways fared no better than London Bridge. His verdict runs thus : " Though there were roads, though property was burdened with obligatory services for their upkeep, though laws every now and again recalled their obligations to the possessors of the soil, though from time to time the private interest of lords and of monks, in addition to the public interest, suggested and directed repairs, yet the fate of a traveller in a fall of snow or in a thaw was very precarious. The Church might well have pity on the way-farer ; and him she specified, together with the sick and the captive, among those unfortunates whom she recommended to the daily prayers of pious souls."

There is a great deal of evidence to justify this verdict,

but evidence in history depends on its choice; and in Thorold Rogers there are other facts that leave England with some efficient mediæval roads, along which horsemen could travel rapidly. Perhaps Rogers may have set too much store by his data; but when we study all the evidence, when we balance it carefully, and visualise all its pictures of well-tested negligence and crime, one thing is beyond all doubt: that the social rule, "Each for All, yet Each for Himself," was a national catastrophe. Its first principle had a very precarious life, though incessant compulsion tried to drive it home to the people's fear of revengeful laws; whereas the second principle—"Each for Himself"—was so popular as a creed that even the divine mysteries beyond death were assailed by egoists, who thought they could buy a place in heaven by giving lands and goods to the Church, no matter what harm they had done in a brief life upon earth. Study Erasmus in his wayfaring letters, and you will breathe the atmosphere of the Middle Ages.

OLD LONDON BRIDGE, BEGUN BY PETER COLECHURCH IN 1176, AND
FINISHED BY A FRENCHMAN, CALLED ISEMBERT, IN THE YEAR 1209

PONT SIDI RACHED AT CONSTANTINE, ALGERIA. BUILT IN 1908–1912

The span of the great arch is 70 metres. The work illustrates the longevity of custom and convention, being inspired partly by Roman aqueducts and partly by the two famous bridges over the Tech at Céret, in France, one of which dates from the year 1321. The span of its great arch is 45 m. 45 cm.

III

CUSTOM AND CONVENTION

YET a pontist must be exceedingly careful when his tramps through any period bring him in touch with ethical problems. He should try to live on the highways of history, not in order to pass judgments on vice and on crime, but because he wants to see clearly, under the form of visual conception, why social

53

concord and equity have never fared well, even the best
forms of civilization being only half-educated barbarisms
that allow their strife to be drilled by a vast number of
active laws. These phases of compulsion go on increasing, yet they fail to resolve into harmony those rapacious
egotisms that compete against each other in the body social
like microbes in living tissues. As soon as a pontist understands his wayfaring through history, as soon as he feels at
home in the general atmosphere of the human drama, he is
glad to be a realist; then nothing that societies do or have
done seems unexampled and inexplicable. To him, for
example, the infanticide practised age after age by savage
tribesmen is not more terrible than the death of babies in
the slums of civilized towns, or than the degradation brought
before his mind by the alert philanthropy that saves little
English children from cruelties. To him, again, the
slaughter on a great battlefield is not more woeful than
the annual sacrifice of lives in street accidents, and railway
smashes, and mine disasters, and sea tragedies; as well as
in games and sports, in nursing the sick, and in all trades
and professions. He is not scared by the fact that the sum
of human life is war, but he is scared by the primordial
customs and conventions that make the incessant war infinitely less humane than it could be and ought to be. So a
pontist in his attitude to history is a sociologist, and not an
abstract moralist. Each body social and its systems of
circulation are to him what patients are to medical students
in a hospital; he has to learn to be attentive to all dis-

ease and to make his diagnoses thoughtfully. Even then frequent mistakes will occur. One thing he must regard as his clinical thermometer: it is the truth that civilizations in their intercourse with right and wrong have been governed by habits and customs and conventions, which have caused most men to be other men; so that most human actions, whether studied in old history or in the current routine of living, are mere quotations from other human actions, instead of being like original ideas in a well-ordered composition. In other words, the ordinary human brain has tried to be automatic, as if to be in harmony with the rest of the vital organs.

Now the architecture of bridges, like that of huts and houses and cottages, never fails to keep before our minds the awful slowness of each reluctant advance from custom to custom, and from convention to convention. I have no words to describe the terror that comes to me when I find in daily use a type or species of bridge so aboriginal in its poor workmanship that a forerunner not only similar to it, but as rudely effective, may well have been employed by the earliest Flint Men, whose delight in imitation was stimulated by all the bridges which Nature had created. Even more, at this moment in England, and even in busy Lancashire, where to-day's machinery abounds, there are primitive bridges which are not even primitively structural; bridges which need in their making not more thought than is given to a difficult sneeze when we are troubled by a cold (p. 60). When I look at them and think of the myriads of generations which in different parts of the world have used bridges akin to these, I am so awed with fear that I feel like a baby Gulliver in a new Brobdingnag where everlasting conventions are impersonated by brainless giants whose bodies are too vast for my eyes to focus.   Often, too, I say to myself: " In the presence of this dreadful conservatism, this inept mimicry that endures unruffled by a thought for many thousands of years, you are as futile as a single microbe would be on a field of battle.   Or imagine that the microbe is in Westminster Abbey, and that it has a blurred sense that makes it dimly conscious of all the many historic things there gathered together; then you have a figure of yourself in your relation to the mingled good and bad in history.   For the Abbey shows in its architecture that convention, though a bane to ordinary minds, is the grammar of progress to the rare men of genius who from time to time shake the world free from its bondage to fixed customs and routines, and compel it to move on to other routines and customs, where it will dawdle until other geniuses come out of the dark and find in new mother-ideas a compulsive force that works a new liberation."

This, indeed, is the only encouragement that I am able to perceive when I watch in history the periodical strife between inveterate conventions and the mother-ideas of genius.   In the case of bridges, for example, the first mother-ideas were those that enabled a primitive craftsman here and there to copy with success the least difficult of Nature's models.   What this man achieved was repeated

OLD BRIDGE OVER THE CLAIN, NEAR POITIERS

by his tools, the ordinary men of his tribe; then other tribes got wind of the discovery and began to make similar bridges, until at last several conventions were formed, and they became widespread and stereotyped. When a convention was very simple and also effective for a given purpose, no one wished to see it developed, so it entered that domain of infertile mimicry where stone tools and weapons remained unpolished for years to be reckoned by scores of thousands. If experience had shown that chipped flint in a rough state would neither cut wood nor break human skulls, then at an early date polishing would have been found out by a savage of genius who yearned to prove that his invention could be made useful; but rough-hewn stones were rudely efficient, so mankind settled itself in a routine and plodded on and on automatically. And thus it was also in the case of many primitive bridges which became so firmly fixed in conventions that now they seem to be contemporary with nearly all the ages of human strife. Not in any other way can we explain their present use by many Europeans, as well as by the natives of Asia, and Africa, and America (p. 145). On the other hand, when a primeval bridge did not serve its purpose efficiently, when it was useless in tribal wars and dangerous in rainy seasons, then a mother-idea paid it a visit from time to time, as we shall see in the next chapter.

Whence the idea came we do not know. It entered a mind that was ready to receive it, coming unbidden from a place unknown like an abiding quest from a spirit world.

The mind that welcomed the idea was neither masculine
nor feminine, it was both, a thing androgynous, for genius
has ever been a single creative agent with a double sex.
The tools with which genius has worked—the selected
traditions and conventions, the acquired knowledge, the
original observation, and the handicrafts of social life—
have ever been plain enough, of course; but to see and
admire tools is not to understand the advent of those
imperishable ideas which not only transform history, but
turn all ordinary men into their mimics and mechanics.
For instance, whenever we light a candle or a fire we obey
the genius of a Palæolithic savage, who, with sparks beaten
from flint into some inflammable grass or moss or fluff from
cocoons, brought into the world the earliest missionaries,
artificial light and heat.   Similarly, whenever we walk
across a timber bridge, whether old or new, we are servants
to the earliest savage who with a stone axe cut down a tree,
causing it to fall from bank to bank of a river or chasm.
Delete from history even two mother-ideas—the invention
of wheels, for example, and the evolution of arched bridges
from Nature's models—and how many civilizations would
you cancel?   Omit from the annals of our "modern de-
mocracy" not more than three mother-ideas: the discovery
of steam as a motive-power, the discovery of microbes,
and the use of metal in bridge building.   In a twinkling
we go back to the middle of the eighteenth century, when
hospitals were cesspools,* when surgery and medicine were

* See the most valuable book on Domestic Medicine by Lister's little-known
forerunner, Dr. William Buchan, of Edinburgh.   The eighteenth edition was published
in 1803, and its pictures of social life are most helpful to a pontist.

wild empirics, when travellers in stage-coaches longed for the general Turnpike Act (a boon delayed till 1773), and when England was unspoiled by jerry-builders and a factory system. A pontist, then, if he understands his subject, looks upon genius as the solar system of human societies, hence he cannot be a willing servant to any mob-rule or mob-worship.

On the contrary, he would gladly see in every town a fine church dedicated to the men and women of genius who with great mother-ideas have tried to better the strife of human adventure. For two reasons I used the phrase "have tried to better." In the first place, the constituents of new knowledge, when mingled with the old customs and conventions, lose much of their good invariably ; and, next, the amalgam thus formed may become explosive. At this moment we see in our new art, the art of flying, how precarious is the charity that mother-ideas bring into the battle-fields of competition. What aeroplanes can do in war is already the only consideration that the mother-idea of mechanical flight receives from the most alert minds ; and very soon military engineers will be called upon to invent bomb-proof covers for every strategic bridge which cannot be displaced by a tunnel. So we compel airmanship to torment us with visions of wrecked cities, when she ought to delight us with bird's-eye views of happier countries.

In brief, the more we study mother-ideas the more clearly we perceive that they in themselves are phases of strife, for they have power to do harm as well as good. Providence for ever tries to quicken the inept human mind, since no blessing is granted to us without its attendant bane. Electricity has dangers of its own, so has fire; Pasteurism has dangers of its own, so has food; radium is curative and very perilous, like the sea or the sun; and all other good things ask us to pick our way with care between danger and utility.

The most tragic element of all in human indiscretion is the mindless routine which has deadened the brain of ordinary men. There is in Lancashire, for example, a charming valley where six or seven old bridges make a few minutes' walk a very long pilgrimage through the history of primitive conventions. Wycollar the valley is called, and antiquaries and pontists ought to go there at once, but not in motor-cars that devour topography as well as miles. One bridge is exceedingly low in the scale of thought and skill; indeed, no prehistoric tool or weapon stands below it. Even the Adam of Evolution, if he ever lived in rock-strewn places, had common sense enough probably to choose a flat stone and to lay it across a deep rivulet, so as to save his children from danger. Such is the most primeval of the Wycollar bridges: three schoolboys could make a smaller one between two April showers. For the stone is not a huge slab ten feet long by four wide, such as we find not far from Fernworthy Bridge, Dartmoor; nor is it like the single slab over the Walla Brook on Dartmoor. It is a long lintel-stone, and in eight or nine strides a little girl would cross it easily.* If the stone were new, and also alone in the valley, no one would think more of it than of a plank used as a temporary bridge; but the stone is very old, and lintel-bridges are ancient customs in the valley of Wycollar. If Nature once in a century allowed bridges to tell their tales, I should expect two of the Wycollar historians to trace their lineage through a great many ancestors until at last they came to a time when the first nomads hacked their way with flint axes through the undergrowth of Lancashire forests, and cursed in primitive words or sounds at the virile brambles whose thorns were sharper than pointed flints.

The second bridge of lintel-stones at Wycollar is a simple adaptation from one of Nature's bridges, the bridge of stepping-stones littered over the beds of rivers by earth-quakes and floods. When the stepping-stones are long you turn them on end and use them as piers; when they are short and squat you pile them up into piers; then lintel-stones are put from pier to pier, and from pier to each bank-side. Here is the A B C of primitive bridge-making with slabs, boulders, and fragments of rock. It needs very much less mother-wit than that which enabled primitive men to survive innumerable hardships, and to breed and rear those

---

* I have two photographs of it, both taken by my friend Mr. C. S. Sargisson, a Lancashire pontist. At one end the lintel rests on a rocky bank and is broken across by long use; at the other end it rests on a slab projecting from the bank, just below a stile of unmortared flags set in a picturesque wall of loose stones. The footway is much worn; and in frosty weather even a temperance reformer might slide from it with his reputation.

true artists who in Palæolithic times, about 50,000 years ago,* turned a good many European caves into the first public art galleries, famous for their rock-paintings and for their sculpture and engravings. Thus the Altamira Cavern, near Santander, in Northern Spain, and the La Madeleine cave in the Dordogne (about eighty miles east of Bordeaux), are among the prehistoric museums, or art galleries, which have given us work very far in advance of the Wycollar lintel-bridges; so far, indeed, that trees and shrubs in the valley ought to blush with shame by keeping autumn tints in their leaves all the year round. This hint from Dame Nature might awaken some little self-reproach in the Lancashire weavers and peasants whose heavy clogs clatter day after day over the lintel-stones, wearing them into troughs where rainwater collects pretty pictures from the sky.

Not long ago a busy official mind in the neighbourhood was troubled by one of the bridges at Wycollar, named the Weavers' Bridge, a dull-witted primitivity made with three lintel-stones and two rough piers in the water. Though the busy official mind was troubled it did not suggest that the bridge should be put under glass and kept with as much care as the perfect skeleton of a mastodon would receive; nor did it wish to build a successor in the cheapest style of industrial metal-work. No; what the official mind advertised as a fortunate inspiration was a foolish little act of commonplace vandalism. It set a mason to chisel out of existence the trough worn in the lintel-stones by generations

* I am quoting this approximate date from Sir Ray Lankester.

of clog-wearers! I have two photographs, now historic, in which the trough can be seen distinctly; but the poor weavers have no such consolation. Their ancestors' work has to be done all over again, and they know that their

IN THE VALLEY OF WYCOLLAR, LANCASHIRE: THE WEAVERS' BRIDGE

great-grandchildren will find in the lintel-stones not a trough but a vague hollow scarcely deep enough to hold a few raindrops. Mr. Sargisson wrote to tell me this pathetic story of a crisis in antiquarianism. But it is fair to add that the busy official mind was content with one foolish act; it spared the rude pillar on the left bank, though this rough stone looks like a small menhir and completes the primeval bridge.

And now let us look at the survival of convention under a form that is even more distressing. Is it true that in many times and lands human beings have been sacrificed not to bridges, but to the spirits of floods and storms which have been feared as destroyers of bridges? One good reference to this question will be found in Francis M. Crawford's "Ave Roma Immortalis." The most venerated bridge in ancient Rome was the Pons Sublicius, whose history dated from the time of Ancus Marcius, who reigned twenty-four years—B.C. 640–616. In much later times, long after the good fight that made Horatius Cocles famous for ever, strange ceremonies and superstitions lingered around the Pons Sublicius. On the Ides of May, which were celebrated on the fifteenth of the month, Pontiffs and Vestals came in solemn state to the bridge, accompanied by men who carried thirty effigies representing human bodies. The effigies were made of bulrushes, and one by one they were thrown into the Tiber, while the Vestals sang hymns or the priests chanted prayers. What did this rite signify? A tradition popular in Rome taught children to believe that the effigies took the place of human beings, once sacrificed to the river in May. This tradition is attacked by Ovid, "but the industrious Baracconi quotes Sextus Pompeius Festus to prove that in very early times human victims were thrown into the Tiber for one reason or another, and that human beings were otherwise sacrificed until the year of the City 657, when, Cnæus Cornelius Lentulus and Publius Licinius Crassus being consuls, the Senate made a law that no man should be sacrificed thereafter."

It is possible, if not, indeed, probable, that the effigies were made at first in order to placate the common people who were indignant over the loss of a festival. We can imagine what would be said to-day if Cup-finals were stopped by Act of Parliament; and the Romans, in their fool-fury over "sport" at second-hand, were always glad to appease their curiosity with shows of bloodshed. Further, in the folk-lore of later times bridges and rivers are connected with the primitive rite of killing women and men as a sacrifice to evil spirits. This dread tradition is related now in the Asiatic provinces of Turkey, as I learn from Sir Mark Sykes, whose "Dar-Ul-Islam" is a book for pontists to read. It was at Zakho that Sir Mark heard the following legend:—

"Many years ago workmen under their master were set to build the bridge; three times the bridge fell, and the workmen said, 'The bridge needs a life.' And the master saw a beautiful girl, accompanied by a bitch and her puppies, and he said, 'We will give the first [life] that comes by.' But the dog and her little ones hung back, so the girl was built alive into the bridge, and only her hand with a gold bracelet upon it was left outside.

"At the foot of this bridge I found the local Agha, Yussuf Pasha, superintending the collection of the sheep-tax, in which as a large landowner he has an interest."

F

Try to visualise in all their details these pictures, passing from to-day's tax-gatherer, a Pasha Lloyd George, into the drama of a very terrible superstition. The workmen can be fitted with fairly good primitive characters, for they do not suggest the sacrifice of a life until the bridge has fallen thrice. As to their master, he is a fiend, since he acts upon their suggestion at once, unmoved by the girl's beauty and the frisking springtime that accompanies her. A little dead hand—and a gleaming bracelet—and the masons chanting at their work, as bridge-builders chant now in Persia: so the drama ends, or so it would end if we could not unite it with a similar legend known almost everywhere in Europe.

Why in the Turkish story the workmen say, "The *bridge* needs a life," I do not know. Their superstition goes away from the river and its evil spirits, and from those other demons, which in olden times made winds so variable. Are we then to suppose that men have defiled the charity of bridges with bad spirits other than those that live in wilted conventions and in modern engineers? I prefer to believe that a bridge that fell three times would muddle the superstition of any workman. In fact, there are many bridges which superstition—not modesty in men—has given to the Devil, and as a rule they have been connected with the same legend, or bogie tale. Mr. Baring-Gould takes a great interest in the bridges ascribed to the Devil, and writes about them as follows in his "Book of South Wales":—

"The Devil's Bridge is twelve miles from Aberystwyth; it is over the Afon Mynach just before its junction with the Rheidol*. . . . The original bridge was constructed by the

PONT DU DIABLE, ST. GOTHARD PASS

monks of Strata Florida, at what time is unknown, but legend says it was built by the Devil.

> Old Megan Llandunach, of Pont-y-Mynach,
> Had lost her only cow;
> Across the ravine the cow was seen,
> But to get it she could not tell how.

* "The Mynach cataract consists of four leaps, making a total descent of 210 feet. The bridge has been thrown across a chasm 114 feet above the first fall and 324 feet above the bottom of the cataract."

"In this dilemma the Evil One appeared to her cowled as a monk, and with a rosary at his belt, and offered to cast a bridge across the chasm if she would promise him the first living being that should pass over it when complete. To this she gladly consented. The bridge was thrown across the ravine, and the Evil One stood bowing and beckoning to the old woman to come over and try it. But she was too clever to do that. She had noticed his left leg as he was engaged on the construction, and saw that the knee was behind in place of in front, and for a foot he had a hoof.

> In her pocket she fumbled, a crust out tumbled,
> She called her little black cur;
> The crust over she threw, the dog after it flew,
> Says she, 'The dog's yours, crafty sir!'

"Precisely the same story is told of S. Cadoc's Causeway in Brittany; of the bridge over the Maine at Frankfort, and of many and many another.

"How comes it that we have an almost identical tale in so many parts of Europe? The reason is that in all such structures a sacrifice was offered to the Spirits of Evil who haunted the place. When a storm came down on the sea, Jonah had to be flung overboard to allay it. When, in the old English ballad, a ship remained stationary, though all sails were spread, and she could make no headway, the crew 'cast the black bullets,' and the lot falls to the captain's wife, and she is thereupon thrown overboard. Vortigern sought to lay the foundations of his castle in the blood of an orphan boy. A dam broke in Holland in the seventeenth

century; the peasants could hardly be restrained from bury-
ing a living child under it, when reconstructed, to ensure
its stability.*

"When the [Cistercian] monks of Strata Florida threw
the daring arch over the chasm, they so far yielded to the
popular superstition as to bury a dog beneath the base of
the arch, or to fling one over the parapet."

There! We have followed a superstition—a vile convention in ignorance and cowardice—from the Pons Sublicius
in Ancient Rome to the Pont-y-Mynach in South Wales;
and the best we can say of it is that in Pagan Rome it went
from human victims to effigies of men and women, while in
Christian times it passed from human victims to dogs.†
Mr. Baring-Gould has told us that in bridges, and "in all
such structures, a sacrifice was offered to the Spirits of Evil
who haunted the place." Yet it was not *in* a structure—a
finished building—that Vortigern wished to offer his sacrifice; he "sought *to lay the foundations* of his castle in the
blood of an orphan boy," so his aim was to placate the
Spirits of Evil before his castle was built. As to his conception of the spiritual agencies to be appeased, it would
mingle his own passions with the fears bred by his primitive fanaticism. For, as Darwin says, "savages would
naturally attribute to spirits the same passions, the same

---

* What does this phrasing mean? I wonder. Is the living child to be reconstructed? in order that its body when buried under the new dam may be strong enough
as a foundation?

† To-day, in some parts of China, a living pig is thrown into a river when a
bridge is endangered by a flood. (See p. 248.)

love of vengeance or simplest form of justice, and the same affections which they themselves felt."

Now in the case of bridges we have to identify primitive men with the terror inspired by storms and floods; a terror difficult for us to understand in our sheltered lives. Have you read Matthew Paris, who lived in the reign of Henry III? If not, go to him and study the tempests that he described, and see how villages were desolated by winds and inundations. Amid these disasters the ignorant would cling to ancient superstitions; fear would be pagan out of doors whatever faith might say in church; and I have no doubt at all that the many so-called Devil's Bridges were as supernatural to the mediæval peasant as were witches. The Dutch of the Middle Ages were more advanced in domestic civilization than our own ancestors; and yet at heart they were cruel pagans, even as late as the seventeenth century, as Mr. Baring-Gould has shown. How very humble human nature ought to be!

Let us pass on, then, to a convention that does not reek like a stricken field. One of the best historians in architecture, Viollet-le-Duc, found in the hills of Savoy a primeval bridge whose structure had been changed very little, if at all, since the days when its ancestors were described by Cæsar and used by the Gauls. It is a timber bridge, known in France as *un empilage*, a thing piled together rudely, and not constructed with art. Indeed, it needs no carpentry, so it is far behind the social genius of prehistoric lake-dwellers. To make a simple Gaulish bridge,

as to-day in Savoy, we must choose a deep-lying river with
rugged banks ; then with water-worn boulders we make on
each bank a rough foundation about fifteen feet square, or
more. Upon this we raise a criss-cross of tree trunks,
taking care that the horizontal trees jut out farther and
farther across the water, narrowing the gap to be bridged
by four or five pines. Each criss-cross must be " stiffened "
or filled in with pebbles and bits of rock ; and across the
unfinished road of pines thick boards are nailed firmly.
Viollet-le-Duc says :—

"Cette construction primitive . . . rappelle singulière-
ment ces ouvrages Gaulois dont parle César, et qui se com-
posaient de troncs d'arbres posés à l'angle droit par rangées,
entre lesquelles on bloquait des quartiers de roches. Ce
procédé, qui n'est qu'un empilage, doit remonter à la plus
haute antiquité ; nous le signalons ici pour faire connaître
comment certaines traditions se perpétuent à travers les
siècles, malgré les perfectionnements apportés par la civil-
isation, et combien elles doivent toujours fixer l'attention de
l'archéologue."

Does anyone suppose that Savoy would have been loyal
to a prehistoric bridge if all primitiveness had vanished
from her social life?

Not that Savoy is the only place where criss-cross
bridges are still in vogue. Much finer specimens are to
be found in Kashmír, thrown across the river Jhelum,
the Hydaspes of Greek historians. At Srínagar, the capital
city, founded in the sixth century A.D., there is a quite

wonderful example, for it has many spans, and corbelled out from the footway is a quaint little street of frail shops, rickety cabins with gabled roofs, and so unequal in size that they are charmed with an amusing inequality.   I have several photographs of this bridge, and in them I see always with a renewed pleasure its ancestry, its descent from the prehistoric lake-villages, those heralds of Venice and of Old London Bridge (p. 216).   All the piers are made with deodar logs piled up in the criss-cross manner ; those that stretch across the river are cut in varying lengths, and each succeeding row is longer than the one beneath it, so the logs in a brace of piers project towards each other farther and farther over the water, till at last they form an arched shape ; not an arch perfect in outline, of course, since the head of it is flattened by the long bearing beams of the roadway.   Still, the arched shape is very notice-able.

A pontist should study these rude arches with care, and connect them with similar arches in the Gaulish bridges of Savoy, and also with the historic fact that the first arches built with *voussoirs* (i.e. arch-stones) were evolved from vaults roughly constructed with parallel courses of stone and layers of timber (p. 155).   It is probable that the parallel layers of timber or rows of logs came before the parallel courses of stone, as the evolution of architecture passed from wood to stone.   Forests much more than rocks and quarries have been an inspiration to primitive builders, as if the handling of wood has quickened in human nature

AT ALBI, ON THE TARN, IN FRANCE, SHOWING ON OUR RIGHT
THE OLD HOUSES, AND ON OUR LEFT, BEYOND THE BRIDGE,
THE GREAT OLD CHURCH, FAMOUS FOR ITS FORTIFICATIONS

an arboreal instinct dating from the family trees in the descent of man.

However, another criss-cross bridge in Kashmír ought to be studied in photographs; it is carried on six piers over the Jhelum at Baramula—quite close to the Himalayas; the piers rise from boat-shaped platforms that meet the oncoming water as boats do, with their blunt stems looking brave as rearguards. The parapet is a simple latticework, and the abutments are masonry. Here we have a type of bridge perhaps quite similar to the one from which the Gauls got their rude methods, long after the craft of the lake-dwellers had left its sheltered moorings and adventured across wide rivers.

Is there any concrete evidence to suggest that the bridge with criss-cross piers has gone through many phases of change, of growth or of decadence? Yes. At Archangel, in North Russia, the criss-cross piers are more primitive; instead of being arched they are upright and stiff; but as the bridge is nearly a quarter of a mile long, and as it is taken down every spring (before the ice breaks up noisily, and the Dwina thunders into a raging torrent), crude workmanship in a hurried routine is excusable. The main point is that a bridge akin to the Gaulish type and to the variation in Kashmír exists in North Russia.

And another variation is met with at Bhutan, in India. Brangwyn has drawn it, and we shall study it later in a page on gateway-towers (p. 272). In the highlands of Eastern Kurdistan, the borderland of Asiatic Turkey and

Persia, travellers find a bridge akin to the Bhutan variety. An excellent book on these highlands has been published,* and its authors, very generously, have written for me some valuable notes on the bridges. Before I quote them in full, let me ask you to remember that in Eastern Kurdistan timber is uncommon; hence the criss-cross bridge has been evolved into another sort of primitive structure—a third cousin, several times removed. A Kurdistan bridge is built as follows: "A site is selected, if one can be found, where two immovable and flat-topped masses of rock face one another across the stream to be bridged: an abutment of unhewn stones is built on these, solid, until a height has been reached sufficient to be safe from any flood.

"Then a bracket of four or more rows of poplar trunks is constructed on each abutment; short stout trunks form the bottom row, and those of each succeeding one are naturally longer than the preceding. Unless the bridge is unusually wide in the footway four poplars are enough to form a row, and the butts of the trees, which are kept shore-wards, are weighted down with big stones as counter-weights to hold them in place.

"The top of each row of trunks projects perhaps five feet beyond the preceding one, so that when a bracket of four rows is completed, it may project perhaps twenty feet over the stream.

"When the corresponding bracket has been completed,

* "The Cradle of Mankind." By the Rev. W. A. Wigram, D.D., and Edgar T. A. Wigram. London, 1914.

two long poplar trunks are slung by withies from bracket end to bracket end, a footway of withy hurdles, resting on faggots, is laid down over all, and the bridge is complete. The length of this centre span is of course limited by the height of the poplars available. I should think fifty feet the extreme possible.

"If the width of the river makes it necessary, one or more piers of stone,—I have seen as many as three,—are erected in midstream, preferably on rock foundations. Each of these carries a bracket on each side, but this double bracket is usually made of 'whole trunks' and these naturally need no counter-weighting.

"As a rule the footway is about four feet wide, and the whole structure is very elastic, so that, as it is guiltless of handrails, it requires a steady head in the passenger. Further, the central span often acquires a pronounced 'sag,' and not seldom an equally pronounced tilt to one side or other. Ancient rule says that the passenger ought not to look down in crossing such a place, lest the sight of water whirling below should unnerve him. In Kurdistan, however, look down he must, and make the best of the hurdles that form the footway; they abound in holes and other traps for the unwary, and a stumble may mean disaster. These bridges, then, though admirably planned (for they are true cantilevers), are not built in the most convenient manner. It is characteristically Oriental, this union of real fineness of design with great casualness in construction and in upkeep. The piers are invariably of stone, never of wood. Good timber is almost unknown in Kurdistan. The poplar grows well, but it is at best only a good pole. Stone, on the other hand, is embarrassingly abundant.

"Dry-stone arches are thrown over smaller streams, but their builders, though acquainted with the principle of the vault, do not venture on a span of more than thirty feet!" *

How do you like the antiquity of conventions? Does it not make you feel that the greatest part of mankind has never shown a particle of desire that its civil institutions should be improved? Note, too, that convention among men is inferior to the instinct of animals, for animals invariably repeat themselves with a passionate interest, whereas we in our formulas grow more and more unfeeling and automatic. Even rabbits when they dig their burrows seem to be guided by inspiration, as if routine work with them is an appetite, like love and hunger; so very different are they from the conservative peasants of Savoy, whose dull routine has delivered down through the centuries a primeval bridge which an hour's thought could have improved.

One day, let us hope, most men will realise that it is woefully commonplace to be as other men; then conventions will go out of vogue. Courts and clubs will invent new and good etiquettes every year; no game will be stereotyped; and laws will command that such and such things be altered and improved by given dates. For example, if an Act of Parliament decreed that during the next ten years all the

* Notes by the Rev. W. A. Wigram, D.D.

railway bridges in England must be made less uncomely
and less at odds with the needs of military defence, I have
no doubt that compulsion, the scout of civil progress, would
discover among engineers more than enough invention.

Railway bridges have been built in obedience to a brace
of conventional arguments. It has been argued, first, that
because traffic and trade are the main considerations, there-
fore art is not a matter to be considered; next, that because
boards of directors have to please their shareholders, there-
fore a most strenuous economy must be advertised in a very
evident manner, even although its results blot fine landscapes with the shame of uninspired craftsmanship.

Thirty-four years have passed since the late E. M.
Barry, R.A., in a thoughtful book, asked the public to understand that modern engineering was not architecture at all,
but mere building; and he chose as an example of horrible
work the Britannia Bridge over the Menai Straits. " Here
we have the adoption of the trabeated principle of large
iron beams laid upon supports of masonry, which rise from
the valley beneath, and tower up above the beams to a
height far exceeding that which is necessary for their
support. I well remember the animated discussions in
scientific circles as to the form and design of these beams,
which were ultimately decided upon as rectangular tubes.
In the many discussions of the merits and defects of
circular, elliptical and square sections, I do not recollect
that a word was said about architectural effect [or about
military convenience and strategy]. Had anyone ventured

to suggest that this, too, was an important matter, and that
an unsightly structure would be an eyesore for all time, he
would have been promptly told that the forms to be
employed were an affair of science alone, and that utility
pure and simple would dictate their arrangement. In the
result a lovely valley was defaced. . . ."

The same convention in mean tradecraft is shown in the
tale about Tennyson and the jerry-builder. "Why do you
cut down these trees?" the poet asked reprovingly.
"Trees are beautiful things." "Ah!" answered the jerry-
builder, "trees are luxuries; what we need is utility."
And what this utility has done for us may be seen in a
thousand railway bridges as bad as those that disgrace
even the Harrow Road, near by Paddington Station.

It is not my argument that every railway bridge in
England is underbred and crapulous; here and there an
engineer has made an effort to be architectural, but the usual
level of taste is exceedingly vulgar, and not in railway
bridges only. Even the Tower Bridge, London, a vast feat
in engineering, is so conventional with a meretricious
mediævalism that it needs the screening dust and mist that
veil the Thames. This is among the modern bridges that
Brangwyn has drawn and painted, raising them into art as
a record of current history. Nothing moves him more than
the huge mechanisms that seize upon to-day's life and turn
it into their obedient slave. Men dwindle ever more and
more in scale as machines become fatal in their enormous
bulk, like Super-Dreadnoughts and the "Titanic"; not to

forget such vulnerable monsters as the bridges of New York, which airships sent forth by Mr. H. G. Wells have already attacked with prophetic success. Is man really doomed to be the tool of machines? Is this to be his final convention?

In one great picture by Brangwyn the High Level Bridge at Newcastle represents our time. Historically the High Level Bridge has much interest; it displaced the Britannia Bridge as an object of scientific veneration, and from the first it has ranked high in the conventional ugliness that the British public has accepted from engineers. When the Britannia Bridge was proved to be a bad railway line (trains were the decisive critics), and when men of science after weighing their after-thoughts began to find fault with the distribution of metal in the section of its tubes, then engineers said, "And now—now we must have a good railway bridge, completely scientific in all respects." It was to be built with two roadways, the one for common traffic passing under a railway, so that business folk might be comforted by the noise overhead, which would be as music to any believer in a pushful industrialism. Six arches of metal would be united to five piers and the abutments; their spans would have precisely the same width, i.e. 138 ft. 10 in., for minds long used to office hours and ledgers would enjoy a dead uniformity. Indeed, everybody was pleased with these plans; and in 1849, when Queen Victoria opened the High Level Bridge, artists alone were unexcited with joy. All the rest of the English world imagined that science, at the cost of only £243,000, had achieved a metal masterpiece. New London Bridge had cost six times as much (i.e. £1,458,311), and her materials were stones, not metals, so once more the north of England had scored heavily over the south. "Besides," remarked the engineers, "we have put into the superstructure 321 tons of wrought-iron, and into the arched ribs 4,728 tons of cast-iron. Economy... Scientific economy.... And we have now in use a perfect example of the true bowstring arch in which no cross-bracing is needed." All this, when discussed at dinners, enriched the flavour of champagne; and opinion became so "heady" that even the "Encyclopædia Britannica" in its eighth edition received the High Level Bridge as an inspired work, and gave to its engineering as much space as the thrifty Romans would have given to all their Spanish bridges and aqueducts.

At last, and all of a sudden, a reaction came; enthusiasm not only caught a chill, it passed in a hurry from its tropical summer into a bad winter of discontent. Scientists went so far as to declare that the High Level Bridge was a youthful indiscretion, advertised publicly in a material which might endure for centuries; and this change of opinion had a great effect on the "Encyclopædia Britannica," whose ninth edition gave only eighteen lines to its former favourite. Even the bowstring arch was praised no longer, "being essentially more expensive and heavier than a true girder."

Such are the comedies invented by our new playwright,

THE TOWER BRIDGE, LONDON

the genius of civil engineers. Still, the High Level Bridge at Newcastle looks well on a misty day; by moonlight it is more impressive than a Whistler nocturne; and in Brangwyn's art it represents our industrial age with a vigour that is manly and impressive.

For the rest, from the pictures in this book you will be able to choose for yourself many a convention in the craft of bridge-building. Study, for example, the arches and their shapes, noting those which have a character of their own. These mark a new departure, and are famous. Thus the bridge at Avignon is admired by technicians because its architect, the great Saint Bénézet, gave to the arches what Professor Fleeming Jenkin has described as "an elliptical outline with the radius of curvature smaller at the crown than at the haunch, a form which accords more truly with the linear equilibrated arch than the modern flat ellipse with the largest radius at the crown." Good Bénézet! Seven hundred and thirty years have gone by since he turned from the Roman tradition of semicircular arches, and designed an excellent arch of his own, a beautiful thing, with a look of triumph in its quiet dignity. Many writers think that L'arc de Saint Bénézet is original also in construction, its vault being composed of four separate bands put side by side in stones of about equal bulk. Sometimes this method of building is condemned as weak, though four of Bénézet's arches have outlived seven centuries of war; and what engineer would feel disgraced if he were baffled by the terrific floods to which the Rhône is subject?

G

Moreover, Bénézet was not an originator in this matter; he borrowed from the Romans. In his time there was a bridge that carried the Via Domitiana over the Vidourle at Pont Ambroise; the vaults of its five arches were built in precisely the same manner, in four parallel arcs or bands that touched each other; and the bridge was notable for other reasons, and thus attractive to all bridge-builders. In the first place, a Bull of Pope Adrian IV, dated 1156, now treasured at Nîmes in the Church of Nôtre Dame, has proved that in the twelfth century a chapel was built either on or from the middle of the bridge; it was dedicated to St. Mary, and it belonged to the chapter of Nîmes Cathedral. A Roman bridge sanctified by a Christian chapel recalls to one's mind the devotion of the Flavian family that placed the monogram of Christ among the ensigns of ancient Rome. Unless the chapel stood out on corbels from the side of the bridge, it must have been a tiny place of prayer, for the bridge was only three metres wide, while the Via Domitiana had an average width of six metres. Further, the roadway across the bridge was peculiar; it followed in gentle curves the contour of the arches, instead of being either flat (as in most Roman bridges) or with a slight incline at the abutment ends (as in the bridge of Augustus at Rimini).* We cannot

---

* To-day only a ruin can be studied at Pont Ambroise: two isolated arches and the lower part of an abutment; but recent French writers draw attention to the technical structure of the arches. In the under surface of each vault four arcs or bands are placed side by side. See Vol. III, Part II, p. 294, "Géographie générale du Département de l'Hérault." Published by La Société Languedocienne, Montpellier, 1905.

suppose that this bridge, so noteworthy in several ways, was unknown to Bénézet, head of the Pontist Friars. Anyhow, the immense Pont du Gard, near Nîmes, a Roman masterpiece, must have been known to him ; and the arches of its second tier have in the belly of each vault three parallel bands of equal-sized stones. If this method of construction be unsound, how are we to explain the heroic stability of the Pont du Gard, the finest of all the Roman aqueducts?

Myself, I do not believe that Bénézet was inexpert as a borrower. We shall meet him again (p. 236), but let us note here that his work is rhythmical and charming ; so it does not belong to the underbred heaviness that bridge-builders often copied from the art of mediæval fortification. This art was an unthrifty engineer ; it employed far and and away too much blind masonry. Castle walls were ten feet thick, and brave soldiers at home feared the light of day, merely to show respect for arrows and machine-worked catapults. They were not discreet ; they made caution too timid and too uncomfortable. Did gallant married knights forget to sleep in their suits of mail? Was a honeymoon in armour a trifle more tiresome than were twelfth-century castles with their arrow slits for windows? For many a year home life was an ill-smelling twilight, particularly to persons of rank ; and from this we may infer that the custom of war during the Middle Ages went hand-in-hand with a superstitious dread of death. Bénézet needed courage as well as genius when he slighted in a graceful manner the ponderous conventions of safety that ruled in his day over castles (1177–1185).   It was his arch that saved the vigour of his design from being dull and clumsy.

Some other arches in French bridges have provoked paper wars.   This is true of those in the bridges at Albi and Espalion, chosen by Brangwyn partly because of their controversial interest, and partly because they illustrate a mood of handicraft which may be called the uncouth picturesque.

AN OLD TOWN BRIDGE IN PERUGIA, ITALY, TO ILLUSTRATE A POINTED ARCH WHICH HAS
IN ITS CURVE A SORT OF LINGERING SENTIMENT FOR THE ROUND ARCH OF THE ROMANS

IV

CONTROVERSIES

STUDENTS are tested and judged by their attitude
to controversies. Common sense should keep them
from partisanship; and when they feel tempted to
look on as mere spectators, they should remember that
crowds at boxing matches are very apt to form wrong
opinions. It is better by far to laugh at both sides by
caricaturing the weak points of a discussion. In a few
days a student will learn which side is the more difficult to

85

caricature, and this knowledge will help him to sift all rubbish from a controversy and to form a judgment of his own on facts and on inferences. As Sir Thomas Browne said, a man should be something that all men are not, and individual in somewhat beside his person and his name.

The bridges at Albi and Espalion have caused some men to break old friendships over a simple question, namely: "When were pointed arches used for the first time in French bridges? At what date were they brought from the East?" As the pointed arch was copied by Europeans, not invented by them, the precise date of the mimicry ought not to excite a pontist; it is a thing for antiquaries to be flurried about. If the question ran in another form: "Was the pointed arch in French bridges an independent discovery?" then a battle and some exploded reputations would be worth while. But no such hypothesis has been put forward by either side in a warm dispute. One party declares that as early as the time of Charlemagne, towards the end of the eighth century, or the beginning of the ninth (768–814), a French builder seems to have played the part of the sedulous ape to Eastern architecture, cribbing the pointed arch, and using it without much skill in the bridge of Espalion, whose construction (as documents prove incontestably) was ordered by Charlemagne himself. In this bald statement there is no challenge, no provocation; it is nothing more than a conjecture supported by a documented fact.

If Charlemagne had been a weak ruler, like Louis the Indolent, it would be fair to suppose that his commands were neglected more often than obeyed; then we could not accept his character as a fact of greater value in a controversy than a command of his mentioned in authentic documents. Let us say that the Black Prince or his father ordered a bridge to be built at a given place; we have documents to prove this, and at the place named in the documents a very old bridge is extant. Should we not read these documents by the light of the reputation won by the Black Prince or by his father? Myself, I should say at once, "His orders were obeyed." And so, too, in the case of Charlemagne. I accept his character as a guarantee that he was obeyed at Espalion; and in this I am supported by Charlemagne's general attitude to roads and bridges. It was he who made many an effort to keep the highways in repair, trying to rescue them from the great disorder into which their administration had been thrown by the decline and fall of the Romans. He created the right to exact tolls, and sanctioned on the roads the use of statute labour and of fatigue duty done by soldiers. During his reign of forty-six years he restored much Roman work and set in movement a system that did not overtax the poor finances of his Empire; but after his death the Empire was divided and continual wars put an end to civil advancement.

As Charlemagne needed a bridge at Espalion we may believe that a bridge was built there between the years 768 and 814. Does the bridge still exist, or was it rebuilt in the twelfth century, or later? There is no evidence on these points; hence the controversy. Those who think it possible, if not probable, that the bridge as it is now, apart from periodical repairs, belongs to Charlemagne's reign, draw arguments from the uncouth workmanship; and even their opponents admit that the bridge is "une œuvre barbare n'offrant absolument aucun intérêt: a barbaric work without any interest at all"* (as architecture). Why, then, should any Frenchman wish to assign this barbaric bridge to a much later century than the eighth? Ah! Here we touch once again the influence of conventions. A belief current among antiquaries has connected the pointed arch with the first Crusade, and so with the last decade of the eleventh century (1095) and the first years of the twelfth. Godfrey of Bouillon, on July 15, 1099, was made King of Jerusalem, and before this date many Crusaders had returned home. M. Degrand says: "At this time, about the year 1100, Crusaders returned to France after their stay in the East, notably at Antioch, where monuments of Persian origin must have been numerous; and without doubt they brought home with them sufficient knowledge to introduce the pointed vault into the national architecture. Thus it is easy to understand why the twelfth century has been chosen as the date for the earliest work done in France with the pointed style. We conjecture, then, that the bridges at Espalion and Albi, in their present state, have not the antiquity which supposition has given to

* See a very helpful book, "Ponts en Maçonnerie," by E. Degrand, Inspecteur. Général des Ponts et Chaussées, and Jean Résal, Ingénieur des Ponts et Chaussées-Two vols., illustrated; Béranger, Paris; price 40 francs.

FAMOUS BRIDGE AT ESPALION IN FRANCE
SAID TO DATE FROM THE EIGHTH CENTURY

them ; and that they must have been rebuilt (*ils ont dû être reconstruits*) after the periods from which their first construction dates."

This argument has a tongue and no legs. Even Nature in the Pont d'Arc at Ardèche had given a pointed arch to France ; * and how can we dare to suppose that no traveller from the East in the time of Charlemagne could have brought with him to Espalion any knowledge of pointed arches ? Was this knowledge guarded so carefully that nothing less than a Crusade could bring it to France? Intelligent soldiers would certainly note the details of Eastern architecture, and when they returned home their talk and their tales would be listened to with eagerness by French craftsmen. More than this we have no right to believe. It is mere hollow claptrap to argue that no French architect or builder could have received earlier news of the pointed arches. But claptrap—is it not the drum of controversy? It makes a great noise, and gives men heart to fight for poor beliefs.

So irrational has this controversy become that even M. Degrand, a most thoughtful pontist as a rule, includes the bridge at Albi in his defective argument, though it cannot be older than the year 1035, because at this date its construction was arranged at a great public meeting held by the Seigneur of Albi and the clergy. Not even then was it possible for a Frenchman to know that pointed arches were common in the East ! M. Degrand accepts the

* See note on p. 6.

date 1035, and thinks it probable that the building was
"begun" then or a few years later; "but," he adds, "we
have no proof that the bridge existed before 1178, in which
year, according to a contemporary document, a body of
troops used it to cross the Tarn." If M. Degrand were able
to prove that Albi Bridge was new in the year 1178, then
we should forget his conventional belief in the first Crusade;
a fact would be very welcome after his parade of idle suppositions.   Further, the meeting of 1035 must guide us until
we know that its decision was *not* carried into action.   It is a
policy of evasion to argue as follows : " In the Middle Ages
building projects were often delayed, as in the case of the
noble brick bridge at Montauban ; * so we cannot attach
any importance to the meeting of 1035 at Albi.   Though
the desire to have a bridge was approved then by the
Seigneur, by the clergy and by the people, yet a hundred
and one things may have intervened between the project
and its realisation.   In 1178 a bridge at Albi was strong
enough to be used without risk by troops, but why connect
it with the meeting of 1035 ? To do so would be rash indeed,
since our aim is to add a pointed arch to the cross worn by
the Crusaders."

So we turn to the evidence of workmanship; and here
again we can shoot at M. Degrand with his own bullets.
To show that Albi Bridge is a clumsy structure without art
is to prove it unworthy of the year 1178, when the Pontist

* See the brilliant sketch by Frank Brangwyn, and the story of the bridge
on p. 254.

Friars were active in France, and when at Avignon the genius of Saint Bénézet was planning a wonderful achievement. The more just fault we can find with Albi Bridge as a piece of building, the more fit we make it for the year 1035. Yet M. Degrand, passing from wayward controversy into art-criticism, gives himself away in an excess of fault-finding. He forgets that the bridge, a bad model as architecture, is uncommonly picturesque, and he writes as follows: " There are seven pointed arches, and their spans vary— without order or regulation—from 9 m. 75 c. to 16 m. ; the piers in bulk are variable also, some of them being 6 m. 50 c. thick, that is to say, two-thirds of the adjacent voids ; they are badly aligned and the spandrils belong almost all to different planes. The breakwaters jut out too far, and meet the current with angles of even less than forty-five degrees ; while the buttresses behind, on the down-stream side, are rectangular and almost without projection. Last of all, there is no ornament to dress the nude spandrils and to set them apart from the parapets. *C'est là, en fait, une œuvre barbare. . . .*"

Let us conjecture, then, that this barbaric bridge at Albi, with its seven pointed arches, may belong, not to the time of Saint Bénézet, but to the year 1035, or thereabouts. Nearly a century ago, in 1822, it was considerably enlarged, but the arches were not rebuilt. The bridge must have been restored many times, but there is no proof that it was reconstructed in the thirteenth century or in the twelfth. Besides, sportsmen in a controversy should be fair. Yet a good many books of reference say: "The Pont du Tarn at Albi, whose first construction goes back to the year 1035 or 1040, is thirteenth-century work"—a calumny on a very beautiful period in the evolution of Gothic architecture. We should have far too much admiration for the Valentré Bridge at Cahors to give the Pont du Tarn to the thirteenth century; and several other bridges in France do ample justice to the successors of Saint Bénézet. For example, there is the Pont St. Esprit, a masterpiece of the Pontist Friars, and a work so vast in length that Brangwyn is never tired of recalling his first impressions of its magnitude.* If, again, we wish to study work that comes to us from the twelfth century, then we turn to the famous bridges at Béziers and Carcassonne.

As to the bridge at Espalion, it has four unequal arches, and three of them are pointed, more or less. Their form is experimental, and seems to mark a first experiment in pointed Gothic. One arch, indeed, when looked at from underneath, might be an ill-planned Roman arch, so poor is its "ogival" or pointed shape; but yet the bridge, as the Brangwyn sketch bears witness, shows how an effort was made to free craftsmen from the convention of semicircular vaults. If we connect it with the age of Charlemagne we may argue thus: "Perhaps the masons were among those who at times restored a neglected Roman bridge; and perhaps the bridgemaster had gained some knowledge of Eastern arches, either at first-hand or from travellers or

* See the picture on p. 293.

PONT DU TARN AT ALBI IN FRANCE. SAID
TO DATE FROM ABOUT THE YEARS 1035-40

from drawings. East and West were united then as they were in much earlier times, so that information from each must have been conveyed to the other." On the other hand, if we guess that the first bridge at Espalion was rebuilt in the twelfth century or in the thirteenth, then we must say also that the town of Espalion was too lazy even to seek advice from the Pontist Friars. Larousse has set forth the position very well: "The most ancient of the extant bridges, constructed in mediæval France, appears to be the one at Espalion (A.D. 780); its date is contested because we find it associated with the pointed arch; but this arch already had been used for two centuries in the East."*

So we may conclude, in a conjecture perhaps strong enough to be called a hypothesis, that the pointed style in architecture may have been brought to France on three occasions: in the reign of Charlemagne, then in the first half of the eleventh century, and then after the first Crusade. There is no need to set much store by the second presumed inspiration, since the idea for Albi Bridge may have been taken from the Pont du Tarn at Espalion.

England as well as France has a controversy over arches; and I mention the fact because of Brangwyn's masterly pen-drawing of the Monnow Bridge at Monmouth —a fortified work of the Middle Ages. In this bridge the arches are ribbed, like those in the bridges at Kirkby Lonsdale, and Warkworth, and Rotherham, at Baslow and

---

* Much more: we shall see (pp. 156,160) that a pointed vault was built in ancient Egypt. The Babylonians also built pointed arches and vaults.

Bakewell, in Eamont Bridge at Penrith, at Ross in Herefordshire (Elizabethan), and elsewhere. When was the
ribbed arch first used in bridges?

The use of ribbed vaulting in English churches dates
from the twelfth century; it came to England from France.
Yet Scotland, the historic friend of France, used it very
rarely in bridges; perhaps only once, in the famous Old
Bridge of Dee near Aberdeen, which dates from the beginning
of the sixteenth century. Mr. G. M. Fraser, a Scotch
pontist, tells me that he has looked in vain throughout
Scotland for another example. Old Stirling Bridge, and
the Brig o' Doon, and the Auld Brig o' Ayr, and Devor-
gilla's Bridge at Dumfries, all finely historic and various,
have plain arches. On the other hand, ribbed arches are
fairly common in North English bridges. One of the best
examples architecturally is the graceful single arch that Sir
Walter Scott loved in Twizel Bridge, that enabled Lord
Surrey to outflank the Scotch before the battle of Flodden
Field.* Why the frugal Scotch were unattracted by a new
and thrifty way of building I cannot explain, unless by
supposing that they loved convention even more than a hard
economy. Viollet-le-Duc estimates that in *arcs-doubleaux*,
or ribbed arches, builders use a third less of tooled and
clavated masonry; hence a great saving not of cost only,
but of dead weight also.

* Twizel Bridge, over the Till, has a very beautiful arch which is slightly pointed;
it has a span of 90 ft. 7 ins., and a distance of 46 ft. separates the parapet from water-
level. Tradition says that a lady of the Selby family built this bridge, one of the most
famous in England.

And there were other economies. An *arc-doubleau* is
the simplest form of ribbed vaulting : at given intervals in
the building of a vault a concentric arch is supposited, or
the vault itself at intervals is made much thicker than
at others. In Poitou, where ribbed bridges were studied
by Viollet-le-Duc, the intervals between the ribs are filled
in with flagging under the roadway ; and with this material
—or with ashlar—the spandrils above the ribs are packed.
When flagstones are used, and rain-water filters down from
the roadway, no harm is done ; the wet trickles away through
the joints of the flagstones, without causing the haunches of
an arch to throw out saltpetre : a mishap that occurs often
when arches are unribbed. I am writing here with the
mind of Viollet-le-Duc, who makes two other valuable
statements : first, that ribbed bridges are notable in Poitou ;
next, that they seem to belong to the beginning of the
thirteenth century, or perhaps even to the end of the
twelfth.

Now it was in 1214 that King John invaded Poitou
without success ; fifteen years later Henry III misconducted
an expedition to the same province ; and again in 1242 he
landed in Poitou to be thrashed at Taillebourg. His aim,
like that of John, was to win back the Empire of Henry II.
May we then suppose that ribbed bridges came to us from
Poitou ? Certainly the mind of England during the first
half of the thirteenth century was drawn towards the sea-
ward provinces of France.

Still, it was the Cistercians of the twelfth century who

introduced ribbed vaulting into English churches,* and why not into bridges as a development therefrom? At a time when bridges were united to the Church in many ways, new methods in sacred architecture would be passed on to bridge-building. Not only were bridges protected by the Church (p. 40), many were built by the lay clergy and by the monastic orders; and when a bridge had neither a chapel nor a little place for prayer, it was sanctified by a shrine, or —and this was usual—by a cross or crucifix raised up from the parapet above the middle arch. It marked the centre of the bridge, and I dare say peasants believed that it prevented evil spirits from passing above running water. Altogether, it is very probable that the first ribbed bridges were built in the twelfth century, though I have no quite conclusive evidence to offer from extant examples.

The six pointed arches in New Bridge on Thames, near Kingston, are very well ribbed, but they are Early English, not Norman; they belong to the early part of the thirteenth century. At Fountains Abbey, Yorkshire, are two small bridges, one Norman, the other Early English; both were built by Cistercian monks, yet neither has ribbed arches, so that I supply you with a fact that runs counter to my hypothesis. At Durham there are two bridges reputed to be of Norman origin, and one of them has two ribbed arches with a span of ninety feet. It is the Framwellgate Bridge at the north end of the city. According to the eleventh

* Read the delightful monograph on Kirkstall Abbey by Sir W. H. St. John Hope and Mr. Bilson of Hull.

LE PONT DE VERNAY, AIRVAULT, DEUX-SÈVRES. A FAMOUS
BRIDGE WITH RIBBED ARCHES, FRENCH ROMANESQUE PERIOD, XII CENTURY

edition of the "Encyclopædia Britannica," Framwellgate Bridge was "built in the thirteenth century and rebuilt in the fifteenth," but no authorities are given, and counter evidence may be accepted as more probable. For example, William Hutchinson * says without hesitation, giving references, that Framwellgate Bridge was built by Bishop Flambard who died in 1128, after holding the See of Durham for 29 years 3 months and 7 days. Flambard "fortified the castle with a moat, and strengthened the banks of the river, over which he built an arched bridge of stone, at the foot of the castle, now called Framwellgate Bridge." In the fifteenth century the bridge was restored by the famous Bishop Fox, who began his reign at Durham in 1494, and died in 1502. There is no evidence to show that the restoration was a rebuilding, and the character of the arches does not belong to the time of Bishop Fox. Even Parker, in his "Glossary of Architecture," 1850, is not surprised that the Framwellgate Bridge should be given to the Norman period, for he mentions this attribution and describes the ribbed arches as perfect. The parapet is scorned as "modern." For many years—I know not how long—a large gateway-tower stood at one end of this bridge, but in 1760 it was taken down.

One of the most famous Norman bridges in Old England was the one that crossed the Lea at Stratford-at-Bow. It was founded and endowed by Queen Mathilda, wife of Henry I. In 1831, eight years before its demolition,

---

* "The History and Antiquities of Durham." Newcastle, MDCCLXXXV.

H

a print was issued of Bow Bridge, and ribs can be seen under two of the three arches.   The central arch is represented in a direct front view, so the vaulting cannot be studied ; but Lewis, who in 1831 published his "Topographical Dictionary of England," found ribs in the three arches.   So a very important question arises here : Was Bow Bridge ever rebuilt ?   M. J. J. Jusserand shall answer this question ; he has read all the evidence, he makes no reference to ribbed arches, he is unbiassed, and his pictures are lively :—

"Whether Queen Mathilda (twelfth century) got wetted or not, as is supposed, on passing the ford of the river at Stratford-atte-Bow—that same village where afterwards the French was spoken which amused Chaucer—it is certain that she thought she did a meritorious work in constructing two bridges there.   Several times repaired, Bow Bridge was still standing in 1839.   The Queen endowed her foundation, granting land and a water-mill to the Abbess of Barking with a perpetual charge thereon for the maintenance of the bridge and the neighbouring roadway.   When the Queen died, an abbey for men was founded at the same Stratford close to the bridges, and the Abbess hastened to transfer to the new monastery the property in the mill and the charge of the reparations.   The Abbot did them at first, then he wearied of it, and ended by delegating the looking after them to one Godfrey Pratt.   He had built this man a house on the causeway beside the bridge, and made him a yearly grant.   For a long time Pratt carried out the contract, 'getting assistance,' says an inquiry of Edward I (1272-

1307), 'from some passers-by, but without often having recourse to their aid.' Also he received the charity of travellers, and his affairs prospered. They prospered so well that the Abbot thought he might withdraw the pension; Pratt indemnified himself in the best way he could. He set up iron bars across the bridge and made all pay who passed over,* except the rich, for he made prudent exception 'for the nobility; he feared them and let them pass without molesting them.' The dispute terminated only in the time of Edward II, when the Abbot recognised his fault, took back the charge of the bridge, and put down the iron bars, the toll, and Godfrey Pratt himself.

"This bridge, over which no doubt Chaucer himself passed, was of stone, the arches were narrow and the piers thick; strong angular buttresses supported them and broke the force of the current; these formed at the upper part a triangle or siding which served as a refuge for foot-passengers, for the roadway was so narrow that a carriage sufficed to fill the way. When it was pulled down in 1839, it was found that the method of construction had been very simple. To ground the piers in the bed of the river the masons had simply thrown down stones and mortar till the level of the water had been reached. It was remarked also that the ill-will of Pratt or the Abbot or of their successors must have rendered the bridge almost as dangerous at certain moments as the primitive ford had been. The

* It is said that he charged eightpence for the passage of a dead Jew! A large sum in those days. A Jewish cemetery was just beyond the bridge.—W. S. S

wheels of vehicles had hollowed such deep ruts in the stone and the horses' shoes had so worn the pavement that an arch had been at one time pierced through." *

This perforated arch proves pretty conclusively that Bow Bridge was never rebuilt; but I look upon doubt as an excellent thing in one's attitude to matters of this kind, partly because fresh evidence may be discovered, and partly because facts are woefully elusive even when they are tackled by judges, and barristers, and juries.

There is one more controversy to be considered : it centres around the famous bridges on Dartmoor, and I will try to put all the main points both clearly and fairly. In this dispute architects contend against antiquaries, and their arguments hold the field. Let me sum them up :—

The "clapper" bridges over Dartmoor rivers are not difficult to study; their construction resembles that of cromlechs and Stonehenges. Their piers were evolved from menhirs, and their table slabs from the mass of rock forming the horizontal member of a cromlech. Nor is it difficult to suggest the evolution through which the clapper bridges have passed, for on Dartmoor itself the evolution is plainly suggested by the rude bridge at Okery and by the single slab at Walla Brook. Any primitive farmer of the Bronze Age had sense enough not merely to put a ledge of granite across the Walla Brook, but to span wider rivers by using menhirs to support large blocks of

* "English Wayfaring Life in the Middle Ages," pp. 45 and 47. See also "Archæologia," Vols. XXVII, p. 77; XXIX, p. 380. Also the histories of Essex.

granite. Timber would not be used, since trees were very scarce on Dartmoor, while granite was so abundant that it must have been very troublesome to farmers.

Now the pastoral life of the Bronze Age was very active in the Dartmoor settlements; all antiquaries make much ado over this fact, yet they fail to see that the circulation of this farm life, the movement here and there of flocks and herds, required bridges, for the rivers then were not less wayward than they are now. Without bridges the farms would have stagnated. And another thing also needed the help of bridges: many domestic fires burnt a great deal of peat and wood, and wood had to be imported from neighbouring districts, probably in exchange for live stock. So, to visualise the farm life is to make it dependent on a ceaseless movement to and fro over very freakish rivers, which after rains and thaws were exceedingly turbulent and perilous. Deep gorges have been worn in the rocks through which the rivers flow; this alone is enough to prove that such wild rivers could not be forded by the tiny sheep and the small cattle of the Bronze Age. Even in mediæval times, as Thorold Rogers has proved, sheep were about as big as Mary's little lamb; they were bred because their wool was the wealth—the Golden Fleece—that made England prosperous; and yet their cultivation failed to add to their national value by increasing their size. Sheep of the Bronze Age were probably smaller still; and how were they to cross the Dartmoor rivers unless bridges were built? Could sheep in those days swim like ducks, or did they float as naturally as logs? And since bridges must have been made here and there in order to keep the farming life from ruin, are we to suppose that the abundant granite blocks would not be used for piers and table stones? Are we to forget the instinctive delight in rude stonework shown everywhere by the dusky, short-statured race which for convenience we call Iberian?

The research of antiquaries may be good or bad. What has it done for the life of these clapper bridges? Has it proved that the present ones are probably younger than the Middle Ages, but that they had many predecessors going back to pre-Roman times? On the other hand, have antiquaries proved that in the Middle Ages a primitive phase of building was revived in Dartmoor, partly because it was good enough for the traffic, partly because it was inexpensive? The absence of lime on Dartmoor would influence the mediæval settlers and govern their building work. But in this discussion it matters not whether the present bridges be old or young; in either case they represent primeval methods. Between the Bronze Period and the Middle Ages all the earliest slab bridges may have disappeared; if so, then settlers on Dartmoor brought with them knowledge enough of cromlechs to recall the Iberian stonecraft, just as in modern times architects have revived phases of Gothic and phases of Classic. Every possibility is entertaining, but why is it that antiquaries in their remarks on the clapper bridges try to be elusive as well as dogmatic? For example, Mr. William Crossing is of opinion

hat the larger clapper bridges have had their age over-
estimated probably because their rough and massive appearance makes them very striking. Why "probably"? He adds
that they are mostly in the line of pack-horse tracks, and
were probably built by farm settlers. "Probably" again!
Yet he gives no evidence. Even Mr. Baring-Gould is
equally dogmatic in devious assertions that have no value
to any architect. Like Mr. Crossing, he attributes the
"clappers" to the period of pack-horses, and sees nothing in
them to indicate a great antiquity. What next? Is primitive stonework insufficiently antique whatever its age may
be? And who is to estimate the age of rude granite
blocks?

I have summed up with fairness the views of architects,
and they ought to hold the field in the judgment of all
pontists. The antiquarian talk about pack-horse tracks has
no cogency, for the prehistoric tracks over Dartmoor are the
first pathways along which the controversy must ramble.
A pontist, then, when visiting Dartmoor, has to do four
things.

1. To visualise the farm life of the Bronze Age;

2. To reconnect it with the rivers and with the neces-
    sary trade in wood for household fires and for
    tool handles;

3. Then he will realise that bridges were essential, and
    that they would be made with the granite blocks
    which Nature had provided.

4. Then, too, he will see that the larger clapper bridges are merely flat cromlechs built over water, and that it matters not when the present ones were put up, since their main interest is their descent from those rude monuments of stone in which the Iberian people commemorated their cult of ancestors, their reverence for the sacred dead.

Near Postbridge, over the East Dart, there is a very bold clapper with three heavy table slabs, each of which is about 15 ft. long and 6 ft. wide. Two piers rise out of the water; each is a pile of granite menhirs that lie flat in the river with their ends looking up-stream and down-stream. The abutments also are layers of granite, and in one abutment the stones are long enough to support on land a very large cromlech. Samuel Smiles believed that this bridge had "withstood the fury of the Dart for full twenty centuries," but there was no need to challenge antiquaries by making a rash statement. For the rest, we must bracket these Dartmoor structures with two other kinds of slab-bridges—those in the valley of Wycollar (p. 60), and those in Spain, at Fuentes de Oñoro. My friend Mr. Edgar Wigram writes to me as follows about the Spanish variety :—

"I include this very rough sketch because it does give some idea of one of the 'Clapper' slab-bridges at Fuentes de Oñoro. The bigger stone would be about 8 ft. long. As to the more important slab-bridge over the Dos Casas rivulet, it stands in a glen where large slabs lie handy. I

THE OLD BRIDGE OVER THE AUDE AT CARCASSONNE IN FRANCE

can speak of it from recollection only, but think it has four spans, about 3 ft. 6 ins. high, or perhaps 4 ft. ; the lintel-stones perhaps 7 ft. or 8 ft. long, centre to centre of piers, and the piers of single stones planted in the river bed, with the longer axes up- and down-stream. A causeway led up to the bridge at each end. Even at the time the solidity of the structure aroused in me a suspicion that it *might* be very old. On the other hand, it may be a recent work of convenience, not of necessity, for the stream in summer is often dry, and in winter it would not be unfordable (except for children) till it had submerged the bridge."

Still, a primitive piece of work, whether done yesterday or 500,000 years ago, comes from a dark mind and a hand without skill ; and the younger it is the more tragic is the meaning of it in sociology. Europeans of the twentieth century A.D. ought to be as far removed from rough slab-bridges as they are from ancestor-worship. Education and personal pride should make them ashamed to use anything that does not represent in its own way the very best that to-day's genius can achieve. For a survival of primitive conventions in a civilized country is a proof that in certain districts the people have feeble minds incapable of pro-longed attention, and therefore glad to find in mimicry a refuge from the pain of thinking. To me, then, primitive bridges are always sinister things ; even when they belong to savages they degrade mankind by showing how mother-wit in men often ceases to be fertile. Between a low degree of intelligence and a fondness for unchanging custom there is at least some relation, for "persons who are slightly imbecile tend to act in everything by routine or habit; and they are rendered much happier if this is encouraged." *

In the next chapter we shall try to follow from the earliest times the slow history of those gifts of the spirit whose growth very often has been arrested; and we shall see once more that weak minds have employed imitation as their scout and custom and convention as their fortified places.

* See Darwin's "Descent of Man," Part I, chapter III.

AT ZUTPHEN IN HOLLAND

CHAPTER THE SECOND
MAN AS THE MIMIC OF NATURE

I

PRELIMINARY CONSIDERATIONS

WE have taken a glance at the bridges made by Nature (pp. 3-4), and now we have to consider their influence on the genesis and development of handicraft. This difficult study has been neglected by men of science; not even Darwin said a word about natural bridges, though they were models to be copied by the sedulous ape in primitive men; and so we must try to be as thorough as possible, within the limits set by a brief chapter.

Where and how is a beginning to be made? The useful and necessary thing is to visualise the fact that varied hints on bridge-building accompanied the descent of man, so the influence of their utility was active through all the linked growth in that organic chain by which the earliest men and their nearest allies were united. Sooner or later the mere use of natural bridges would generate in some minds a desire to copy them; and although we are quite ignorant as to when this desire came for the first time out of the darkness, yet we may suppose, without any great extravagance, that it belonged to the same period of handicraft as the earliest manufactured tools and weapons, which were a development from stone clubs and spears fashioned into shape by earthquakes and volcanoes, the first armourers of the Stone Age. As soon as a tribe, guided by a savage of genius, began to copy three or four object-lessons in Nature's perennial school for mimics, the imitation of several others would be suggested by the same trend of thought, sooner or later. It is reasonable to believe that hand-made weapons preceded hand-made bridges, as hunting and fighting were the strongest motive-powers behind human needs and actions. To slay was the herald of to build, so the first bridges of handicraft ought to be placed in a likely inference among the later doings of Palæolithic hunters and warriors.

A horrible slowness marked each advance from a bad copy of a natural bridge to a slightly better one. In fact, only a few brilliant creative minds—not more than two or three thousand—separate our own social order from the strife of Palæolithic savages. Into the coarse dough of humanity an infrequent genius has put some enchanted yeast. And we must needs believe that the dead routine of imitation, to which human nature has ever been enslaved, held primeval man even more relentlessly than it holds ourselves. One misfortune more than any other delayed a creeping progress: it was the fact that mankind had no cause to fear the most intelligent creatures among the lesser organisms. If snakes and beasts of prey had been as clever as were bees and ants and beavers, men could have saved themselves from extermination by one means only—by a rapid advance from frequent good ideas into great achieve-

ments.   Day after day the large human brain would have
been called upon to produce large protective thoughts, and,
had it failed to produce them day after day, the human race
would have been food for enterprising rivals.   We have no
guess why Providence withheld from mankind this high
discipline, this fateful choice between death and a swift
intelligence ; but we do know that the most dangerous
of the lesser organisms have been the least quick-witted,
and that men in their intercourse with natural things have
shown a lethargic mimicry.   Their cave-dwellings were
stolen from cave-lions and cave-bears ; their pit-dwellings
were copied from the holes and tunnels burrowed by many
animals ; and in their lake-dwellings they collected hints
from five sources : natural bridges, the platforms built by
anthropomorphous apes,* the habits of waterfowl, the
beaver's dam and "lodge," and the nests of birds.   In the
round hut, which was made with branches and wattle-and-
daub, stick nests were united to the plasterwork of rock-
martins.   Yes, a good workman in the construction of mud
walls does no more than rock-martins have done in all the
ages of their nest-building.   When these birds make their
nests they use wet loam stiffened with bits of straw, and
each layer is allowed to harden before another is put on in a
thickness of about half an inch for a day's work.†

* The orang in the Eastern islands, for example, and the chimpanzee in Africa,
build platforms on which they sleep.

† White of Selborne notes this fact.   And Darwin notes two others of equal
interest.   He says : "The orang is known to cover itself at night with the leaves
of the Pandanus ; and Brehm states that one of his baboons used to protect itself
from the heat of the sun by throwing a straw mat over its head.   In these several

Even more remarkable is the fact that men may have borrowed from several birds the idea which enabled them to pass from round huts into oblong cabins. In Australia, for instance, there are three birds—genera of the same family—that build arched bowers with long sides; and Darwin tells us to regard them as " co-descendants of some ancient species which first acquired the strange instinct of constructing bowers for performing their love-antics." One species of Australian bower-birds, the fawn-breasted variety, erects a platform of sticks as a foundation for its gabled hall of courtship, that measures nearly four feet in length and eighteen inches in height. This structure is charmingly decorated, and if we could magnify it to the size of Westminster Hall we should be amazed by its beautiful architecture. Unmagnified, it is a model to all primitive men, for it shows far more invention than a wigwam or than a charcoal-burner's hut.

As soon as a student begins to understand what man-kind has copied in Nature's wonderful school for mimics, he cannot fail to take delight in natural bridges and their influence on handicraft. At first he is humbled painfully by the small amount of creative wit that a million years or so have gleaned from the big human brain ; but soon the novelty of feeling humble is more attractive to him than the vile habit of flattering human nature.*

habits we probably see the first steps towards some of the simpler arts, such as rude architecture and dress, as they arose among the early progenitors of man." Darwin refers to architecture as well as dress because of an earlier sentence on the platforms built by anthropomorphous apes.

* But for this habit we should be less horrified by the acts of German " culture " in a time of war. I add this note to my proofs, September 26, 1914.

II

AMONG THE HERALDS OF MAN

IT was during the Upper Miocene age that two or three big apes migrated into Europe, probably from Africa, and passed from explorers into colonists. One of them was the Dryopithecus, a creature almost as tall as a man, and closely allied to Hylobates. He illustrated that organic art of caricature in which young Dame Nature excelled, many of her experimental efforts having Gargantuan humour in their shapes and proportions.

When food was scarce the Dryopithecus became a nomad, a sort of four-handed Odysseus who was very well able to fight his own battles, whether he wielded a heavy stick, or hugged his foe, or from the shelter of a tree dropped missiles that cracked heads and made backbones exceedingly painful. Hugging seems to have been his *forte*, after clawing and fierce blows had prepared the way for a close embrace; and by his expert ferocity in defence and in attack he earned for himself the right to be a forerunner of several entertaining creatures, notably the gorilla and the chimpanzee and primitive man. He was inquisitive enough to use every natural bridge put in his path by good fortune.

At first I see him on four sorts of natural bridge, and

no fault can be found with his activity. He crawls along fallen trees over some torrents and chasms; across a flooded river here and there he leaps in a shambling, lopsided fashion, when stepping-stones and boulders rise above water-level; he roams into hilly districts where many a ledge of rock spans a dangerous gap; but he enjoys himself most of all when a suspension bridge of branches enables him to amble from tree to tree across a deep-lying river pent up between high cliffs.

In these four bridges, each of them generic, Nature has arrived at utility in her usual manner, by alternating growth and violence. The fallen tree, for instance, from which all timber bridges have been evolved by handicraft in a sequence of gradual improvements, belongs to the utility of Nature's violent moods; and this applies also to the bridge of stepping-stones. Earthquakes and floods distributed boulders over the beds of rivers, and from these boulders handicraft has developed piers and abutments. On the other hand, a bridge of long boughs—and I have used many a one myself—is a symbol not merely of growth but of abundance, and also of endurance. But it is not to be looked upon as the only suspension bridge along which our arboreal ancestry capered, and from which primitive mankind took, and take, hints in bridge-building. Let us remember also the pendent bridge of lianes, and of other tough creeping plants, which in many warm countries grew, and grow, from tree to tree, forming strong cables. On such a high-swung bridge I can see the Dryopithecus, suspended by his hands, and learning tricks as a gymnast, while his mate squats between the fork of a branch and collects fleas from her baby.

When photographs of natural bridges lie around me on a table, there is another vision that comes before my mind in a succession of vivid pictures. I behold a shaggy little animal, partly an ape, partly a man, who stands upright on a fallen tree; below his feet a river in flood foams among rocks; and over there, beyond the peaked hills, a blood-red sunset makes a wondrous tragedy of colour. Somehow the little animal is awed by the flaming sky, and stares at it fascinated, his protruded mouth wide open, and his teeth gleaming. His arms are thin, sinewy, capable, hairy, and very long; they hang at full length, and their prehensile fingers grasp two sticks, one long and pointed, another short and knobbed. His breastbone looks weak as his shoulders droop forward, and horizontal lines of wrinkled skin run from each armpit across the narrow chest. His legs are short and somewhat arched; and their feet grip wood as a habit. The eyes, overhung by a ledge of bone, shimmer with a peculiar suspicion, an instinctive cunning, very vigilant and fierce, that protects even tired sleep with the alertness of a sentinel. The body is daubed with yellow ochre and iron ore, as if to rival the coloured life seen everywhere in Nature; but through this decoration much uneven hair is noticeable, and a coarse beard surrounds the face with a ruff rather similar to that which now gives pride to the *Cebus capucinus*. The head is becoming human, a real Pandora box, whence many banes and a few blessings will escape continually, and spread far and wide over the earth. At present this creature is a wild beast in the terrible nursery stage between apehood and savage manhood. Already he has lost the athletic ease and grace of his tree-top cousins. Not only is he out of joint with them, but his own lot is very perilous, a never-ending war against hardships and dangers. Beasts of prey know how weak he is; most animals outrun him; birds in their swift flight escape from his weapons, and he feels rage and jealousy when monkeys at play leap long distances from bough to bough. Out of his nature comes a pitiless hatred for all living creatures. Do you not see this earthling, this Adam of Evolution, part ape and part man, standing alone on a windfall bridge, with a river in flood below his feet, and the sun a radiant crescent, blood-red, dipping below that far horizon of peaked hills?

And yet this biped has been moved by the sunset, and also by an idea of his own, whose history can be read in deep lines of ploughed earth that run from the bridge to a wood over there, a hundred yards away. At this distance from the river a tall tree was blown down, and a tribe of ape-like men, guided by their leader, dragged it to the bank-side and put it across the waterway, taking long days over the wonderful task. Nature at last has discovered a mind that can think in imitation. Her tree-bridge has a rival.

At this moment the picture changes. A female creature

appears, accompanied by several children. She is uglier than the male, because she suffers much more; her family grows too fast, and for a long time its members are unfit to defend themselves. Never for an hour can she put aside her motherhood. Other animals are occasional parents, because their young are soon able to do their own business; while she, our Eve of Evolution, for ever anxious about her helpless little ones, is an incessant mother through the few brief years of her fertility. Perils encompass her and them, and in a short time she is worn into old age. But she loses her youth creatively; there is not a privation nor a pain that her constant motherhood fails to make into a spiritualising of the heart, into a *Vita Nuova*, into the starting-point for a fresh development. So she is humanised by suffering and love-humanised in spirit, that is to say—long ages before her body has matured into womanhood. It is she who endows children with quickened minds and with social inclinations; and it is she who encounters with a yielding but tenacious courage the wild beast that male passions breed and perpetuate. Also—and this is very important—she is by temperament a practical worker, whereas the male is not; he thinks all the time of adventure, and his moods are incalculable. Even his paternity is coarse-handed, and subject to furious greeds and lusts. His brain is active enough to be awed by the strife of Nature and weak enough to be crippled by a little reason. His character threatens to check his evolution. Where the climate is hot, and food grows abundantly, he makes no progress; bad times alone compel him to work, and to pass very slowly, with a dogged reluctance, from handicraft to handicraft. His higher education begins when he chips a stone into a pointed weapon and feels the rhythmical enjoyment that accompanies invention and manipulation. In fact, handicraft is the earliest public school, the first university; it helps motherhood to transform the brute male into a being somewhat better,* a primeval savage. Yet naturalists have confirmed themselves in three bad habits: they say too little about handicraft, they admire man far too much, and they patronise woman. When they do not bury Woman in the term Man, they glance at her with a condescending half-pity, as bibliophiles glance at second or third editions; and so it is worth while to do some justice to our primitive foremother, the Eve of Evolution.

With her incalculable partner, the irrational male, she and her family wander from district to district. At times they settle under a rock-shelter or in a cave, and make footpaths from it to watering-places and hunting-grounds. Here and there a river is crossed by stepping-stones, and more than one ravine is spanned by branches and by a fallen tree. What is their attitude to these things? The windfall tree-bridge, like every other gift from Nature, is a

---

* Better in many respects, but not in all; for as Darwin points out, it was the self-condoning mind of man, not the instinct of any brute beast, that came to use infanticide as a custom. "The instincts of the lower animals are never so perverted as to lead them regularly to destroy their own offspring." Only arguments can choose and approve unnatural habits.

bane to them as well as a boon, for it is a road open to dangerous animals; as such it is a thing to be guarded, and many a fight in its defence occurs, creating traditions of bravery which are long remembered.

Further, as time goes on, and the progenitors of man become more human, the pressure of competitive life draws ever more and more attention to the incompleteness of natural bridges. For example, stepping-stones may be useless when they are needed most of all, in wet seasons and after storms; and the tree-bridge is so narrow that warriors cross it only one by one, so their slow attack gives a terrible advantage to a brave defence. These hindrances, so obvious and so unpleasant, make appeal to the inventive faculty that a few men possess. Not much is required. From four or five seedling ideas a great many improvements will grow; and now is the moment for us to choose a vague tentative date for the beginning of this gradual development.

Most people are bored by prehistoric archæology, because its earlier periods are as undated as is the oblivion of coma. So a date in obscure history, however tentative it may be, is very helpful; the mind rests on it, somehow, anyhow, and feels that the lost legions of the dead years left some oases in the Saharas of ancient time. And this point is not the only one that concerns the general reader who *does* generally read. In recent years the antiquity of handicraft has been extended very much by a "find" of eagle-beaked flint implements, with other tools, below the Pliocene deposits on the East Anglian Coast. The eagle-beaked flints are undoubtedly of human manufacture, and they carry back the ancient stone period of man to the Tertiary times. Sir Ray Lankester writes on this important subject, and his knowledge helps us a great deal, though we have to recover it from entangled sentences. For example* :—

" Evidence has been for twenty years or more in our possession (in the form of stone implements) of the existence of man in Europe in the warm period which preceded the Pleistocene, with its glacial clays and drifts and its gravels deposited on the sides of existing river valleys, sometimes 800 feet above the level of the bed to which the stream has now worn down its excavation, many miles wide. The discovery within the last four years of beautifully worked flint implements of the shape of an eagle's beak (called ' rostro-carinate ') and of other service-able forms below the marine Pliocene shelly sands—known as the ' Red Crag ' in Suffolk—separates the migrations and mixtures of human tribes and groups, of which we have any knowledge, by a huge chasm of geologic time from the date of the earliest European population. The best geologists have come to the conclusion that half a million years (and it may well be twice as many) separate us from the days before the Crag Sea laid down its shelly deposits on the East Anglian Coast. Yet there were skilful men—not mere ape-like creatures using sticks and roughly-broken stones, but men capable of making and admiring

* " Daily Telegraph," September 8, 1913, p. 5.

GOTHIC BRIDGE AT VILLENEUVE-SUR-LOT, FRANCE

symmetrical, well-finished flint tools, and of using them to clean skins and to plane wood—living a human, creative, dominating life here in Western Europe in those immensely remote days. Probably enough, as great a period as separates those skilful men from us separated them from the earliest unskilful 'commencing' men of the tropical zone."

Yes, probably enough, but yet we must not suppose that handicraft in Western Europe has ever had a standard of uniform merit. As our own work is very often inferior both to that of the Romans and to that of the Middle Ages, so the eagle-beaked tools may denote nothing more than a local industry which a man of genius had originated. No other implements have been dug up from Pliocene deposits in other European localities, hence students of art and architecture cannot accept the generalisation advocated by Sir Ray Lankester. As well suppose that the whole of Western Europe produced in the same age many painters equal to the Van Eycks, or many bridge-builders of a piece with Caius Julius Lacer, or the good Saint Bénézet. It is enough to believe that at a date to be known vaguely as 500,000 B.C., a craftsman of genius lived and laboured in a district of Western Europe, now called the East Anglian Coast. How far his influence extended, or how long it lasted, we have no inkling yet; but it may have been the influence, not of a rare genius, but of a school tradition which migrating tribes had spread through many parts of Europe. Anyhow, the eagle-beaks are historic facts and their manipulative skill gives us the right to make reasonable inferences.

For example, we may infer that if the craftsman who made an eagle-beaked tool showed intelligence in some other useful ways, he did no more than common justice to his humanity. Suppose he cut down a tree with his flint axe, choosing one that grew aslant over a chasm or across a river; or suppose he piled stepping-stones together in the middle of a waterway, and then used this pier as a support for two tree-trunks whose far ends rested on the banksides. Neither of these ideas has more mother-wit than that which has enabled ants to bore tunnels under running water, and to make active bridges by clinging to each other in a suspension chain of their wee brave bodies. Not many human minds in any period of history have been as diligently rational as ants; but let us risk the conjecture that the first advance in bridge-making began among the rostro-carinate workmen probably more than half a million years ago.

To cut down a tree, in order to get a bridge at a chosen place, was a good idea in primitive enterprise, but it was not enough; it gave but little additional help in tribal wars, since it repeated the narrow footway, the main drawback of windfall tree-bridges. Two or three trees laid side by side were necessary, and at least two piles of stepping-stones to carry enough trees over a fairly wide river. Such were the first improvements that war and social life demanded from the wit of primitive mankind, and often they were de-

manded in vain for many long ages. Even at the present
time there are tribesmen who feel well pleased with themselves when they make single and double tree-bridges.
I am told, for instance, by Mr. T. Beddoes, a traveller and
trader in Equatorial Africa, that often in his wanderings he
has made and used a tree-bridge to cross a narrow creek,
following a native method for the sake of its ready convenience. " The natives," he writes, " cut down the tallest
trees on a bank of the waterway that they intend to bridge,
then they make a handrail with bush-rope fastened to short
upright sticks which are placed about three feet apart.
Bush-rope is made from creepers or from long cane vines.
Sometimes an attempt is made to flatten the upper surface
of the tree ; but this work is uncommon, as African natives
are lazy ; they detest manual labour. There are trees that
grow to an enormous height ; one of them measured a
hundred feet odd, so fairly wide creeks and streams can be
bridged. But canoes are the favourite means of crossing
rivers ; they carry light loads well enough, and they need
less labour than bridge-building."

This peep into the aboriginal mind reveals a dire
stagnation. But although no other thing in Nature is
less uncommon than human initiative, yet the men of the
eagle-beaked tools may have made tree-bridges, and also
such stone bridges as the lintel-slabs at Wycollar (p. 60).
For this work required nothing more than imitation, while
the eagle-beaks added some invention to a deft handicraft.
Many an earthquake had made a slab-bridge, and other

models were formed by the lava from volcanoes which hardened into a thick crust over many gaps in the land.

From these bridges—a tree cut down with a flint axe and a single boulder or slab laid from bank to bank of a stream—came three lines of descent in very slow, yet fertile handicraft; and to the history of each a long book could be given. Let me name them one by one :—

1. The Slab-bridge with stone piers.
2. The Tree-bridge with stone piers.
3. The Tree-bridge with timber piles.

III

THE SLAB-BRIDGE WITH STONE PIERS

IN this we follow an evolution from unhewn fragments of rock upheld by stepping-stones to Cyclopean slabs of hewn granite and marble supported by well-made stone piers. The halting development of this bold stone-craft was loved and fostered by that original people which for convenience we call Iberian, and which at some unknown period migrated from Asia, "and swept round Europe, whilst a second branch colonised the Nile basin and Northern Africa, and a third streamed east and occupied China and Japan. The master idea in the religion of this people was the cult of ancestors, and the rude stone monu-ments, menhirs, cromlechs, and kistvaens they have left everywhere, where they have been, all refer to commemora-tion of the sacred dead. The obelisk in Egypt is the highly refined menhir, and the elaborate, ornamented tombs of the Nile valley are an expression of the same veneration for the dead, and belief in the after life connected with the tomb, that are revealed in the construction of the dolmen and kistvaen." *

What could have been simpler than the building methods of the Iberians? We see them at Stonehenge, which dates

* "A Book of North Wales," by S. Baring-Gould, pp. 2–3.

125

from about the year 1680 B.C., according to the astronomical
calculations of Sir Norman Lockyer and the late Mr. F. C.
Penrose.*   Here we have the primitive circle of large stones,
and the rugged trilithon (two rude uprights, or menhirs
connected by a long table slab or lintel).   There is a feeling
for massive construction, but it is barbaric.   The clapper
bridges over Dartmoor rivers belong to this elementary craftsmanship.   Each is a cromlech repeated in several spans
over water, no matter when it was built (p. 100).   Among the
ancient Egyptians there were kindred bridges; and the
Chinese have managed to preserve in a formidable handicraft an Iberian fondness for the trilithon.   Mr. O. M.
Jackson tells me that many slab-bridges in Sichuan have
lintels about twenty feet in length; they are decorated by
sculptors with a dragon's head and tail at the junction of
two lintels and a stone pier.   Every dragon's head looks
upstream, and the tail curls out on the downstream side;
so the slabs appear to rest for security on the back of a
guardian dragon.

There is a Chinese bridge of lintel-slabs, concerning
which very different descriptions have been written, but
even the most moderate account makes it more than four
and a half times longer than the Pont Saint-Esprit (p. 293).
Gauthey writes about it as follows :—

"At Loyang, in the Province of Fo-Kien, on an arm of

---

* These calculations can be studied at the British Museum side by side with an
excellent model of Stonehenge.   On the supposition that Stonehenge was a sun-
temple, its date has been astronomically determined as about 1680 B.C., with a possible
error of two centuries either way.

he sea, there is a bridge with three hundred spans; its con-
truction went on for eighteen years and employed twenty-
ive thousand workmen.   Technically it belongs to the
ame class as the bridges of ancient Babylon, which are
aid to have been made with long and flat stones laid from
ier to pier.   If Loyang Bridge be 8800 metres in length,
s some writers affirm, then its piers will be 4 metres 87 in
hickness, and its spans in width will measure 24.36 metres.
The footway is 22.74 metres.   The long slabs are 5 metres
hick and 3 metres wide.   As for the piers, they are 23 metres
n height, and bear marble lions carved from blocks 7 metres
ong."

Gauthey gives a drawing of this bridge, and his measurements are taken from the Atlas of Martimmart.   They have
n air of great exaggeration.   As Gauthey remarks, " It is
difficult to believe that the tabular stones are as large as
hey are presumed to be : their bulk is more than threefold
reater than that of the obelisk at Rome in the Place de
Saint-Pierre.   Besides, M. Pingeron speaks of them as
eing fourteen metres long by a metre and a half in thickness and in width, so he diminishes by a full half the
ength of Loyang Bridge.   Even with this reduction it
s a wonderful achievement, more than four and a half
imes longer than the Pont du Saint-Esprit."*

The dimensions given by M. Pingeron may be accurate ;
hey represent a hugely magnified clapper bridge decorated
vith sculpture and carried on tall piers for a distance of

* Emiland Gauthey, " Traité de la Construction des Ponts," A.D. 1809–1816.

4400 metres, in a series of three hundred spans. The marble lions, I suppose, ornament the parapets above the piers, like those on the bridge of Pulisangan (p. 310). Marco Polo visited the province of Fo-Kien, where Loyang Bridge is said to be, and stayed at the city of Kue-lin-fu, known to-day as Kien-ning-fu. Here he was greatly struck by " three very handsome bridges, upwards of a hundred paces in length, and eight paces in width."* Not a vivid description, yet enough to prove that notable bridges in Fo-Kien have had a long history.

* "The Travels of Marco Polo." Everyman's Library, p. 315 It is to be remembered that Marco Polo's " paces " are geometric.

IV

TREE-BRIDGES WITH STONE PIERS

THE most famous bridge in this kind is the one built by Trajan over the Danube, just below the rapids of the Iron Gate. Trajan required it for his wars against Dacia, which in A.D. 106 he brought to a successful end, the Dacian leader Decebalus being slain and his people subdued. The bridge had played its part, yet Hadrian, the next Emperor, who began his reign ten years afterwards, looked upon it as a dangerous highway, open to incursions from Dacian revolts, and for this reason he destroyed some piers and the footway. Perhaps Hadrian was jealous of Trajan's work, for two fortified gates and a handful of Roman troops could have defended the bridge against barbarians.

There has been much controversy over this great structure. Its architect was Apollodorus of Damascus, who designed also the Trajan column placed in the centre of the Forum Trajanum. A bas-relief on this column represents the bridge, but in a manner at odds with the written description given by Dion Cassius, who held important offices under Commodus, Caracalla, and Alexander Severus, A.D. 180–229. Dion Cassius wrote a history of Rome, in eighty books, and a small portion of this work has come down to us entire. His evidence then is worth having, and it states that the bridge had twenty piers of hewn stone, 150 feet high and 60 feet wide, with openings between them of 170 feet, spanned by arches. Doubt has been thrown on the accuracy of this description, because the bridge on the Trajan column is unsuited to a span of 170 feet; "nevertheless thirteen piers are still visible out of the twenty, according to Murray's 'Handbook.' The writer has not been able to find any accurate measurement of the width between these piers, but as the 'Handbook' speaks of the length of the bridge as perhaps 3900 feet, and as the Conte Marsigli, writing from personal observation, in a letter to Montfaucon, gives the total length as probably 3010 feet, there can be no doubt that the spans were very considerable and that the representation of the design in the bas-belief is almost wholly conventional. The one point as to which it gives clear information, not supplied elsewhere, is that the superstructure was of wood."*

In other words, this colossal work was a descendant of the earliest tree-bridges, in so far as the footway was concerned. Whether arched timbering was carried from pier to pier to uphold the roadway, as in the bas-relief, is a question of no great moment; the horizontal bearing beams would need support, no doubt, since they had to span openings far wider than the longest trees; and it

---

* Professor Fleeming Jenkin's "Essay on Bridges."

s useless for us to guess in what way this support was carried to them from the lofty piers, which were built with enormous blocks of stone. The main point is that one phase of bridge-building, whose first models were fallen trees lying astride rivers and chasms, seems to have culminated in the masterpiece of Apollodorus of Damascus. Much inferior work of the same kind, very varied and entertaining, has been common everywhere; some of it belongs to Kurdistan, for example (p. 73); and in the Lledr Valley there is a good Welsh specimen called the Pont-y-Pant, whose wooden footway is primitively rustic, and whose piers are fragments of rock gathered from the river-bed and piled together. I have found at Thirlmere a quaint thing which is partly a dam and partly a bridge. The dam, an undulating wall of unmortared stones, has at equal intervals a few angular openings over which wooden hand-bridges are thrown. It would be easy in a shallow river to make a fish-pool by heaping boulders into a dam of this rude sort, and the completed work would rank no higher than the beaver's contests against running water. So I tell myself that many a tribe in the great period of prehistoric art, about 50,000 years B.C., ought to have built for itself a bridge as elementary as the Pont-y-Pant and a perforated dam as uncouth as the one at Thirlmere.

From this untutored handicraft we look back again at the great art of Apollodorus, whose vast bridge over the Danube was near the ancient town of Nicopolis.

What a long travail in the gestation and birth of infrequent ideas! Even half a million years ago a man of the eagle-beaked tools may have put a boulder under a tree-bridge because the tree was thin and swayed too much on a windy day; half a million years ago, and yet we do not feel ashamed of the Pont-y-Pant!

V

TREE-BRIDGES WITH TIMBER PILES

LET me restate the first periods in their history:—

    1. A windfall tree lying astride a gap in the land.

2. A windfall tree dragged from a wood and put astride a gap in the land, perhaps by a tribe of semi-human creatures directed by a superior mind.

3. A savage of genius, perhaps as early as the Tertiary period, cut down a tree in order that it might span a dangerous creek or an abyss in the mountains. Intelligently, with the aid of a flint axe, he copied the work done by many a gale of wind; and in this act of simple mimicry he discovered the first principles of secure bridge-making. The footway was strong, and branches from the tree-trunk gave support to clutching hands. Any bough that blocked up the footway was topped off. Even to-day we find in country woods a good many rustic bridges hewn from tree-trunks, and guarded at the sides by hand rails of dressed branches. Their footways are no wider than the planed surface of a well-grown tree.

4. Another savage of genius, thousands of years later, maybe, took a hint from a troublesome inconvenience which

from the first had been present in tree-bridges. The footway being too narrow, he put two or three trees side by
side, so that two or three warriors might cross it abreast,
instead of weakening their attack by an advance in single
file.

But this improvement suggested other changes of much
greater value both to war and to social life. However
carefully the trees were laid side by side, their rounded
surfaces left a valley between them; and gaps were formed
by curved trunks and by gnarled excrescences. So the
widened footway had drawbacks of its own. Often, on a
rainy day, naked feet would slip, for the trees were polished
by long use; and many a slip would either break or strain
an ankle. Yet the wit of mankind would bear these
troubles with a grumbling patience; thousands of years
may have passed by unprofitably; but sooner or later a man
of genius would perceive that every defect in a bridge suggested an improvement. The valley between the tree-trunks
could be filled in with soil and pebbles and turf; a round
foothold polished by long use and slippery after rain, could
be flattened and roughened; and where the trees diverged
from each other, making traps for the unwary, invention
could be busy for a long time. Why put the trees close
together? If they were separated by half a stride, then
covered transversely with brushwood and turf, a much
better bridge would be made without much effort. Again,
suppose the long beams were thin saplings that shook too
much underfoot, particularly when a tribe of shouting

warriors ran across them in a hot attack.   To steady such a bridge with props would be a great convenience, and timber props would serve as conveniently as boulders and piled stones.   A criss-cross of logs made an excellent pier,* for example, and forked boughs, which entered into several phases of primitive handicraft, made good piles.† We know not when these quite simple improvements gave some dignity to manual work, but their inception needed only a little mother-wit.   Some Quarternary men ripened a great deal more in their arts, as painters and sculptors and engravers.

In this monograph several descendants from the aboriginal tree-bridge are studied briefly, and I refer you to the Index.   Some varied English specimens are given in Francis Stone's "Norfolk Bridges"; and from Don Antonio de Ulloa (1716–1795) we can learn how wooden bridges have long been made in the mountainous parts of South America.   They "consist of only four long beams laid close together over a precipice," and they "form a path about a yard and a half in breadth, being just wide enough for a man to pass over on horseback."   Here the beams have a flat surface, and lie together like boards on a floor. It is primitive handicraft of a low sort, for the beams would carry a much wider footway.

* For criss-cross piers, see Index.

† Forked boughs were used in the building of roofed walls, and bent trees in the building of gabled cabins.

VI

SOME TYPICAL TIMBER BRIDGES

AS there is no room here for a pedigree of timber bridges, let us choose a few examples which are particularly famous in history. It will be enough if we take three: (1) a prehistoric lake-village, (2) the Pons Sublicius of the Romans, and (3) the wonderful work done in the eighteenth century by two Swiss carpenters, the brothers Grubenmann.

Lake and marsh villages were the highest form of prehistoric bridge-building; their thronged platforms, dotted with round huts, not only put a defence of water between home life and prowling foes, but heralded all the housed bridges that the world has seen during its periods of written history. Whether we study Old London Bridge, or the criss-cross bridges with frail shops in Kashmír (p. 71), or the booth-bridges of China (p. 210 *note*), or the roofed timber bridges of Switzerland (p. 291), we are concerned with a pedigree that starts out from the first Neolithic lake-dwellings. But the later stone period, known as Neolithic, is not very old. Between it and ourselves there is a span of about nine thousand years, or a few thousand years more.*

* Sir Ray Lankester, "Daily Telegraph," August 27, 1913, p. 6.

But British lake-dwellings are attributed to a time still later, the Bronze Age, whose date in the British Isles may be fixed tentatively at from 1200 to 1400 B.C.* Further, as pit-dwellings lasted to the days of Tacitus among some Germanic tribes,† so a British lake-village here and there defied progress till the coming of the Romans. There was one at Glastonbury, and its "Late Celtic" routine of life has been studied carefully from its remains.

Standing on an artificial island formed by a series of timber bridges, it occupied nearly three and a half acres, and its round huts, about sixty in number, were intermingled with a few square cabins that marked the most recent enterprise. Low walls were erected with upright posts driven into the artificial island at a distance of about a foot from each other; then this framework was wattled and plastered with clay. A few rough slabs of lias stone made a doorstep, a piece of timber lay across the threshold, a wood fire crackled on a central hearth, and every household wanted to feel entirely safe, for a tall and tight palisade enclosed the little colony. In this primitive defence a great many poles were set up side by side; they ranged in height from five to ten feet. Wolves and war were feared very

---

* Robert Munro's "Archæology and False Antiquities," p. 12.

† Tacitus remarks of these wild tribesmen: "They are accustomed to make artificial caves in the ground, and they cover them with great heaps of dung, so as to form a shelter during the winter, and a storehouse for the produce of the fields. For in such dwellings they moderate excessive cold, and if at any time an enemy should come, he ravages the parts that he can see, but either discovers not such places as are invisible, and subterraneous, or else the delay which search would cause is a protection to the inmates."

much, evidently; and yet the villagers were devoted to that self-decoration with which men and women for many a long period had tried to rival the patterned colours given by Nature to birds, and beasts, and insects, and fish, and snakes, and flowers, and stones. They loved rings, cut from amber and jet and glass; wore bracelets, some of bronze, others of Kimmeridge shale; glass beads had their vogue, and clothes were fastened together with bronze safety-pins, or with split-ring brooches of bronze. Perhaps the women were truly feminine, and wore a monstrous head-gear, outraging their good looks in fashionable efforts to renew their beauty.

Drawing closer to this village perched up on primitive bridges, we find in it some weavers and spinners, a few wood-carvers who were true artists, some carpenters who had lathes, and some clever smiths who made iron knives, awls, spades, bill-hooks, gouges; and a few ambitious potters decorated their work and gave it a careful finish. Harvests were grown somewhere, as women used querns to grind the corn. Good little people! They wanted to be pacific and artistic; fighting did not set their genius; and so they vanished. How could they hope to protect the gift of life when British war-chariots and Roman soldiers began to fight in the neighbourhood, obeying the dread mysterious law of fruitful carnage? They slunk away from the fierce midwifery of war, fearing the long self-sacrifices of a painful renaissance.

Their gentle enterprise lasted from about the second or

third century B.C. to the Roman occupation. Among the remains of their village several skulls have been found, mild-looking skulls of a long shape, like those which have been taken from the long barrows. It was an Iberic tribe that trifled with peace and art, showing an epicene fervour akin to that of our cooing sentimentalists. Perhaps the Romans allowed the village to fade out of being, or perhaps they cleared it away as a futility, for neither Roman coins nor Roman wares have been found on the site, though remnants of Roman villas and potteries have been unburied in the vicinity.*

It is certain that most of the Roman bridges were built with timber. Thousands of trees were cut down when a paved road was constructed, so that cheap material for bridge-building was always at hand when the road was carried over ravines and rivers.† Besides, if a great many stone bridges had been built by the Romans, in Britain and elsewhere, many remains of the piers would have been found

---

* Boyd Dawkins, "The British Lake Village," 1895; Sidney O. Addy, "The Evolution of the English House"; "The Times," September 19, 1895; "Manchester Guardian," September 22, 1896; and A. Bulleid, "Somersetshire Arch. and Nat. Hist. Society's Proceedings," 1894, reprinted in 1895.

† The making of a Roman road was a formidable enterprise. H. M. Scarth, in his "Roman Britain," relates how a portion of the Fosse Road at Radstock, about ten miles south-west of Bath, was opened in February, 1881, and that its work showed the following details in constructive method. 1. Pavimentum, or foundation, fine earth, hard beaten in. 2. Statumen, or bed of the road, composed of large stones, sometimes mixed with mortar. 3. Ruderatio, or small stones well mixed with mortar. 4. Nucleus, formed by mixing lime, chalk, and pounded brick or tile; or gravel, sand, and lime mixed with clay. 5. Upon this completed foundation the *summum dorsum*, or surface of the paved road, was laid with infinite care. So the men of a day built roads for the centuries, and were proud to be servants to the unborn.

in all big rivers. We know, too, that the Romans were tolerant in their attitude to native bridgemen, since the criss-cross piers of the Gauls outlived the Roman Empire by many centuries.

We know not, neither can we learn, how the Romans themselves made timber bridges. Even their Pons Sublicius, a sacred monument, hallowed by historical traditions and by its connection with religious ceremonies, was described imperfectly. To this day experts quarrel over its technique and over its position on the Tiber. Colonel Emy has tried to reconstruct it, but his attempt differs from that of Canina, and we cannot choose between them. The utmost we can say is this—that the Pons Sublicius was a tree-bridge resting on piles, and dating from the times of Ancus Marcius, who reigned from B.C. 640–616. If the chief priests did not build it, they certainly kept it in repair, always using wood with a pious regard for a venerated past; and with their help it existed as late as the reign of Constantine (A.D. 306–337), when it was mentioned in the " Notitia," and when a bridge was named after it at Constantinople. But the Pons Sublicius became obsolete as a highway for traffic, and then a good understudy bridge of stone—the Pons Lapideus—was built close at hand, and was known sometimes as Pons Sublicius, a title of honour. Sir William Smith believed that these bridges were outside the city, beyond the Porta Trigemina, and that the wooden one was built by Ancus Marcius in order to connect the town side of the Tiber with a new fortress erected on the Janiculus.

We pass on now to the brothers Grubenmann, whose best work was destroyed during the war of 1799. Ulric and Jean Grubenmann were village carpenters, born at Teufen, in the canton of Appenzell. Ulric seems to have been the abler of the two; certainly he was a man of true genius who spanned great distances by his unrivalled use of corbelled and trussed timber bearings. It was in 1755 that he began his suspension bridge at Schaffhausen, and in 1758 this work was complete. There were two spans in a distance of 364 feet, and they formed an elbow that pointed upstream. The abutment near Schaffhausen was 171 feet from the angle, and from the angle to the opposite shore was 193 feet. Ulric had decided that the bridge should cross the Rhine in one magnificent flight from abutment to abutment, but the town authorities interposed and told him to find use for a stone pier belonging to a bridge which a flood had ruined in 1754. Being a Swiss by birth and by training, Ulric Grubenmann followed an ancient tradition in Swiss carpentry, covering his bridge with a solid roof; and so perfect was the bridge, so admirably scarfed, trussed, strutted, braced, bolted up, and suspended, that only two faults could be found with it: the roof was too heavy, and the parts were too dependent on each other. An injury to one portion of the structure might have been disastrous to the whole bridge—a vital consideration in a warfaring time.

Grubenmann's methods were simple. "The braces proceeding from each abutment," said Telford, "are continued to the beam which passes along the top of the uprights, and the lowest of these general braces are actually united under that beam, thereby forming a continued arch between the abutments, the chord line of which is three hundred and sixty-four feet, and the versed sine about thirty feet. These braces are kept in a straight direction by the uprights, which are placed seventeen feet and five inches apart. If this bridge had been formed in a straight line between the abutments I can see no reason why this form of construction should not have supported a roadway of about eighteen feet in breadth, as well as a slight roof; because, in that case, all the weight arising from the braces which proceed from the middle pier would have been saved, and the roof might have been made much simpler and lighter."

While Ulric Grubenmann was working at Schaffhausen, his brother Jean built a similar bridge at Reichenau, two hundred and forty feet in a single span; and some years later the two brothers constructed their Wittingen Bridge over the Limmat, near Baden, giving to it a span of three hundred and ninety feet. They were famous now, and their influence travelled from Europe to America, where it found in Bludget an able interpreter, Bludget's bridge over the Portsmouth River being similar in technique to the bridge at Schaffhausen. Since that time the evolution of timber bridges has remained in the United States of America, where it has ranged from the criss-cross of logs for bearing piles to the most intricate combinations of lattices and trusses. Very often there is far too much ntricacy, and no thought at all is given to military considerations (p. 352). ꭓ" Many wooden American bridges are trusses which almost defy analysis, the designs being, however, obviously suggested by an attempt to combine at least two of the three main types of bridges. No advantage whatever is gained by a combination of this kind; on the contrary, great disadvantage is almost sure to follow its adoption, namely, that it will be impossible that each part of the structure should, under all circumstances, carry that portion of the load which the designer entrusted to it. For suppose a bridge constructed partly as a girder and partly as a suspension bridge, the girder being very stiff and deep, the chain perfectly flexible with considerable dip. Let the chain and girder be each fit to carry half the passing load. It is perfectly conceivable that the deflections of the two should be so different that the girder would, under the actual load, break before the chain was sensibly strained, or the difference in the relative dip of the chain and depth of the girder might be such as to cause the former to give way first."*

* Professor Fleeming Jenkin. If any reader wants to continue the study of timber bridges, let him turn to Colonel Emy and to the huge volumes compiled and edited by Hosking. But it is clear enough that timber bridges belong to the past; in these days they are ludicrously out of joint with the needs of social life, owing to the rapid advance which "progress" has made in artillery, in high explosives, in airships, and in aeroplanes.

VII

PRIMITIVE SUSPENSION BRIDGES

WE have seen (p. 114) that the first suspension bridges were of two sorts: (*a*) long branches which had grown across rivulets and chasms; (*b*) thick and tough creeping plants by which many forest trees were festooned to one another. It is a vast evolution from these natural things to the art of Ulric Grubenmann, the forerunner of metal suspension bridges.* Unfortunately it is also an evolution which we cannot follow through many consecutive phases, artists and historians having failed to record its growth. We cannot suppose that the

* These date from about the year 1816, when Galashiels Bridge was constructed. It was only 112 ft. in length. But in 1819 Telford designed the Menai Bridge, in which the span of the catenary is 570 ft. and the dip 43 ft. The success of this work gave rise to much imitation, and in several places very great projects were carried through with success. At Pesth, for instance, the span was 666 ft., and at Fribourg 870 ft. But engineers, having no imagination and but little prudence, went too far, so they had to retreat from their cocksureness. Soon it became evident that a long suspended bridge of metal suffered much from the lateral oscillation caused by wind, and that its flexibility made it unfit for railway traffic. "The platform rose up as a wave in front of any rapidly advancing load, and the masses in motion produced stresses much greater than those which could result from the same weights when at rest. Moreover, the kinetic effect of the oscillations produced by bodies of men marching, or even by impulses due to wind, may give rise to strains which cannot be foreseen, and which have actually caused the failure of some suspension bridges. On the 16th of April, 1850, a suspension bridge at Angers gave way when 487 soldiers were passing, and of these 226 were killed by the accident." —Professor Fleeming Jenkin.

ancients neglected suspension bridges; from the spider alone they must have learnt that pendent ropes made a good bridge; but we know not what they achieved in this airy handicraft.   Many people of to-day show in primitive hammock-bridges that their ancestors were influenced by the work of spiders.   In countries so far apart as China and Central Africa and Northern India, for example, there are hammock-bridges of cane and osier, netted elaborately at the sides and swung by bamboo cables, as in China, or by ropes made from the silky fibres of the Nilgiri nettle, as in the Bermulda Hills. Whatever sort of primitive rope is employed, its first model was the gnarled and twisted stem of a vine-like creeping plant.

Perhaps the most ancient suspension bridge in China is the one known as *Liu Soh* or *Lew saw*, literally a slip rope. A bamboo cable is fixed from side to side of a ravine, not in a level line, but a little aslant, so as to form a mild sort of switchback.   A traveller carries a wooden saddle with a deep groove in it; the groove fits the bamboo cable, and straps fasten the saddle and give confidence to the jockey, who travels at a rapid speed when he is fat.   On his return journey he is pulled up the bridge by ropes.   In the mountains of Sichuan there are hundreds of these single cable-bridges.*   What are they but lianes and vine stems *plus* a little human primitiveness?

Don Antonio de Ulloa, the Spanish Admiral, describes

* From information kindly supplied by the Rev. O. M. Jackson.

L

a Peruvian bridge closely allied to the Chinese Liu Soh, and called the tarabita. Ulloa noticed it on several rivers, but particularly on the rapid Alchipichi. The tarabita is only a single rope made of bujuco, or ox-hide thongs twisted into a cable from six to eight inches in thickness. It is extended from one side of the river to the other, and anchored firmly. On one bankside it is controlled by a wheel, or winch, that makes it either taut or slack. A leather cradle is hung from the tarabita by two clasps that have rounded heads; two ropes are stretched across the river and bound to the travelling clasps; a wayfarer sits in the cradle and is pulled across by the guide-ropes. Even mules are slung from two tarabitas, according to Antonio de Ulloa, whose book on South America was published in 1748, at Madrid. An English translation appeared in 1758, and ran into five editions. Let me give a quotation from the fourth, issued in 1806. It concerns a venerable suspension bridge akin to the bamboo variety made in the mountains of Sichuan in China :—

"Over the river Desaguadero is still remaining the bridge of rushes invented by Capac Yupanqui, the fifth Ynca, for transporting his army to the other side, in order to conquer the provinces of Collasuyo. The Desaguadero is here between eighty and a hundred yards in breadth, flowing with a very impetuous current under a smooth, and, as it were, a sleeping surface. The Ynca, to overcome this difficulty, ordered four very large cables to be made of a kind of grass which covers the lofty heaths and mountains of that country, and called Ichu by the Indians ; and these cables were the foundation of the whole structure.   Two of them being laid across the water, fascines of dry juncia and totora, species of rushes, were fastened together, and laid across them.   On these the two other cables were laid, and covered with the other fascines securely fixed, but smaller than the first, and arranged in such a manner as to form a level surface ; and by this means he procured a safe passage for his army.   This bridge, which is about five yards in breadth, and one and a half above the surface of the water, is carefully repaired or rebuilt every six months, by the neighbouring provinces, in pursuance of a law made by the Ynca (Capac Yupanqui), and often since confirmed by the kings of Spain."*

In the first volume of his book, chap. VII., Antonio de Ulloa visits the Andes, and finds there some tree-bridges, some stone bridges, and some complex bujuco bridges.   The stone variety he does not describe, but he writes interestingly about the bujucos.   When six cables have been made by twisting together strips of ox-hide they are suspended across a river, not in a single row, but in two tiers, the lower one with four cables, the upper with two.   Over the lower tier branches and canes are laid transversely ; and when this floor is braced to the upper cables, there is a sort of cage within which travellers can walk in safety while the bridge swings.

* "A Voyage to South America," Antonio de Ulloa, translated from the Spanish by John Adams, Fourth Edition, Vol. II, p. 164.

"On some rivers of Peru," says Ulloa, "there are bujuco bridges so large that droves of loaded mules pass over them; particularly over the river Apurimac, which is the thoroughfare of all the commerce carried on between Lima, Cusco, La Plata, and other parts to the southward." Humboldt passed over one of these pendulous bridges, and Miers crossed another which was strong enough to bear the traffic of pack-mules, though it was two hundred and twenty-five feet in span.

And now we must pass on to a half-suspension bridge which is very common among the N'Komis, a tribe that inhabits the Fernan Vaz district in Equatorial Central Africa. It is a bridge built with Y-shaped sticks. Two parallel rows of these pronged branches are driven into the bed of a stream, and into the banksides; then long runners are put between the forks to bear a footway of sticks laid across them transversely.

Mr. Thomas Beddoes, an African trader, and traveller, draws my attention to this bridge of forked branches; and tells me also that in the Agowe district, but far inland from the banks of this river, he came upon a primitive suspension bridge partly made with very thick vines—vines as thick as a man's leg—which were joined together into a couple of natural ropes long enough to be suspended from trees over a creek about two hundred feet wide. Perhaps a yard separated them, and they were parallel to each other. When anchored to the trees at a height of four or five feet above the bank, they form the upper part or parapet of the bridge. As for the footway, its bearers were saplings—young trees from ten to twelve feet long and three or four inches in diameter; they were lashed together into a continuous runner, and two such runners were laid from the banksides over the creek, to carry a hurdle pathway of canes or sticks. Then the upper part of the bridge was braced to the saplings with thin vines, which were tied to their supports at intervals of about a foot, and which served the purpose of suspension rods, for they counteracted the strain on the saplings when a native crossed the narrow footway.

It would be easy to write much more about primitive swing bridges, but enough has been said to stimulate thought and discussion. Not one of them has a brighter intelligence than that which we find in many prehistoric handicrafts.

VIII

NATURAL ARCHES—THEIR SIGNIFICANCE AND THEIR INFLUENCE

LONG before the germ of humanity in some anthropomorphous apes became slowly fertile in a mysterious
gestation, Nature had weathered many rocks into
hollowed and vaulted shapes. Some were yawning sea-
caves, whose arched mouths gulped in the tidal waves, and
whose caverned bodies gurgled or boomed with the noise of
deepening water.* Others were vaults gradually fretted
into being by subterranean torrents, such as we find to-day
at Saint-Pons, in the Cevennes, where the river Jaur is
nourished by an abundant spring which in a second, through
the mouth of a low-arched cavern, pours a thousand litres
of fresh, sweet water. Others, again, were genuine arched
bridges, such as we find to-day in the Pont d'Arc, over the
river Ardèche (p. 6). In England we have several such

---

* Such caves are frequent on the coast of Pembroke, in the Little England
beyond Wales. Lydstep Arch is a far-famed example, and the Devil's Punch Bowl,
opened within the area of a prehistoric camp by the falling in of the roof, has an archway to the sea. "Bocherston Mere is a very small aperture, which, like a widening
funnel, spreads out below into a large cavern. During the prevalence of gales from
the south-west, the sea, driven by wind and tide in at the arched entrance, is ejected
through the upper hole in jets of foam and spray some forty or fifty feet high, like
geyser spouts. The limestone naturally pierced with caverns lends itself to be thus
riddled and rent."—S. Baring-Gould, "Book of South Wales," p. 196.

bridges, notably the Durdle Door on the coast at Lulworth, whose arched span must owe at least a part of its shape to the troubled action of sea-waves. "La Roche Percée" at Biarritz—a crinkled, lava-like formation—is inferior to our Durdle Door ; and "La Roche Trouée," near Saint-Gilles Croix-de-Vie, though remarkable as a square-headed aperture, has a lower place still in the pontine work done by Nature.*

Perhaps the most wonderful rock-bridges are those at Icononzo, in New Grenada, over the torrent of Summa-Paz. There are two, and one of them soars up and up to a crown that spans the water at an altitude of ninety-seven metres. How could men of genius fail to be architects when Nature set before their eyes great vaults, not only varied in shape, but at times of a stupendous height ? In different ways she produced surbased arches, pointed arches, semicircular arches, all more or less ragged in their outlines, but each a model for progressive mimicry and adaptation.

Here is not the place to dally with the causes of their formation, such as uneven weathering and the scour of running water subject to high tides or to terrific floods. As rivers in the course of many ages deepen and widen their channels, they reach now and then a strata of fissured rock, and their eating action is very rapid when they are

* There is no need to multiply examples, for every reader must have seen how rocks have been vaulted, and lands tunnelled, by underground rivers. At one part of her course, for example, the Guadiana flows underground for twenty miles, forming a vast bridge above which 100,000 sheep can pasture.

able to undercut the softer rocks by fretting their way along apertures or crevices. Many an earthquake has made such inlets for river water, and earthquakes may have shattered some rocks into vaulted shapes. Whether glaciers have played a part in the hollowing of rocks into arched caves and bridges I do not know; but rock-basins are attributed to the erosive power of glaciers, so why not some rock-bridges also? It is a question over which geologists ought to quarrel as they did over rock-basins.*

But the main point is that the archways made by Nature not only suggested the arched bridge of handi-craft, but heralded all the lovely styles of building which have used vaults, domes, turrets, towers, spires, steeples, and arched openings—gateways, porches, and windows. There is a rival art, as we know, an art which has glorified the long lintel-stone carried by pillars; but it has never won from the genius of great men the highest technical inspiration. To it we owe much work of a noble dignity, but in the powerful aspiration of this work there is but little upward flight; it is not near at once

---

* When the glacial theory of their formation was young and argumentative it encountered at first a sneering opposition from Sir Roderick Murchison, the famous geologist, who in 1864 wrote as follows to Sir William Denison: "In my anniversary address to the Geological Society you would see the pains I have taken to moderate the icemen, who would excavate all the rock-basins by glaciers eating their way into solid rocks." But he failed to "moderate the icemen"; and Sir Roderick himself, a few years before his death, gave what is called "a tardy acquiescence" to their evidence. He became a frigid iceman. As Dr. Robert Munro has said, evidence which may be clear and convincing to one trained mind may not have the same effect on another—a fact which should at least warn us to be tolerant in matters of opinion.

PONTE DELLA PAGLIA
AT VENICE, *RENAISSANCE*

to the point of heaven and the point of home. In fact, its masterpieces weigh down heavily on the earth instead of rising towards the light. Not till we come to genuine *archi*tecture—to the art that employs arches and vaults and domes—do we find united in the same edifice a majestic weight and a buoyant fervour. This union of qualities may be found in a supreme Roman bridge, such as the Puente Trajan at Alcántara, but it reigns most beautifully in a Gothic cathedral, whose bulk, earth-bound and vast, has in it what Goethe defined as a petrified music, lofty and spiritual. Rome built for man and the ages, while Gothic art has a symphonic ardour expressed in a creed of hope that transcends all terrene things.

The work done by Nature in various archways, some pointed and many round-headed, is a surprise to many persons. Yet Nature's custom is to build in curves and circles, as in the trunks of trees, and the shapes of flowers, and the forms of birds' nests. She hates angles, and particularly right angles; these she makes in her moods of violence, when she flashes into zigzag lightning, or splinters trees and rocks with an earthquake. We ourselves are accustomed from early youth to squared shapes in handicraft, yet our actions often speak to us of mankind's primitive fondness for circular huts and round pit-dwellings. We find it difficult to walk forward in a straight line, the steps we take having a tendency to curve; and untaught boxers never hit straight from the shoulder, their arms swing in segments of a circle. Art students, again, begin by drawing "too round," so they have to be shown how "to square their touch." Are you tempted to believe that the spinning of our globe has transmitted to all living things the routine of its movement?

In any case, let us keep well in mind the different symbolism implied by curves, angles, straight lines, and circles. Squares and oblongs denote repose and weight, while circles and curved lines are identified with everything in the universe that denotes life, mystery, intelligence, fertility, light and heat, movement and speed, and space illimitable. Human progress itself is a circular ascent along the finest spiral lines, for civilization as a whole never comes back to the same conditions, but creeps above them to some trivial extent. The greatest circular or rounded shapes are the sun, the full moon, our own little world, the human skull, and the human heart; eggs, flowers, nests, the shapes of bones, and the wheel, without which dilatory progress would have been far and away too pedestrian. The first wheel was a rolling stone; afterwards men noticed that a log touched by accident on a hill rolled down for some distance; and at last a person of genius cut solid sections from a tree-trunk and made the earliest wheel of handicraft.

Just one more point ought to be noticed with sympathetic care: that arches in art are more suggestive than circles; they have the mystery of a beautiful part taken from a whole—a whole that looks methodical. We feel this mystery whenever we watch how the moon grows from a silver crescent into a radiant circle. A thing complete dulls an attention that looks on, whereas growth or the suggestion of growth has the stimulus of hope and faith. To culminate is to begin a decline. Even the circle of the sun would be tiresome but for the grey days that renew a truism into a gracious truth. This explains why arches in art make an appeal to the imagination that circles never equal. For example, wheel-windows in Gothic architecture never have the magic of pointed windows. Our eyes travel around them and cannot escape in a flight upwards. Nature, then, when she produced arches, brought into the world a very noble inspiration, and therefore very remote from the dull and slow mimicry of mankind.

In fact, the earliest known vaults of handicraft have but a trivial age in the vast antiquity of human life. Let us take a rapid glance at them, so as to note their rudimentary construction. They are built not with stones directed towards the intrados, but with stones in horizontal courses that jut out one beyond another, just as Nature's archways in stratified rocks have a succession of layers. At Abydos, one of the most ancient cities of Upper Egypt, there is a vault of this primitive sort in the temple of Rameses the Second, who reigned for sixty-seven years, from about 1292 to about 1225 B.C.* Another is found at Thebes in the temple of Ammon-Rē, but the most ancient specimen of all is at Gizeh, in the great pyramid of Menkaura. Now Men-

---

* Dates in Egyptian history are obscure, but these give the period approximately.

kaura belonged to the Fourth Dynasty, so that his date is more than 3000 years B.C. His sepulchral chamber is ceiled with a pointed arch—not a true arch, of course, the stones being merely cantilevers opposite to each other, with their undersides cut to the pointed shape. To understand the structural method, close your hands together at their full length, then open them gradually into the form of a pointed arch : the united finger-tips represent the apex of the vault, and the curving fingers represent the long archstones. Here is a departure from the horizontal layers of stone, but with these also pointed arches have been built.

For instance, Italy has a very good example at Arpino, in Campania. "Arpino occupies the lower part of the site of the ancient Volscian town of Arpinum, which was finally taken from the Samnites by the Romans in 305 B.C. . . . The ancient polygonal walls, which are still finely pre-served, are among the best in Italy. They are built of blocks of pudding-stone, originally well jointed, but now much weathered. They stand free in places to a height of eleven feet, and are about seven feet wide at the top. A single line of wall, with mediæval round towers at intervals, runs on the north side from the present town to Civita Vecchia, on the site of the ancient citadel. Here is the Porta dell' Arco, a gate of the old wall, with an aperture fifteen feet high, formed by the gradual inclina-tion of the two sides towards each other."*

This ancient gate has a pointed arch ; it belongs to the

* "Encyclopædia Britannica," 11th edition, article "Arpino."

so-called "Cyclopean style." Sir William Smith gives an illustration of the Porta dell' Arco, and refers to "the very singular construction," in which successive courses of stone "project over each other till they meet, so as to form a kind of pointed arch." Yet the construction is in no respect very singular, being the simplest way in which rude arches can be copied from Nature's models. With toy bricks of wood a child can build a Porta dell' Arco.* On the other hand, art and science go together in the building of an arch with voussoirs and keystones. A long evolution separates this workmanship from the gateways at Arpino and Tiryns and Mycenae, though we cannot follow it through its gradual improvements. It is an evolution with many breaks, many related forms having perished ; but experts note a difference between the Porta dell' Arco at Arpino and similar vaults both at Mycenae and at Tiryns, where the craftsmanship dates from the Heroic Age in Greece.

The main entrance at Mycenae is called the Lion Gate, from the famed triangular arch and relief above its huge lintel-stone. The arch belongs to the method of laying stones in horizontal courses that jut out towards each

---

* M. Degrand, in his "Ponts en Maçonnerie," draws attention to the fact that arches of this elementary sort have been discovered in Mexico where they represent a dead civilization to which no date can be assigned. Degrand draws his information from two books ; "Histoire du Royaume de Quito," par Don Juan de Velasco, Paris, 1840, and "Monuments anciens du Mexique," par de Waldeck et Brasseur de Bourbourg, Paris, 1866. At Palanqué, in a building supposed to be a temple of the sun, a large bay that opens into the sanctuary has an elliptic arch formed with courses of dressed stone that project one beyond the other : "*un arc surbaissé formé d'assises de pierres de taille posées avec une forte saillie les unes par rapport aux autres.*"

other across an opening; and the decorative sculpture represents two lions that stand face to face; they are separated by a pillar and their front legs rest on a low altar-like structure that supports the pillar. The same device occurs in cut gems and in goldsmith's work of the Mycenaean age; and the lions recall to memory those with which some Chinese bridges have been ennobled (pp. 127, 311).

Even more remarkable are the beehive tombs at Mycenae; there are eight in all, and some others are found in the neighbourhood. Pausanias regarded them as the places where Atreus and his sons hid their treasures, but now they are looked upon as the tombs of princely families. The most important of them, just outside the Lion Gate, is called the Treasury of Atreus. It has two rooms, a square one cut in the rock, and a round one with a pointed dome. This chamber is fifty feet in height and in diameter; we go to it along a horizontal passage twenty feet wide and a hundred and fifteen feet long, with side walls of squared stone sloping up to a height of forty-five feet. "The doorway was flanked with columns of alabaster, with rich spiral ornament, now in the British Museum; and the rest of the façade was very richly decorated, as may be seen from Chipiez's fine restoration. The inside of the vault was ornamented with attached bronze ornaments, but not, as is sometimes stated, entirely lined with bronze. It is generally supposed that these tombs, as well as those excavated in the rock, belong to a later date than the shaft tombs on the Acropolis." *

In the Treasury of Atreus there are two points that interest architects more than any others. The first is the contrast between admirable decoration and hugely primitive stonework; and the other is the fact that the annulary courses forming the domed and circular chamber have this particular character, that the lateral joints of the stones hardly tend at all towards the centre. Moreover, again and again the stones are separated by a space, and this interval is filled up with small rubble which seems to have been pressed together with the greatest care. These irregular courses, whose inside diameter grows less and less as the circular wall grows higher and higher, forms at last a sort of pointed dome over the great tomb. M. Degrand says very well : " A vault of these proportions must count as a memorable work. Its construction here and there makes use of colossal stones, and it subsists almost intact after more than thirty centuries of existence. At a pinch its architect and workmen could have erected some masonry bridges in accord with the same technical method."

In wide arches of this sort the resistance of good mortars would have been called upon to play the leading part; but in arches of narrow span the stones could

* " Encyclopædia Britannica," article " Mycenae "; see also Sir William Smith, " Dictionary of Greek and Roman Geography "; and note what M. Degrand says in his " Ponts en Maçonnerie."

have been used dry, and such arches may well have displaced many a primitive footway of logs that rested on stone piers.

The Egyptians built some real arches, not with long stones carefully shaped into segments of a circle, such as we find in some Chinese bridges (pp. 313–14), but with hewn blocks whose joints converged toward a common centre. In Ethiopia, for example, in one of the pyramids of Meroe, there is a semicircular arch composed of voussoirs; and two pyramids at Gebel Barkel have arched porticoes with voussoirs that tend to one point. Their shapes differ, one arch being pointed and the other round-headed.* The pyramids of Gebel Barkel are puny in style, and belong to a very late date in old Egyptian history.

As we have seen, a triangular arch may be studied above the Lion Gate at Mycenae. Triangular arches are uncommon, but Brangwyn has chosen a good example of a much later date from Kashmír. The builders found it easier to set up a triangular scaffold than a rounded one.

As for the semicircular arch, early examples of it have been discovered in Asia Minor, among the ruins of Phrygian cities; in Acarnania, the most westerly province of ancient Greece; and also in that part of Central Italy where the Etruscans, by their powerful civilization, heralded Rome. It was in Etruria that Rome cradled her infancy, for she borrowed from the Etruscans many of her building

* See E. Degrand, Vol. II, p. 124; and see also the "Traité d'Architecture," by Léonce Reynaud.

methods and many of her civil institutions, both religious and political. Among the gleanings that she harvested we find the round-headed arch, which became a symbol of Roman conquest and colonisation. Perhaps it was employed at Rome for the first time in those great sewers,

IN KASHMÍR : A PRIMITIVE BRIDGE WITH TRIANGULAR ARCHES

extant still, which were attributed to the statesmanship of Lucumo Tarquinius, the legendary man of wealth who with his wife and retinue migrated in a splendid manner from Etruria and became a Roman citizen. If the sewers were built about 600 years B.C., then the history of round-headed vaults, as Rome collected from many nations the

M

toll of enlightened obedience, extended over more than a thousand years.

In the next chapter we shall try to understand the Roman genius, but here we must recall to mind two preliminary points : one is the aboriginal arch of tree-trunks that Cæsar found in Gaulish bridges (pp. 70, 72), the other is the fact that the Romans left in Britain a version of their round-headed arch that is simpler and more rustic than any other. It was copied frequently by mediæval bridge-builders, and to-day many of the copies are known locally as Roman. Brangwyn represents one of these imitations in Harold's Bridge at Waltham Abbey.

Perhaps this bridge may date from Harold's time, but it is a feeble thing in comparison with the Roman example near Colne, Clitheroe, whose simple and effective structure is bolder in aspect than the New Port at Lincoln, a genuine Roman gateway. There is but one arch in the Roman bridge near Colne, and its voussoirs have no masonry above them, the footway being protected by large cobbles which are easy to displace when they become outworn. Perhaps the width of this bridge may have been great enough for Roman wheels and British chariots, but I doubt if a coster with his cart would make the crossing.

Along the ancient tracks of Lancashire there are many single-arch bridges with a Roman aspect, but without an authentic air of stalwart dignity. The one near Colne looks genuinely Roman, while the others speak to me of a Roman tradition enfeebled in much later times by a rather timid craftsmanship.   Mr. C. S. Sargisson has examined these bridges carefully, and from him I have received some excellent photographs.

A bridge belonging to the same school is to be found at

BRIDGE AT WALTHAM ABBEY ATTRIBUTED TO HAROLD

Monzie, near Crieff, in Perthshire; there are several in North Wales, the best example being Pandy Old Bridge at Bettws-y-Coed; and a good English specimen, quite as entertaining as Harold's Bridge at Waltham, should be noted at Hayfield.   Nothing can be simpler than this use of a single rough ring of voussoirs ; and it justifies the inference that Roman pontists were niggardly in Britain, since they stereotyped a narrow bridge without parapets, and erected no tremendous aqueduct and no bridge of enduring fame, such as we find elsewhere in Europe. If Rome had foreseen the future history of Britain, and had given way to jealousy, she could not have been more parsimonious in her British bridge-building.

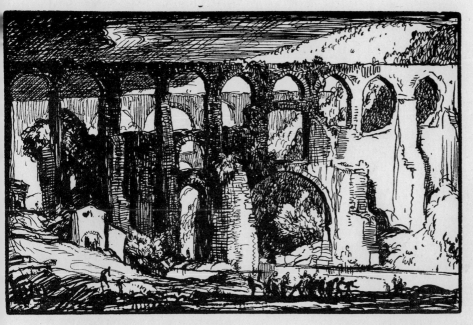

SMYRNA: ROMAN BRIDGE AND AQUEDUCT—THE POINTED ARCHES ARE EASTERN
RESTORATIONS

CHAPTER THE THIRD

A FEW WORDS ON THE ROMAN GENIUS

I

WHAT are we to think of the Roman bridges and aqueducts? Are we to be men in our attitude toward them? or shall we try to see them with the unfriendly eyes of Grecian supermen?

It seems to me that many Grecian supermen are terrible persons in their criticism of architecture. Often they are so cocksure in their contempt for Roman art that they write down their verdicts without any thought, and also in uncouth English, as if a slatternly habit of mind were a fit companion for their proclaimed belief in the supremacy of Greek masterpieces. Years ago, in the "Encyclopædia Britannica," one of these superlative judges told the world that Roman bridges and aqueducts "were really of a more engineering than architectural character, being in the main utilitarian." What does this ungainly language mean? Was a Roman temple less utilitarian than a Roman aqueduct? less needful as a part of the national life? Why should a lover of Greek art write absurdly on the Roman genius? I am told, for instance, by another Grecian, that the Pont du Gard, a Roman masterpiece, three or four leagues from Nîmes, in France, has "rough masonry." What next? A very strong man, a Sandow, in comparison with a Tom Thumb, is a man of rough muscle and sinew, and if Tom Thumb is to be our standard of symmetry and grace, then Sandow is a masterful error in proportion and vitality. To describe the Pont du Gard as "rough" is to be a pigmy in a very foolish attitude to Roman power; and it proves also that the critic has a defective appreciation of his own vaunted hobby, the might and magnificence of Greek architecture.

Does anyone know why British writers are reluctant to admire in art those virile gifts of the spirit that win victories and promise a great future? Why is it that our criticisms are honeyed with sweet phrases? We prattle about "tender sentiment," and "exquisite refinement," and "gracious and gentle tact," as if these female qualities only and alone could make fame permanent in the arena of the centuries. Is a passion for "refinement" to turn us into valetudinarians? Surely the Roman genius, in a supreme monument such as the Pont du Gard, is the very tonic for which we ought to have an inborn care and liking? Yet some professors of taste, being devotees of the epicene, condemn it as a "rough" genius, just as bad climbers revile the Alps.

When J. J. Rousseau visited the Pont du Gard he was awed into silence by the immensity of the three arcades. For the first time in his life he understood the grandeur of the Roman spirit in adventurous achievement. "Le Pont du Gard," he wrote in his "Confessions," "était le premier ouvrage des Romains que j'eusse vu. Je m'attendais à un monument digne des mains qui l'avaient construit; pour le coup, l'objet passa mon attente, et ce fut la seule fois en ma vie. Il n'appartenait qu'aux Romains de produire cet effet. L'aspect de ce simple et noble ouvrage me frappa d'autant plus, qu'il est au milieu d'un désert où le silence et la solitude rendent l'objet plus frappant et l'admiration plus vive ; car ce prétendu pont n'était qu'un aqueduc. On se demande quelle force a transporté ces pierres énormes si loin de toute carrière, et a réuni les bras de tant de milliers d'hommes dans un lieu où il n'en habite aucun ? Je parcourus les trois étages de ce superbe edifice,* que le respect m'empêchait presque d'oser fouler sous mes pieds. Le retentissement de mes pas sous ces immenses voûtes me faisait croire entendre la forte voix de ceux qui les avaient bâties. Je me perdais comme un insecte dans cette immensité : je sentais, tout en me faisant petit, je ne sais quoi qui m'élevait l'âme, et je me disais en soupirant : ' Que ne suis-je né Romain ! ' Je restai là plusieurs heures dans une contemplation ravissante ; je m'en revins distrait et rêveur, et cette rêverie ne fut pas favorable à Mme. W——. . . . Elle avait bien songé à me prémunir contre les filles de Montpellier, mais non pas contre le Pont du Gard ! On ne s'avise jamais de tout."

I give this quotation in the original French because the flavour of Rousseau cannot be translated. As well try to keep the flavour of champagne by mixing this wine with water. Besides, I wish to contrast the elusive vanity of

* If Rousseau walked along the three tiers of this bridge-aqueduct, then he had what climbers call "a good head," for there is but little space between the piers and a most unpleasant fall into the river Gardon. Most of us have passed over the top, leaving Alpinists to explore the rest of this wonderful structure.

Rousseau with the alert and appealing manliness of Charles Kingsley, another ardent devotee of the Pont du Gard. In 1864 he wrote as follows to his wife :—*

"My first impression of the Pont du Gard was one of simple fear. 'It was so high that it was dreadful,' as Ezekiel says. Then I said, again and again, 'A great people and a strong. There hath been none like before them, nor shall be again for many generations.' As, after fifteen miles of the sea of mulberry, olive, and vine, dreary from its very artificial perfection, we turned the corner of the limestone glen, and over the deep blue rock-pool, saw *that thing* hanging between earth and heaven, the blue sky and green woods showing through its bright yellow arches, and all to carry a cubic yard of water to Nismes, twenty miles off, for public baths and sham sea-fights (*naumachiæ*) in the amphitheatre, which even Charlemagne, when he burnt the Moors out of it, could not destroy!—Then I felt the brute greatness of that Roman people ; and an awe fell upon me as it may have fallen on poor Croc, the Rook, king of the Alemans— but that is a long story—when he came down and tried to destroy this city of the seven hills, and ended in being shown about in an iron cage as *The Rook*. But I doubt not when he and his wild Alemans came down to the Pont du Gard they said it was the work of dwarfs—of the devil? We walked up to the top, through groves of *Ilex*, *Smilax*, and *Coronella* (the first time I have seen it growing), and then

* "Charles Kingsley: His Letters and Memories of his Life." Edited by his Wife. 1879. Vol. II, pp. 176–7.

we walked across on the top. The masonry is wonderful, and instead of employing the mountain limestone of the hills, they have brought the most splendid Bath oolite* from the hills opposite. There are the marks cut by the old fellows —horse-hoofs, hatchets, initials, etc., as fresh as paint. The Emperor (1864) has had it all repaired from the same quarries, stone for stone. Now, after 1600 years, they are going to bring the same water into Nismes by it. When we crossed, I was in a new world. *Genista anglica*, the prickly needle furze of our commons (rare with us), is in great golden bushes; and box, shrubby thyme, a wonderful blue lily, bee-orchis and asters, white, yellow, purple (which won't dry, for the leaves fall off). Then wild rosemary, and twenty more plants I never saw. We went below into a natural park of ilex and poplar (two or three sorts), and watched such butterflies and the bridge, till C—— said, 'This is too perfect to last,' which frightened me and made me pray. And there was reason—for such a day I never had in my life of beauty and wonder . . . . and yet there

---

* Sir William Smith, in his great "Dictionary of Greek and Roman Geography," gives a detailed account of the stonework. "The stone of this bridge is a yellowish colour. Seen under the sun from the west side, the bridge has a brightish yellow tint, with patches of dark colour, owing to the weather. The stone in the highest tier is a concretion of shells and sand, and that in the lower tiers appears to be the same. In the stones in the highest tier there are halves of a bivalve shell completely preserved. The stone also contains bits of rough quartzose rock, and many small rounded pebbles. In floods the Gardon rises 30 ft. above its ordinary level, and the water will then pass under all the arches of the lowest tier. The piers of this tier show some marks of being worn by the water. But the bridge is still solid and strong, a magnificent monument of the grandeur of Roman conceptions, and of the boldness of their execution."

is one thing more glorious and precious than the whole material universe—and that is a woman's love. . . ."

A classic tradition says that the huge stones in the Pont

THE PONT DU GARD FROM ABOVE THE FIRST TIER; SHOWING BELOW THE MODERN BRIDGE FOR GENERAL TRAFFIC OVER THE GARDON

du Gard were joined together by iron clamps.   Is this true? Each iron clamp, if any were used by the masons, connected a voussoir to an interior archstone.*   From time to time the Romans employed iron rods bent at the ends and

* Later we shall see that Perronet, a famous bridge-builder of the eighteenth century, used iron clamps for this purpose.

astened into stones with molten lead; such rods have been discovered among the ruins of a Roman bridge over he North Tyne, at Chollerford, near Hexham. This was a bridge with a wooden superstructure, probably, as no roussoir has been found among the litter of pier-stones.

The Pont du Gard is very tall; it soars, and to a height hat exceeds forty-seven metres. The first tier has six arches, the second has eleven, the third has thirty-five. In the middle tier the length is 257 m. 90 cm. Note, too, that the architectural centre of the design is determined by the rocky channel of the Gardon; we find t not in the centre of the bridge but on the north in the arch under which the river flows. It is the biggest arch of all, with a span of 25 m. 30 cm., while the neighbour on each side is narrower by nearly six metres. The other bays of he first arcade dwindle in span to 15 m. 75 cm.* As to the centre of the second tier, it corresponds with that of the first, for the largest vault is above the river; it carries four little arches of the third arcade, while its companions support only three. Some critics see nothing more than the unequal size of these arcades, when the real point is to find the architectural centre, whence the composition radiates, majestic and imperious. The topmost arches and their crowning dignify the whole structure with a completeness akin to that which is given to a long range of columns by a fine entablature and cornice.

* I believe these measurements to be strictly accurate, unlike those in many books of reference.

And we must note the symbol of prosperity—a phallus —carved twice in low-relief on the Pont du Gard. On the western side it graces a springing voussoir in the third arch of the second tier; and there is another on the keystone of the greatest arch, where the river passes. Here the emblem is a double phallus, and when it is touched by sunlight it looks as young as hope, not as uncertain as prosperity.

We cannot put a date on this Roman masterpiece, because in this matter there are differences of opinion. M. Ménard, historian of Nîmes, attributes the work to Agrippa, son-in-law of Augustus, who is said to have ordered its construction about nineteen years before the Birth of Christ. The architecture belongs to the Tuscan order. Its vaults are semicircular, and spring from ledges, or imposts, about 50 centimetres high, and as much in projection. There are four parallel rings of stone in the vaults of the first tier, and three in the second, while the third tier has either one or two. This Roman method of building the under surface of an arch, by laying stones in parallel bands or rings, side by side, but not bonded together, was copied in the Middle Ages (p. 82). One point more : the water channel of the aqueduct, placed on top of the third arcade, is 1 m. 30 cm. wide and 1 m. 60 cm. high ; it is nearly blocked up with a thick deposit of lime, but when this substance is detached we find on the side walls a deep layer of cement coloured red. The bed of this channel is a solid floor, 22 cm. in thickness, and its component parts are small pebbles mixed with lime and gritty sand.

Like other antique monuments, the Pont du Gard has been ravaged by the brutality of mankind. At the end of the seventeenth century, for instance, during years of religious warfare, so called, the Pont du Gard was often crowded with fugitives and with troops, who made a footway for themselves along the upstream side above the first arcade by means of a strong platform corbelled out from new imposts. Over this road cavalry and artillery passed at full speed, not only shaking the bridge, but causing the topmost tier to develop a curve which is still noticeable. At last the province of Languedoc interfered, and in 1670 careful restoration was begun.

Years later, in 1743, the *états généraux* decided that a good highway should be built up against the eastern side of the Pont du Gard; and this new bridge, finished in 1747, was perhaps justified by its utility, though it harmed a classic monument. There have been a good many modern restorations, and one day the aqueduct itself may be brought into use again, in accordance with the wishes expressed by a great many persons.*

* Let me add to this account a few details from Sir William Smith's " Dictionary of Greek and Roman Geography." " It is generally said that the bridge is entirely built of stones, without mortar or cement. The stones of the two lower tiers are without cement; but the arches of the highest tier, which are built of much smaller stones, are cemented. At the north end of the aqueduct the highest tier of arches and the water channel are higher than the ground on which the aqueduct abuts, and there must have been a continuation of small arches along the top of this hill; but there are no traces of them, at least near the bridge. On the opposite or south side the aqueduct abuts against the hill, which is higher than the level of the channel. There is no trace of the hill having been pierced; and an intelligent man, who lives near the bridge, says that the aqueduct was carried round the hill, and that it pierced another hill further on, where the tunnel still exists. . . ."

II

FRANCE happens to be rich in fine relics of Roman bridge-building. Among her antique monuments there are remains of three aqueducts, at Fréjus and Lyon and Luynes; and every pontist has seen photographs of the aqueduct at Lambèse, in the department of Constantine, Algeria. At Vaison, in Vaucluse, over the river Ouvèze, we find an important Roman bridge, built on two rocks, with a single arch not less than thirty metres in span; and along one embankment is a range of tall and narrow arches that start out from the abutment of the bridge. The Pont de Vaison is not in all respects representative of the best Roman work, for its voussoirs, instead of being rimmed and extra-dossed, are fitted into the spandrils (p. 282). I do not know the date of this bridge, but Vaison descends from a famous Roman town, Vasio by name, mentioned by Mela (ii. 5) as one of the richest towns of the Narbonensis.

It is common knowledge—or it should be—that the Romans adorned some of their bridges with a triumphal arch; and it happens, by rare good fortune, that France owns a small example of this Roman pride. It is the Pont Flavien at Saint-Chamas, which in a single arch, forty-two feet wide, spans the rocky bed of the Touloubre. At each entrance there is a triumphal arch seven metres high, flanked at each side by two Corinthian pilasters, upon the summit of which the entablature rests. There is a stone lion at each extremity of the entablature; it stands rampant and looks out into the open country, as if to symbolise for ever the wakeful power of Roman thoroughness. Only one of the four lions belongs to Roman workmanship; the others are much younger, and their proportions are bigger. This bridge, again, which I believe to be unique, bears an inscription, from which we learn that it was founded by a certain L. Donnius Flavus, a flamen of Rome and of Augustus. But the name Augustus was a title of veneration given by custom to all the Cæsars, so that Donnius Flavus and his bridge have uncertain dates.

And now we will take a devious walk along some Roman roads through Gard-Hérault, to see what we shall find in the way of antique bridges. From north-east to south-west the region is crossed by the Via Domitiana, which runs from Lyons to the Pyrenees, going over the Rhône at Arles, and passing by Nîmes, Pont Ambroise, Substantion, Saint-Thibéry, Béziers, and Narbonne. At Pont Ambroise the river Vidourle is partly spanned by the ruins of a very picturesque Roman bridge, but its points of interest belong to an earlier chapter (p. 82). Near Castelnau, or Substantion, the Via Domitiana crossed the river Lez by a bridge now wholly destroyed; its abutments can be seen when the water is low, but they add nothing to our knowledge of Roman masonry. In mediæval times this bridge was called

N

the Pont Lairou, Lero being the Latin name of the river Lez.

Not far from Saint-Thibéry the Via passed over the Hérault at that point where, in the seventeenth century (about the year 1678), the river was split into halves by a great flood, which formed the Île des Bénédictins; the Roman bridge is on the western branch of this divided river. Four arches exist, but originally there were nine, with spans ranging from ten to twelve metres. The piers have cutwaters both upstream and downstream, with circular bays nearly two metres high for the relief of spate water. The facing stones are long, and the filling is local volcanic rubble. This bridge was wrecked by a flood before the year 1536.

The Via Domitiana was carried over the Orb, and then, following the ancient road of Colombiers, it crossed the Capestang by a Roman viaduct called the Pons Selmis or Pontserme, which in 1430 was repaired with 500 quarters of stone $2\frac{1}{2}$ pans long by $1\frac{1}{4}$ pans thick and wide. It was a tremendous viaduct, its length being 1500 metres; the width did not exceed three metres. In the sixteenth century it fell in for want of repair. At the present time only an isolated arch remains, with fragments of two others. In a document of A.D. 782 this bridge is called Pons Septimus.

Another Roman road left Nîmes in the direction of Larzac, and near Lodève apparently it joined the ancient road from Saint-Thibéry to Millau; at Sommières it crossed

the Vidourle by a magnificent Roman bridge which had no
fewer than seventeen arches. To-day only eight arches are
visible, the others having been buried under a great accumu-
lation of soil on both banks.* Yet the Pont de Sommières,
though deprived of nine arches, has a high place among the
Roman monuments.

I have now to mention a Roman byway that branched
out from the main road on the right bank of the Vidourle,
at a little distance from Sommières; it ran toward Substantion, passing by Castries and joining the Via Domitiana
near Vendargues. At Boisseron it crossed the river
Bénovie, a small tributary of the Vidourle, by a bridge
which to-day is extant, though disfigured by modern work.
It has a shelving parapet and road, but we cannot describe
it as a gabled bridge (p. 27). There are five arches of
unequal size, the piers on the upstream side have cutwaters,
and rectangular bays above the cutwaters ease the pressure
of floods.

Frank Brangwyn has drawn for us the wreck of a Roman
bridge over the Loire, at Brives–Charensac, in the neighbourhood of Puy; and the big arch, which springs from
water-level, is particularly interesting because it has a
double ring of voussoirs. The smaller arch belongs to the
Middle Ages, for it has a pointed shape.

We pass on to Spain, which has been called the land

* See Grangent, Durand et Durant, "Description des Monumens Antiques du
Midi de la France," Paris, 1819, I, p. 113, and Plate XL; see also "Géographie
Générale du Département de l'Hérault," published by the Société Languedocienne,
Montpellier, 1905. Vol. III, part II. p. 310.

of bridges and aqueducts. A pontist may live there for many years and be happy all the time. Even a hurried author, who visits the antiquity of Spain as a mere journalist, and who mimics vainly the travel books of Alexandre Dumas, finds that the many bridges put some thoroughness into his

RUINS OF A ROMAN BRIDGE OVER THE LOIRE AT BRIVES-CHARENSAC, FRANCE

own work, acting as a drag on the far-sought and dear-bought liveliness with which the million may be charmed. There is the case of S. R. Crockett, who was commissioned to be lively and daring among the Spaniards, so he published in 1903 "The Adventurer in Spain," a poor copy both of Borrow and of Dumas. "I would like to write

a book—copiously illustrated—upon Spanish bridges alone,"
he told his readers in a moment of zeal, adding briskly,
"that is, if I thought anybody could be found to buy it."
In one passage thought and enthusiasm very nearly broke
loose from the discipline of "a popular style":—

"Many bridges, too, there were—wonderful in a country
where, as in Spain, there are neither roads to travel upon
nor waters to cross—nor even, it may be added, travellers
to cross them. Yet in our first hour we had passed, we five
apprentice Carlists, at least as many admirable bridges—
clean-shaped, practical, suited to the place and to the landscape as a becoming dress fits a pretty woman. This is
a rare thing in bridges, and one which is almost never to
be found in new countries, where a bridge is invariably an
outrage upon the surrounding scenery. Queer bridges we
found—triangular bridges, unnecessary bridges, of wood
and stone and straw and stubble—but never ugly bridges."

Mr. Crockett did not understand the rivers of Spain,
many of which after a storm leap from their dry beds into
raging torrents, and give rough-and-tumble lessons to
bridge-builders. From Roman times to our own, these
freakish waterways have inspired noble work, that cannot
well be rated at too high a level. At Mérida alone a
pontist can dream over the past for several months, not only
studying the remains of three Roman aqueducts, upon which
storks hold their parliaments, but making friends with two
Roman bridges, one of which puts the Roman genius in

scale with the Guadiana. It is a huge structure, not less than 780 metres in length, with sixty-four arches of granite. Books of reference mention eighty-one arches, but this number includes the relief bays for floods tunnelled through the piers above the cutwaters. Some writers believe that the greater bridge at Merida was built under Trajan, while others give it to Augustus, who founded Mérida as a home of rest for the veteran soldiers of his last campaign. In 686 the Visigoths restored this bridge ; in 1610 it was repaired by Philip III ; in 1812, during the siege of Badajoz, seventeen of the arches were wrecked in order to close the river. At the northern end we find a Roman castle, now in ruins, so we are able to study a battle-bridge dating from those times when Rome turned wars into colonies.

The Roman bridges of Spain may be divided into five classes :—

1. Those which are low and many-arched, as at Mérida and Salamanca.

2. Those which have two or three arches with shelving parapets and roads, as at Alcantarilla* and also near Villa del Rio;†

---

* Two arches over the Salado river, some thirty miles below Seville (p. 367).

† Between Córdova and Andujar, over a small tributary flowing into the Guadalquivir from the south. This bridge has three arches, one a good deal larger than the others ; bays are driven through the spandrils for spate water to pass through. The masonry consists of stone in big blocks, and the craftsmanship has a very peculiar feature: the voussoirs are notched or joggled one into the other, like those in the Elizabethan bridge at Ross-on-Wye, Herefordshire. This technique is a thing to be remembered: it occurs in no other Roman bridge that is known to me. The notching adds much to the endurance of an arch ring, yet it has never entered into the

3. One or two with a single arch, as at Ronda ;

4. Several in which Roman and Moorish masonry are combined, as at Córdova ; and

5. There is one Roman bridge so lofty that its parapet is separated from the river-bed by a distance of more than fifty-nine metres. I refer to the famous Puente Trajan over "the melancholy Tagus" at Alcántara. This herculean masterpiece has six arches, his length is a hundred and eighty-eight metres, and the roadway is eight metres wide and quite level. A triumphal archway thirteen metres high stands in the middle, but I regard its Roman origin as doubtful, as the design is not quite in scale with the majesty of the bridge.

Who can say how many writers have tried to describe the Puente Trajan? No description can summon up before the mind an image of his marvellous power and nobility, for these qualities produce a feeling of awe and take from us the wish to write. That he came from an architect and was put together by common masons, huge stone after huge stone, is a fact very hard to believe, as only two things in this bridge mark the littleness of man: one is the archway, that fails to triumph with a Roman spirit, and the other is an arch of modern workmanship. Everything else recalls to my mind a good saying that fell from Marshal Ney when

technical routine of bridge-builders. Perhaps the dovetailing of the stones has been looked upon as too costly, for it needs much skill and care and time. Mr. Edgar Wigram drew my attention to this little-known Roman bridge, and to the one at Alcantarilla (p. 367).

he noticed in the aqueduct of Segovia the startling difference between the craft of modern masons and the ancient
Roman art in thorough construction. In the fifteenth
century some vaults of the Segovian aqueduct were
destroyed by wars, and Isabella the Catholic had them
rebuilt in the most careful manner. Yet the work was not
careful enough, for in less than three hundred years the
reconstruction had to be renewed, while the Roman art
remained youthful and immovable. In 1808 Marshal Ney
was greatly impressed by these facts, and, pointing to the
first arch of the modern portion, he said : "C'est ici que
commence le travail des hommes." Even the people of
Segovia feel that their soaring aqueduct has in it something
far beyond their reach, something grand enough to be called
superhuman. Custom has deadened their admiration, of
course, has enabled them even to build silly little houses
amid the shadows thrown by their antique monument; but
yet they doubt the human origin of such perfect masonry
and give it to the Evil One, who comforts himself with
a tremendous deed of architecture whenever he is greatly
bored by the feeble gullibility of mankind.

Nothing is more difficult than to express in words this
unhuman character of the best Roman bridges, which reveal
eternal manhood and courage in the work done by the men
of a day. For instance, here is the Alcántara over the rocky
gorge of the Tagus. He was erected for Trajan by Caius
Julius Lacer; and we know that Lacer was buried quite
close to his bridge, and that his tomb remains on the left

THE ROMAN AQUEDUCT AT SEGOVIA IN SPAIN, WITH
MODERN HOUSES CLUSTERED AROUND ITS BASE

bank. These facts are trite and tame, but when we turn from them to the supreme bridge we pass from bald history into a creation that seems miraculous.

"It is long before the eye can learn to grasp his * full dimensions; all around him is rock and mountain, there is nothing to give scale. We are warned of this . . . by the camera, for the lens will not look at so wide an angle. . . . Presently, as we peer over the parapet into the depths of the gulf below us, we realise that there is a man down there walking by the waterside, with a dog that seems to bark though we cannot hear the sound. Slowly our eyes measure the voussoir above which we are standing; it is a twelve-ton block of granite; and the huge vault with its eighty such voussoirs seems to widen and deepen beneath us as we gaze; for the brook that it spans is the river Tagus, whose waters have their source three hundred miles away.

"Thus hint by hint we have pieced together the astonishing conclusion that the span of each of the two great central arches is rather wider . . . than the interior of the dome of St. Paul's; and that the height of the railway lines above the Firth of Forth is twenty feet less than that of the road above the Tagus! What must the scene be like in winter, when the waters are foaming against the springer stones one hundred and forty feet above their summer level! How vast the strength of these massive piers which for eighteen hundred years have defied the fury of the floods!

* This bridge is a soldier, and claims masculine pronouns.

"Where now is the great *Via Lata* that ran from Gades to Rome? Where are the famous cities which it threaded on the way? The vine and olive grow in the forum of Italica, and the Miracles of Mérida are a dwelling for the stork. But here at the wildest point of all its wild journey our eyes may still behold a memorial which nature has assailed in vain : 'Pontem perpetui mansurum in sæcula mundi';—the monument of Caius Julius Lacer, more enduring even than Wren's." *

Many persons believe that Wellington's troops, in 1809, blew up one of the smaller arches, but this is untrue. The history of the ruined arch has been given by Larousse. It was cut on two occasions. In 1213 the Saracens destroyed it, and Charles the Fifth rebuilt it in 1543. Two hundred and sixty-five years passed, and then the French in 1808 were compelled by the policy of war to wreck the same arch, and I have already described how Wellington bridged the gap with a netting of ropes— a suspension bridge of ships' cables—covered with planks (p. 16). This temporary work was displaced by a wooden arch, which in 1818 was burnt down ; and between this date and the Carlist wars no restoration seems to have been attempted. "The Spaniards were long content with a ferry," says Mr. Wigram. But now they have renewed the arch "in its native granite, a feat of which they are justly proud. Only, seeing that no cement at all was used in the original building, it was really a little too bad of them to

* "Northern Spain," by Edgar T. A. Wigram, London, 1906, pp. 231-2.

insist upon pointing *all* the joints!" True ; but the workmen were modern, not Roman, and it was humility on their part to advertise their cement, their most evident strength.

THE BRIDGE AT ZARAGOZA, PARTLY ROMAN

The Moorish words *Al Kántarah* mean THE BRIDGE, and we know that the Titanic masterpiece of Julius Lacer has but few rivals. Let us put it side by side with the most stately bridges at Isfahan in Persia, whose august charm is not so masculine (p. 268) ; then we do honour to the finest pontine architecture in the world. The Alcántara is a King, a Cæsar, while the two Persian achievements are Amazon Queens.

Several bridges in Spain have the honorary title of being Roman, either because they exhibit a combination of Roman and Moorish masonry like the sixteen-arched example at Córdova, or because they may have in them some Roman workmanship, like the Puente de Piedra over the Ebro at Zaragoza, which has seven arches and six very massive piers, far too ungainly to be Roman. Indeed this bridge dates from 1437, but it was built on a classical site, and on Roman foundations. Some houses give interest to the up-stream side of the piers, but their roofs do not rise above the level of the parapet.

As for the bridge over the Guadalquivir at Córdova, it is more Moorish than Roman, for most of the Roman arches were destroyed by the eighth century, and they were reconstructed by the Arabs, who established themselves at Córdova in 711. Recently this bridge has been so much repaired that it looks almost new. A big tower, very Moorish in style, the Calahorra, keeps guard at the end remote from the town; and the city entrance has a worn classic gateway and an elevated statue of Saint Raphael, the patron saint of Córdova.

THE HUGE DEFENSIVE BRIDGE AT CORDOVA IN SPAIN. ORIGINALLY ROMAN, BUT REMODELLED BY THE MOORS IN THE NINTH CENTURY RECENTLY SO MUCH REPAIRED THAT LOOKS ALMOST NEW

III

A FEW remarks must be made on the technique of
Roman bridges and aqueducts. Vitruvius mentions a method known as *opus quadratum* in
which stones were put in regular courses of headers* and
stretchers†; they were big stones, about two feet by four
feet and two feet high, as in the Marcian Aqueduct dating
from B.C. 145.‡ Each stone was bordered with a draft cut
one and a half inches wide, and the middle surface was
roughed with a pick. This technique may be studied in
the aqueducts at Segovia and Tarragona. The arches
were set back at their springing behind the imposts, leaving
ledges upon which the scaffolds rested.

Not all the Roman aqueducts were of stone. The one
named after Nero was in brickwork of the finest kind; and

---

* The stones laid end-foremost.   † The stones laid at full length.

‡ There is conflicting evidence on the date of this monument. Pliny attributed
the Marcian Aqueduct to Ancus Marcius, whereas Strabo and Frontinus conjecture
that the building got its name from Marcius Rex, a pretor, who in the year B.C. 145,
or thereabouts, restored some ancient aqueducts whose first construction did not go
back beyond the year 272 B.C. Sextus Julius Frontinus, governor of Britain (A.D. 75–
78), was the author of two monographs that are still extant—one on the Roman
aqueducts, and another on the art of war. He was nominated *Curator Aquarum*, or
Superintendent of the Aqueducts, in 97, nine years before his death. Sir William
Smith tells us that the earliest aqueduct was not older than the year B.C. 313. In
earlier times the Romans had recourse to the Tiber and to wells sunk in the city.
During the sixth century of the Christian era there were fourteen aqueducts at Rome.

another, the Alexandrine, that brought water to the Thermæ of Alexander Severus, was faced with bricks over concrete. At Minturnæ, a town of the Volci, a decorative effect was given to the wall surfaces by means of coloured tufa arranged in geometrical patterns. This is enough to show that the virile conservatism of Rome did not stereotype building methods.

Many persons believe that the Romans built aqueducts because they were unacquainted with the hydraulic principle that water in a closed pipe finds its own level. Yet Vitruvius gives an account of the leaden pipes that distributed water in Roman towns ; and Pliny says that this piping was used very often for rising mains to carry water to the upper floors of houses. But lead pipes might burst, and they were costly ; it was cheaper to build aqueducts, for their materials belonged to the State and slave labour was in vogue.*

Finally, we should pay attention to the Roman aqueducts because they were an apprenticeship in the building of lofty and daring arches. In the Anio Vetus, for example, which dates from about the year B.C. 272, some of the arches rise to a height that exceeds ninety feet. And any architect who conceived and brought to completion a fine aqueduct, such as the Pont du Gard, or the wonderful structure at Segóvia, deserved to take rank with Caius Julius Lacer. No problem of bridge construction would have baffled his matured knowledge.

It is said that the earliest vaulted bridge of the Romans

* Mr. R. Phené Spiers has written admirably on these technical matters.

was erected under the elder Tarquin, about six hundred years before the Birth of Christ. Emiland Gauthey says, for example, " Pont Salaro, à Rome, sur le Teverone. Cet ouvrage, composé de trois arches en plein cintre, de 16, 6 à 21 metres, et de deux arches plus petites, de 6, 8 metres, fut élevé sous Tarquin l'ancien, six cents ans avant J. C." Yet there is no evidence to justify this dogmatism. The bridge may have been a timber one, like the Pons Sublicius. It carried the Via Salaria over the Anio (*Teverone*) about two and a half miles from Rome, and was called usually the Pons Salarus. Livy speaks of it under another name, Pons Anienis, and makes it the theatre of an immortal fight, the one between Manlius and a gigantic Gaul, B.C. 361. In single combat Manlius killed the barbarian, and took a chain (*torques*) from the dead body, and put it around his own neck, as a proof of his victory, winning by this act the surname of Torquatus.

The Pons Salarus does not appear again in early history. By the year B.C. 361 it may have been made into an arched bridge of stone, though it was not till B.C. 313 that the first aqueduct to Rome was constructed. In any case, however, we learn from an inscription, which Sir William Smith accepted as authentic, that the Pons Salarus was rebuilt in the sixth century A.D., by Narses, general and statesman, in the reign of Justinian. If in this reconstruction any earlier work was preserved, we must look for it in the smallest arches described by Gauthey, for we find narrow spans in the earliest Roman aqueducts. Those of the Marcian are

only eight metres.   The Ponte Salaro existed till 1867,
when it was blown up during a panic caused by Garibaldi's
march to Rome.   A fortified castle stood above one side of
the central arch, rising from the footway, whose width was

PONTE ROTTO AT ROME, ANCIENTLY THE PONS PALATINUS OR SENATORIUS

more than eight metres.   The bridge was about a hundred
metres long, and its vaults were built with exceedingly
heavy stones remarkable for their bossage work.   A wood-
cut of this late Roman bridge is given by Professor
Fleeming Jenkin, but it differs from the illustration in
Emiland Gauthey's "Traité de la Construction des Ponts,"
Paris, 1809–16, Vol. I.

There has been so much controversy over the antique bridges at Rome that the steadiest head becomes giddy while reading Palladio, Becker, Bunsen, Piranesi, Sir William Smith, and other experts. Perhaps we may be on safe ground when we step delicately on tiptoe into the historic environment of the Pons Palatinus, a bridge which seems to have been erected in the year B.C. 179.* A good part of this bridge was rebuilt in the time of Pope Gregory XIII (1572–85), but in 1598 it was wrecked by a terrible flood, and people began to speak of it as the Ponte Rotto, or broken bridge. From Palladio's book on architecture, printed at Venice in 1570, we learn that the Pons Palatinus, or Senatorius, was known also as the Ponte Santa-Maria, so Rome must have been horrified when a classic bridge recently dedicated to the Virgin was overthrown by a spate, which spared the Pons Cestius and the Pons Fabricius.

The arches of this bridge were rather more than twenty-four metres in span, and their large archivolts were boldly prominent. The piers, about eight metres thick, were protected by angular cutwaters, and above each cutwater was a tall niche flanked by pilasters whose capitals touched the broad cornice that framed the spandrils in a vigorous manner. Each spandril was ornamented with a sea-horse

* I take it that the Pons Palatinus, or Senatorius, mentioned by Palladio, was the bridge called by ancient writers the Pons Aemilius, whose piers were founded in the censorship of M. Aemilius Lepidus and M. Fulvius Nobilior, B.C. 179; the arches were finished some years later, when P. Scipio Africanus and L. Mummius were censors. Becker and Canina assume that the Pons Aemilius became the Ponte Rotto, and Degrand and others identify the Palatine bridge of Palladio with the Ponte Rotto.

o

carved in relief; and this decoration was foiled by the plain, deep parapets whose horizontal lines were diversified here and there by a projection. Brangwyn's drawing of the Ponte Rotto gives all the architectural character, and we see that this bridge was a great Roman citizen, manly and brave and noble. Further, when we speak of any bridge as virile as this one arch, we have a right to use masculine pronouns, "he" and "his" and "him." The trivial word "it" is a feeble neutrality that belongs to a great many bridges, both ancient and modern; but a Cæsarian achievement like the Pons Palatinus, or the Pont du Gard, or the Puente Trajan at Alcántara, takes rank among the rare deeds that do honour to a splendid manhood; and this we should recognise in our pronouns.

Palladio says that in his time, from 1518 to 1580, three other bridges over the Tiber, at Rome, were in good preservation. Let us take a glance at them:—

1. The Pons Ælius, called then, as now, the Ponte Sant' Angelo, built by Ælius Hadrianus, who reigned from A.D. 117 to 138, and who erected his bridge as a passage over the Tiber to his own mausoleum, which forms the ground-work of the present castle of St. Angelo. An earlier bridge connected the Vatican and its neighbourhood with that part of the city which Caligula and Nero had beautified with gardens; and remains of it still exist near S. Spirito. The date of its disappearance I do not know, but in the days of Procopius, the sixth century of the Christian era, the Pons Ælius was the only communication between the city and the

Vatican district. Either legend or truth says that the Ælius had a bronze cover upheld by forty-two pillars. If this gleaming roof ever existed (and writers should be afraid of pretty details in ancient history), it must have been damaged very much when the parapets were broken down in the fifteenth century. This accident was caused by a great crowd that lost control of itself on the bridge, when thronging to St. Peter's to receive the Pope's benediction. At last the parapets gave way, and ninety-two persons were either drowned or crushed to death. Long afterwards, as we know, Giovanni L. Bernini (1598–1680) designed balustrades of iron and stone, but dwarfed them with ten huge statues commissioned by Pope Clement IX (p. 324). The figures of St. Peter and St. Paul at the city entrance were put up by Clement VII. The bridge itself—or himself, shall we say?—has a technical inspiration akin to that of the Pons Palatinus; but there is less ornament, and above the cut-waters, instead of tall niches, we find rectangular pillars with plain capitals, upon which Bernini erected pedestals for his "breezy angels."

2. The Pons Fabricius, connecting Rome on the city side with the Insula Tiberina. In very early times this island in the Tiber was united to each bankside by a bridge, and hence it was called *Inter Duos Pontes*. The present Pons Fabricius was either founded or restored by L. Fabricius, curator viarum in B.C. 62, as appears from the inscription on it, and from Dion Cassius. It is mentioned by Horace as a bridge very attractive to suicides :—

. . . jussit sapientem pascere barbam
Atque a Fabricio non tristem ponte reverti.

Since Palladio's time, if not from a much earlier date, the
Pons Fabricius has been known as the Ponte Quattro Capi,
because its entrance from the left bank has a protective
emblem, a quadrupled head of Janus, the guardian deity of
gates, and a divinity with many other occupations, all very
alert and troublesome. So we must add this pagan emblem
to the other symbols of religious faith with which bridges
have been sanctified. In 1680 the Pons Fabricius was
repaired by Pope Innocent XI. There are two arches, each
with a span of 25, 34 metres; and there used to be two
other arches, only 3, 50 metres wide, pierced through the
abutments, but they have disappeared among the houses on
each bankside. The bridge in its greatest width measures
a little more than 15 metres. It has a bold cornice ornamented with mutules, and its relief bay for spate water is
flanked by pilasters. M. Degrand says of the Pons Fabricius: " C'est le premier pont dans lequel les têtes des voûtes
ne forment pas des demi-circonférences: l'intrados est un
arc de cercle de 25 m. de rayon et de 20 m. de flèche."
Here we find a starting-point for the lovely arch invented
at Avignon by Saint Bénézet (p. 81).

3. The Pons Cestius, on the other side of the island,
known to-day, and in Palladio's time, as Ponte S. Barto-
lommeo. Yet its inscription, which is mentioned by Canina
and by Sir William Smith, speaks of it as Pons Gratianus,
and commemorates its repair by Valentinian, Valens, and

Gratian. It has but one arch, nearly a metre less in span than those of the Pons Fabricius. These two bridges, according to Piranesi, were founded in a very remarkable manner, on reversed arches built under water. Gauthey gives two drawings of this construction, but he does not guarantee the truth of Piranesi's details.

Five other antique bridges crossed the Tiber at or near Rome, but Palladio found nothing more of them than a few remnants. Already I have spoken of two, the Pons Sublicius and its understudy (p. 140). On the left bank, facing the church of S. Spirito, Palladio saw remains of the Pons Triumphalis; but Piranesi and Bunsen do not agree with Palladio. They place the Pons Triumphalis beyond the Pons Ælius, and Sir William Smith thinks it probable that the remains near S. Spirito belong to a bridge which the *Mirabilia* names Pons Neronianus, and which ancient topographers describe as Pons Vaticanus. Then there was the Janiculine bridge upon the foundations of which, between 1471 and 1484, Pope Sixtus IV had erected the Ponte Sisto. As the Janiculine bridge went from the Janiculum to the Porta Aurelia, it was known also as Pons Aurelius; and in the Middle Ages it seems to have been called Pons Antoninus. As for the Ponte Molle, anciently the Pons Milvius, it belonged to the Flaminian Way, crossing the Tiber beyond the walls of Rome, a mile and a half outside the city. Its founder was said to be the earlier Æmilius Scaurus, who died about eighty-five years before the Birth of Christ. Yet it certainly existed in

B.C. 207, for Livy relates how the people poured out of Rome as far as the Milvian bridge in order to meet the messengers who brought tidings of the defeat of Hasdrubal. This may have been a timber bridge, and Æmilius Scaurus may have displaced it for a stone bridge during his consulship, B.C. 110.

Only a few fragments of the Pons Milvius existed in Palladio's time; and so the Ponte Molle now extant has a false reputation of being Roman. In fact, it is a very poor structure, badly designed and very uncouth.

IV

THERE was in Italy a Roman bridge built of white Istrian stone that Palladio admired much more than any other; indeed, he admired it too much, for he copied it in most of his pontine architecture, as if he had no right to make use of his own originality! And since his time many architects have cribbed from the same shining model, the Ponte Augustus over the Ariminus, at Rimini. Two Roman bridges are found in the neighbourhood of this town, one with seven arches and one with five; both date from the same great era, and in both the roadway is not carried through on the same level, but has an ascent at each end, like the two bridges of Roman origin at Vicenza. It was the bridge with five arches that Palladio preferred at Rimini, and his fondness for it—or, rather, for *her*, as this Roman bridge has a charm somewhat feminine—is approved by recent experts, and notably by R. Phené Spiers and M. Degrand. She is a bijou among bridges, and not a male prodigy, like the Puente Trajan. Her arches are small in span, ranging from 8 m. 77 to 7 m. 14, according to Gauthey,* the narrower ones being at the sides, and the three larger

---

* Degrand says 10 m. 56 and 8 m. 1. R. Phené Spiers gives 27 ft. for the spans of the three central arches, and the side ones about 20 ft.

bays in the middle. Their form is semicircular, and their
springing does not rise from low water-level, like that of the
arches in the Roman bridge at Mérida ; it is placed four or
five metres* above low water, and this planning adds light-

PONTE MAGGIORE OVER A RAVINE OF THE TRONTO AT ASCOLI-PICENO IN ITALY ;
BUILT IN THE MIDDLE AGES, BUT ROMAN IN STYLE

ness and grace to a fortunate design. As usual, the piers
are too heavy, their thickness being about equal to a half
of the adjacent voids ; they are protected by very vigorous
cutwaters that break the current with angular wedges of

* Gauthey says four, Degrand says five.

ninety degrees. The spandrils are decorated with niches, and every niche is flanked by pilasters carrying entablature and pediment. A beautiful cornice supported by modillions crowns this bridge, which was begun by Augustus and finished by Tiberius.

Brangwyn is fascinated by the bridges at Ascoli-Piceno, the Asculum Picenum of the Romans, that gleams on a terrace dominating the Tronto, about twenty miles from Porto Ascoli on the Adriatic. The town is defended by ravines, across which four great bridges are thrown. The Ponte di Porta Cappucina is a Roman bridge, a fine example with a single arch of 71 ft. span ; and the Ponte de Cecco is Roman. It has two arches and belongs to the Via Salaria. As for the Ponte Maggiore and the Ponte Cartaro, they are mediæval, but the former is an adaptation from Roman aqueducts, and in the latter there appear to be some traces of antique craftsmanship. All these great viaducts are marvellously constructed, for they resisted the earthquake that shook Ascoli in 1878.

V

VERY little is known about the Eastern bridges constructed by the Romans. In Jebb's "By Desert Ways to Baghdad" an illustration is given of a Roman bridge over the Tigris at Diarbekr; and on the same river, at Hassan, between Diarbekr and Mosul, there are ruined piers of another Roman bridge. Again, at Shushter, in Persia, we find a dike and a bridge ascribed to the Roman Emperor Valerian, whom Shapur the First took prisoner at Edessa, A.D. 260. The dike is called the Band-i-Mizan, the bridge the Pul-i-Kaisar. But if Valerian helped to build these huge monuments, very little Roman work now remains; seventy yards of dike and bridge were swept away in 1885; and the Pul-i-Kaisar has been rebuilt several times. Indeed, as Brangwyn's pen-drawing shows, the arches (there are forty in all) differ in style as well as in size and material.

"Persian tradition has it that Ardashir (either Artaxerxes of the old Persian kings or Ardashir of the Sassanians) built the first dike across the river Karun in order to raise the water of the river to the level of the Darian canal. The dike became destroyed and was renewed under the Sassanian Shapur I, by Roman workmen sent for by Valerian, who had been captured by the Persian king in

260. That Valerian had a part in constructing these remarkable works does not rest upon any historical basis;
we may, however, believe that the Sassanian Ardashir, or
his son Shapur I, finding that the river, with its bed in

THE PUL-I-KAISAR AT SHUSHTER IN PERSIA. ITS LENGTH IS 560 YARDS,
AND ITS ROADWAY IS 7 YARDS WIDE

friable soil, was daily getting lower and finally threatened
to leave the town and the Mian-do-ab district dry by not
filling the Darian canal, engaged Roman workmen. The
Gerger canal was cut and the river diverted from west to
east of the town. The old river then became emptied and
its bed was raised and paved with huge flags, to prevent

further erosion and washing away of the soil and a conse-
quent fall of the river. Then the Band-i-Mizan and the
great bridge were erected. . . ." *

In every chapter of this monograph other references to
Roman work will be found.

* Sir A. Houtum-Schindler, c.i.e., " Encyclopædia Brit.," 1911, article
" Shushter."

I

MEDIÆVAL England was a forrestial country, and many a roadside wood gave shelter to footpads and bandits, who planned ambuscades, and amused themselves with rape and rapine and murder. If they were less ready to cut a throat than to broach a tun of wine* the terror inspired by their evil reputation told lies that duped everybody. In fact, travellers were pitied by Acts of Parliament, but they had greater faith in the Church, which enabled them to renew their failing courage with frequent prayer at shrines by the wayside. Saint after saint was called to their aid; and from the time of St. Dunstan the Church reckoned the building of bridges among the most urgent duties of charity. Some good must have been done, yet rivers and journeys were feared very much; fords were common, and an ambush near a

---

* See the Statute of Winchester, A.D. 1285, and Statute 2, Richard II, A.D. 1378; see also the Rolls of Parliament. Among the most dangerous rogues were many lawless barons and their retinues, against whom the Law protested vainly. In A.D. 1138 we find them mentioned by the "Gesta Stephani," and till late in the fifteenth century the partisans of nobles were feared on the roads. But for them the Wars of the Roses would have been less horrible, and wayfaring life would have been less barbarously at odds with those Christian virtues which were proclaimed everywhere by great symbols of religion: manor churches, hopeful cathedrals, vast monasteries, wayside chapels and shrines, and quiet homes whispering with the prayers of gentle nuns. Brutal strife among Christians had made the world into a new Garden of Gethsemane over which the Spirit of Christ brooded and wept.

ford was a peril difficult to encounter. In the "Ballad of Abingdon Bridge," which dates from the time of Henry V, we see what fords were like and how their guardians behaved to travellers. "Another blissed besines is brigges to make," the rustic poet cries, thinking of unfortunate wayfarers who were washed from their saddles into a flooded river :—

> And som oute of their sadels flette [fall] to the grounde,
> Wente forthe in the water wist no man whare,
> Fyve wekys after or they were i founde,
> Their kyn and their knowlech [acquaintance] caught them up with care.

And this life-tax claimed by rivers was not the only trouble. The keepers of a ford knew no pity, but got their toll in relentless ways, taking bread from the beggar's wallet and "a hood or a girdel" from "the pore penyles." Very often, too, great woods encircled riverside towns and manors, so that outlaws after dark could steal up close to the houses and the bridge; it was then that pilgrims welcomed with the greatest relief the cresset-lights that glimmered from some friendly building on the bridge—from a chapel, or a defensive gateway, or a small bickering windmill, or a good watermill buttressed against a pier and rising high above the parapet.

And now we must pass in review six old species of bridge :—

1. The Housed Bridge, such as we find in Brangwyn's beautiful monochrome of the quaint bridge at Kreuznach, in Germany.

OLD BRIDGE WITH HOUSES AT KREUZNACH, ON THE RIVER NAHE, IN PRUSSIA. AN OLD MILL BRIDGE, SEEMINGLY

2. The Shrined Bridge, as in Brangwyn's alert impression of the Gothic bridge at Elche, in Spain.

3. The Bridge of Mills, as represented in the very romantic sketch of the old and broken bridge at Millau, in Southern France, at the confluence of the Tarn with the Dourbie. Another example, much modernised, exists in France, at historic Meaux, about thirty-two miles from Paris.

4. The Chapelled Bridge, as at Wakefield, and Rotherham, and Pisa, and Avignon (see Frontispiece), and elsewhere.

5. The War-Bridge, which in Brangwyn's art receives the most varied and vigorous recognition. Never before have they been studied so completely by an artist.

6. The Bridge of Shops, as at Venice in the Rialto.

P

II

WE ought not to be surprised that mediæval bridges were connected in a self-evident manner with all the principal motive-powers of social life. They were excellent places where kings and nobles could show off their military ambition, and where the Church could be active in good work done for the safety of wayfaring. Shops on a bridge were valued because of the continuous traffic that brought trade to their doors; and a few private houses on a market bridge gratified a middle class vanity, that took pride in paying the higher rents of a business thoroughfare. To live on Old London Bridge was a distinction; to be a tradesman on the Ponte Vecchio in Florence, or on a timber bridge in Paris, was to be prosperous, for no bridge of shops was wide enough to be unpopular among those who had money to spend. Can anyone explain why the feminine joy of going to market has ever been most adventurous in narrow streets, or in short streets of a medium width ? *

* There seems to be only one exception to this rule. I refer to some Chinese bridges of the thirteenth century, mentioned by Marco Polo in his account of the city Sin-din-fu, now called Ching-tu-fu, situated on the western side of the province of Se-chuen, of which it is the capital. Marco Polo says: "The city is watered by many considerable streams, which, descending from the distant mountains, surround and pass through it in a variety of directions. Some of these rivers are half a mile in width, others are two hundred paces, and very deep, over which are built several

Whatever the reasons may be, here is a point to be remembered when we study such a bridge as the Rialto, at Venice, which carries three little streets on an arch twenty-four feet six inches high, and ninety-one feet in span, with a soffit about seventy-two feet wide. To-day the Rialto shops are trivial and mean, but in the great time of the Republic they displayed the most luxurious oddments of fashion, and delighted the idle rich. Very often it is said that the Rialto was built from a design by Michelangelo, as if this wonderful master of a tragic and supreme dignity could have amused his leisure with such a pretty whim in ornate building ! Modern criticism shows a very poor taste when it repeats this old fallacy, or when it describes the Rialto as a masterpiece of architecture dating from the Renaissance. In comparison with the bridges of Isfahan, which belong to the sixteenth and seventeenth centuries, the Rialto is a mere toy. Its origin is the subject of

large and handsome stone bridges, eight paces in breadth, their length being greater or less according to the size of the stream. From one extremity to the other there is a row of marble pillars on each side, which support the roof; for here the bridges have very handsome roofs, constructed of wood, ornamented with paintings of a red colour, and covered with tiles. Throughout the whole length also there are neat apartments and shops, where all sorts of trades are carried on. One of the buildings, larger than the rest, is occupied by the officers who collect the duties upon provisions and merchandise, and a toll from persons who pass the bridge. In this way, it is said, his Majesty receives daily the sum of a hundred besants of gold." According to the Latin editions of Marco Polo, the booths or shops were set up in the morning and removed from the bridge at night. If so, then the width of these bridges, described by Marco as "eight paces," must have been more than twenty-four feet, since booths would have obstructed such narrow footways. Marco Polo's great editor, Colonel Yule, interpreting the description of another bridge, proves that the "paces" must be geometric.

Rondelet's "Essai Historique sur le Pont de Rialto," where
we watch a great competition between Palladio and
Antonio da Ponte. Palladio was the greater man, but the
Senate rejected his designs,* and in 1588 Antonio da Ponte
built his arched scaffold or centring and laid the first blocks
of Istrian marble.

In Brangwyn's picture the Rialto is gay enough to
belong to the joyous times of the Republic; and by comparing this picture with the pen-drawings of the bridges at
Isfahan, in Persia, it is easy to note the difference in spirit
between two cities that attained in the same age their
greatest prosperity. In 1590, Isfahan became the capital
of Persia; and by this year Venice had recovered from the
destructive fire of 1577, and was beautifying herself in
many ways, as with the Piazza di San Marco.

At Isfahan no fewer than five old bridges cross the
Zendeh Rud, the most ancient being the Pul-i-Marnun,
which was built by Shah Tahmasp, who reigned from 1524
to 1575. It is not a great bridge, so it stands apart from
the Pul-i-Khaju and the vast Bridge of Ali Verdi Khan,
which undoubtedly are among the finest bridges in the world.
Their beauty has such a gracious power, such brightness
and grandeur, that even the Roman bridge at Alcántara
may seem to rival it unsuccessfully. Brangwyn has drawn
these Persian masterpieces, but the Pul-i-Khaju alone

* Degrand, in his "Ponts en Maçonnerie," gives a reproduction of Palladio's
drawing, which represents an imperial scheme, far and away better than Antonio da
Ponte's.

THE RIALTO, VENICE DESIGNED IN 1588
BY ANTONIO DA PONTE, ARCHITECT

belongs to this section on housed bridges—except in some
architectural points common to both.   Their arches are
Moorish, and their builders may have borrowed from the
Romans an idea which has come down to our time in at
least one antique monument, namely, the ruined aqueduct

THE PUL-I-KHAJU OVER THE ZENDEH RUD AT ISFAHAN, PERSIA

at Lyon, not far from Saint Irénée.   Through the piers of
this aqueduct arches are cut transversely, so as to form a
side arcade all along the length of the structure.   These
lateral arches vary much in size, and some of them have
been built up.   I know not for what purpose they were
used ; but they lighten the piers, which are uncommonly

massive. It is this arrangement—a vaulted gallery cut through the sides of piers—that we find also at Isfahan in the two historic bridges of the Sefi kings.

The Pul-i-Khaju has been described many times, but Lord Curzon's account of it is by far the most valuable :—

"The Pul-i-Khaju is shorter than the bridge of Ali Verdi Khan, being only 154 yards in length, owing to a contraction in the bed of the river, which here flows over a ledge of rock. The structure consists, in fact, of a bridge superimposed upon a dam. The latter is built of solid blocks of stone and is pierced by narrow channels, the flow in which can be regulated by sluices. This great platform is broken on its outer edge, the stones being arranged in the form of steps descending to the river-level. Upon the platform or dam repose the twenty-four main arches of the bridge, which is of brick, and the chief external features of which are four projecting two-storeyed hexagonal pavilions, one at each corner, and two larger pavilions of similar shape in the centre, a third storey being erected upon the roof of the more westerly of the two. As in the case of the Julfa Bridge,* the basement is pierced by a vaulted passage, running the entire length of the bridge through the piers on the top of the dam, and crossing the successive channels by stepping-stones six feet deep. The main roadway of the bridge, twenty-four feet broad, is also flanked by a covered gallery on each side, leading to the hexagonal pavilions, and opening by a succession of arches on to the outer air.

* The Bridge of Ali Verdi Khan.

Finally, there is a terrace-walk at the top, which was originally protected by a double parapet and screens. The pavilions were once adorned with rich paintings and gilding, and with panels containing inscriptions. The decoration is now more jejune and vulgar, and the spandrils of the arches are mostly filled in with modern tiles. In olden days this bridge was a favourite resort in the evening, where the young gallants of Isfahan marched up and down, or sat and smoked in the embayed archways overlooking the stream. Now it is well-nigh deserted save in the springtime, when the snows melt in the mountains, and in a few hours the Zendeh Rud is converted from a petty stream into a foaming torrent. Then the good folk of Isfahan crowd the galleries and arcades of the bridge, and shout with delight as the water first rushes through the narrow sluices, then mounts to the level of the causeway and spills in a noisy cascade down each successive stairway or weir, and finally pours through the main arches, still splitting into a series of cataracts as it leaps the broken edges of the dam." *

Such is the Pul-i-Khaju. Her architect's name is unknown, but she dates from the time of Shah Abbas II, who reigned between the years 1641 and 1666. Even in photographs she is a bridge of enchantment where from time to time all the tired geniuses of the world should go for a romantic holiday ; the pavilions certainly await the coming of worthy guests, who would save them from the vulgar

* Lord Curzon's book on Persia.

decoration which has displaced the old paintings and enrichments. That vaulted arcade in the basement, running transversely through all the piers, and crossing the channels by huge stepping-stones (one of the earliest bridges copied by primitive man from Nature's object-lessons), has a great historic interest, though in pictures and photographs it attracts very little attention. Was it suggested by a Roman model, or was it rediscovered by the originality of a great architect? I have searched long for an answer to these questions, but in vain.

Perhaps Old London Bridge at her best, after the building of None-such House, in 1576, may have been as entertaining to the eye as is the magic of the Pul-i-Khaju, though inferior to this masterpiece as a work of art. The earliest representation of Old London Bridge comes to us from the fifteenth century, in a miniature that graces the poems of Charles d'Orléans.* It shows five piers much broader than the adjacent voids, also a line of picturesque timber houses jutting out from the parapet, and a great chapel of apsidal form, with wrought pinnacles and two tiers of decorated windows. This Gothic church, dedicated to St. Thomas à Becket, rises from water-level to a height exceeding that of the tallest house on the bridge.

In Howell's "Londinopolis" (edition of 1657) it is said that during King John's reign, 1199–1216, a mayor of

---

* British Museum, the MS. 16 F. ii, Fol. 73. The little picture is drawn from nature; a bad reproduction of it appears in M. Jusserand's good book on "English Wayfaring Life in the Middle Ages."

London, 'being master workman of the bridge, builded from the foundation the large chappel on the bridge upon his own charges, which chappel was then endowed with two priests and four clerks, beside chantries." It was put on the east side ; there were two storeys, one with an entrance from the river, the other with a porch on the roadway. So boat-farers had their own place of worship on London Bridge, and they walked to their praying-stools over a pavement of black and white marble. Both storeys were brilliantly lighted ; in the upper one there were eight windows.

The first architect of Old London Bridge, Peter Cole-church, "priest and chaplain," died in 1205, and was buried in the Chapel of St. Thomas, just twenty-two years after Saint Bénézet was laid to rest in his bridge chapel at Avignon. Between 1176 and 1183 Colechurch may have had some correspondence with Bénézet, for both were heads of religious bodies engaged at the same time on similar work. "Their letters to one another would interest engineers," remarks Professor Fleeming Jenkin, as if engineers alone were attracted by Old London Bridge.

In 1176, when Colechurch prepared his designs, every-body was excited about a great and very useful enterprise. The King, the clergy, the citizens of London, even country-folk, endowed the bridge with lands or sent money to hasten its completion. The Archbishop of Canterbury subscribed a thousand marks. During the sixteenth century the list of donors was still to be seen "in a table fair written for posterity," treasured in the chapel on the bridge.*   Stow makes no reference to the mayor who at his own expense built the chapel ; he says only that Colechurch was buried "in the chapel builded on the same bridge in the year 1205." Four years later the bridge was finished by three "worthy merchants of London—Serle Mercer, William Almaine, and Benedick Botewrite, principal masters of work." Their director-in-chief was a Frenchman, brother Isembert by name, whose magnificent bridge at Saintes had delighted King John, and who was chosen to superintend the finishing of Old London Bridge a little while before the death of Colechurch.

In July, 1212, a terrific fire occurred on the bridge, beginning at the Southwark end, but spreading to the houses at the north end also ; no fewer than 3000 persons lost their lives. Citizens gathered at the north end to watch the spectacle, and were overtaken by the swift-travelling flames and by panic also. Many jumped into the river and were drowned ; others were killed by falling timbers, and many were scorched to death. Again and again, in after years, London Bridge and her chapel were ravaged by fire ; as in 1300, in 1471, in 1632, in 1666, and in September, 1725.

Here is Stow's picture of the houses :—

"The building was of timber, very substantial and beautiful, for the houses were three stories high, besides the cellars, which were within and between the piers, and over the houses were stately platforms, leaded, with rails and

* J. J. Jusserand, p. 49.   See also in Stow.

ballasters about them, very commodious and pleasant for walking and enjoying so fine a prospect up and down the river, and some had pretty little gardens with arbours."

All this fine architecture was destroyed in the Great Fire of 1666, but a still better pile of buildings was put up, and now the houses were separated by a roadway twenty feet wide. In earlier times the passage between the houses ranged in width from twelve feet to fourteen. At last, in 1756, every house on the bridge was pulled down, but the chapel was granted a few years more of life. Guess why? Because some vandal or other was willing to use the chapel as a warehouse. At about the same time the chapel on Rotherham Bridge, Yorkshire, was a tobacco shop. As for the merchant who leased the Chapel of St. Thomas à Becket, he built a new ceiling with heavy beams that crossed each other; soon he tired of his warehouse, and then—then the historic old fane was destroyed. A city is like a board meeting—from time to time it has a conscience.

Two other historic facts find a place here. In March, 1782, the right of toll was discontinued, so that Londoners were separated from a direct personal interest in the welfare of their bridge, just as free education separates parents from their most sacred duties. Eight years earlier, in 1774, the waterworks of little windmills were destroyed by fire, after bickering for 192 years under the shadow of Old London Bridge.

The end was drawing near. New London Bridge was begun on March 15th, 1824. George Rennie made the designs after studying the Bridge of Augustus at Rimini, and his brother, Sir John Rennie, directed the workmen on a site 200 feet west of the Old Bridge ; just as Peter Colechurch crossed the Thames a little west of the earliest known timber bridge built by Londoners.* It took only seven years to carry out the designs of Rennie, whereas Colechurch and his successor, the Frenchman Isembert, were busy for thirty-three years. On August 1st, 1831, New London Bridge was opened by William IV, and by the second year of Victoria's reign the old bridge was dead and gone. It had taken a long time to murder her, fragment by fragment, but yet she lived almost as long as the first Westminster Bridge, designed by M. Labelye, which lasted from 1750 to 1853.

One purpose of Old London Bridge has been forgotten : she was an arcaded dam, and she deepened the water for shipping on the eastern side. According to Arber's reprint of "Euphues and his England," there were twenty arches in all, "whereof each one is made of excellent freestone squared, every one of them being three-score foote in height, and full twenty in distance one from an other." This latter statement is incorrect. The arches ranged in width from 18 feet to 32 feet 6 inches, and the piers varied in breadth from 25 to 34 feet ; they were raised on strong elm piles, covered with thick planks bolted together, and they occupied not less than two-thirds of the waterway.

* This was finished in 1014 ; in 1136 it was burnt down, and in 1176 Colechurch started upon his brave enterprise.

NEW LONDON BRIDGE, DESIGNED BY GEORGE RENNIE, AND CARRIED OUT
BY HIS BROTHER, SIR JOHN RENNIE. OPENED TO THE PUBLIC IN 1831

Yet modern engineers played the fool with this ancient break-water. Several arches were thrown into one large span, so the Thames poured through the bridge with an increased and uneven force; the ground current developed a scour that dug deep holes under the piers, and into these holes tons of stuff were poured ineffectually, for the scour continued to undercut the foundations. Even Labelye's bridge at Westminster was affected very much by this new devilry in the ground current of the Thames.

It was Euphues who described the old bridge as "a continuall streete, well replenyshed with large and stately houses on both sides." To-day we have one bridge well replenished with houses (unless the vandalism of trade has made a recent feast of it), but its architecture is not large and stately. I refer to William Pulteney's Bridge at Bath, an experiment of the eighteenth century, when amateurs trifled with architecture, and architects trifled with amateurs. The structure is sedately prim and dull, but yet it is admirable, for it has tried to renew in England a generative tradition that links every housed bridge to the earliest lake-villages.

So I am glad to say that the crippled old buildings on the High Bridge at Lincoln—a favourite subject of Peter de Wint—have been restored. This work was done, and done very well, thirteen years ago, under the direction of two architects, and a long account of the repairs, with a full-page illustration, was published in "The Builder," March 21, 1903. The illustration shows the back view of the houses with the bridge beneath and beyond. The restoration is conservative and excellent, but time alone can mellow it from a thorough newness into a ripe completeness. Even then it will be a poor little monument when compared with its Florentine superior the Ponte Vecchio, which history gives to Taddeo Gaddi and the fourteenth century.

The Ponte Vecchio has but one fault—the long and level roof, which has two parallel lines of a most unpliant straightness. Why should an architect put himself at odds with the curved witchery that Nature gives to her sky-lines and horizons? In other respects the Ponte Vecchio has a charming citizenship haunted by romance. Even the beaked piers are not too large, though they are said to date from the year 1355. Perhaps they were remodelled by Renaissance art; certainly they have a style not unlike that of the great Ammanati. As for the three arches, they are well balanced, their roadway has a gentle slope, and their shape goes about half-way between a cycloid and a surbased round arch. The cycloid form appears in the arches of another Florentine bridge, Ammanati's masterpiece, the incomparable Ponte della Trinità. Some of the many-windowed tiny cots that project from the parapet of the Ponte Vecchio seem to be stuffy compromises between tombs and homes; they would be fit resting-places for the occasional ghosts that men of science welcome, after infinite hesitation unrelieved by humour.

But I regret always that from the Ponte Vecchio I can

get no idea of the effect made in nature by Old London Bridge. Is there extant any bridge that helps us to realise the work of Colechurch and Isembert? The once famous watermills at Meaux, in Brie, and the Pont du Marché there, are somewhat of an aid in this matter. Brangwyn visited them in 1913, and was fascinated. Some writers say that the first watermills at Meaux were built in the twelfth century; and on a recent photograph taken from a picture I read: *Meaux, Les Moulins sur Pilotis, xii. siècle.* But these mills disappeared before the year 1835, and they belonged to the end of the fifteenth century, not to the twelfth. Viollet-le-Duc put this date on record, together with the fact that the bridge and its mills were entirely of wood.* In 1420 the English captured Meaux, and they held it till 1438, when they were defeated by the Constable de Richmont. Had they retained the little town till the end of the century, we might venture to suppose that the timber bridge and its wooden mills were built by our ancestors, in order to keep themselves in mind of Old London Bridge. The modern mills are many-storeyed places of business, and they stand very erect on stone piers. To-day the Pont du Marché has eight stone arches, and a single row of early timbered houses. I have four photographs of it, and in each it is charming. Next summer I

---

* Viollet-le-Duc writes as follows (vol. 6, p. 410): "Dans les villes, on profitait souvent des arches de pont pour établir des moulins, et même alors les ponts et moulins, bâtis en bois, ne formaient qu'une seule et même construction. Avant 1835, il existait encore à Meaux, en Brie, un pont de ce genre entièrement en bois ainsi que les moulins y attenant; cet ensemble datait de la fin du xvᵉ siècle. . . ."

may see it in nature, but if a pontist travelled to see all the bridges that attract him, he would need a life of several hundred years and a river Pactolus to finance his research.*

Is there any reason why England should not have a great bridge of shops, or of watermills, or of houses? Let Brangwyn and Mr. Lutyens collaborate, and then we shall have a masterpiece indeed! Here and there we have a small bridge with a watermill close at hand; there is one in Sussex between Midhurst and Easebourne, for example, but I know not one that warms my patriotism with a glow of pride. Viollet-le-Duc draws three charming pictures of French mill bridges which have disappeared. There was the Pont aux Meuniers at Paris, that crossed the great arm of the Seine below the Pont au Change, facing the Palais; it resembled the Millers' Bridge at Meaux. A great stone bridge at Châlon-sur-Saône was decorated with round towers above the piers, and between these towers, on the right of every arch, a little mill was busy. This mediæval arrangement, so rich with a quaint citizenship, lasted till the seventeenth century. Over the Loire at Nantes was another picturesque bridge that united in itself the merits of many good burgesses. Impudent houses with peaked roofs were balanced on the piers and throve well as shops; a footway of wood was corbelled out from the parapet; and between some of the piers windmills behaved like human

---

* Alas! The Great War has done much harm to the Pont du Marché at Meaux. To-day (September 26, 1914) I saw a photograph of its crippled condition. One arch at least is ruined, and mended roughly with timbering.

THREE-ARCHED BRIDGE AT VENICE, OVER THE CANAL
OF ST. GIOBBE. BRICK AND STONE. *RENAISSANCE*

creatures, for the harder they toiled over the business of daily bread, the more loudly they complained. Their noise implied that corn was very hard to crush; and the reluctant movement of their revolving wind-sails was an image of self-pity.

As mediæval towns of importance were encompassed by walls and defended by castles, there was little free space; hence the building of a new bridge was always a great event; it enlarged the civic life and prepared a foundation for a new street or for a fresh line of defensive works. Thus the Bridge of Saintes was a long line of fortifications (p. 300), while the bridges of Paris were housed and populous, unlike many a village where poor Jacques, in the midst of unceasing war, lived the life of a hunted wolf. Unfortunately, the tenants of Paris bridges wanted to thrive at their landlords' expense, and at last they ruined the landlords, who were bridges, not men, I am sorry to say. The great corbels that supported the houses pressed too heavily on the spandrils; caves and hiding-places were dug into the piers; and when the houses were removed from the Pont Notre-Dame and the Pont Saint-Michel, it was found that every tenant had misused his home, even to the extent of excavating secret chambers behind the haunches of an arch. For human nature has ever claimed the privilege of doing justice to itself in actions of foolish violence.

For instance, it is disgusting to read about the desecration thrust upon English bridge chapels after the reign of

Q

Henry the Eighth. As an example we can take the Chapel of St. Mary on Wakefield Bridge, Yorkshire, a beautiful piece of Decorated Gothic dating from the fourteenth century. After the Reformation it became many profane things, including an old clothes shop, a warehouse, a den of flax-dressers, a newsroom, a cheesecake house, a tailor's shop, and I know not what else; so "we think upon her stones, and it pitieth us to see her in the dust." At last— it was in 1847—an effort was made to rescue her from further degradation : quite a big effort, for it cost £3000, yet the cause had nothing to do with sport or with self-advertisement. To raise so much money in the service of history was a great achievement. But the chosen architect was less fortunate than he might have been ; he was one of those Victorian "restorers" whose zeal at times was excessive. In a few months the Chapel of St. Mary was rebuilt, almost, so thorough was the renovation. Even the original front was torn off and carted to the grounds of Kettlethorpe Park, where it still remains, I believe ; and not enough care was shown in the choice of building materials, for the new work was carried out in Bath stone and Caen stone, which were much too soft for the Wakefield atmosphere. Indeed, the new front perished so quickly that in less than forty-five years a part of its detail looked more friable than the ancient work at Kettlethorpe ; and a second renovation became necessary.

The subscriptions raised for these remodellings and repairs call to mind the fact that in much earlier times

Wakefield Bridge and its chapel were objects of charity. For example, in 1391, the fourteenth year of Richard II, William de Bayley, of Mitton in Craven, left *C sol ad confirmacionem cantarie in Capella Sce Mariæ sup Pont de Wakefield;* and a deed dated the 27th of September, 1454, the thirty-second year of Henry VI, mentions a yearly dole of three shillings to be paid to the bridge chapel at Wakefield. At an earlier date, in 1398, two chantries were ordained in St. Mary's Chapel, thanks to the generosity of William Terry and Robert Heth, who obtained licences from Richard II "to give and assign to two chaplains celebrating divine service in the chapel of St. Mary, on Wakefield Bridge, lately built, ten pounds rent in Wakefield, Stanley, Ossett, Pontefract, Horbury, Heckmondwike, Shafton, Darfield, Preston, Jackling, and Frystone by the water." Norrison Scatcherd gives this quotation from a document in the archives of the Hatfield family, but I know not what to say of it; for a charter of an earlier date mentions a sum of £10 and two chaplains (p. 230)

However, the chapel is built on a little island in the river Calder, and the plan is arranged below so as to offer the least resistance to the river. "The extra width required for the chapel above is obtained by corbelling out on each side, which gives a total external width of about twenty feet. The total length is about forty-five feet. The front towards the bridge is very elaborate, and is divided into five ogee-headed compartments, with buttresses between. Three of these, the centre and two ends, are doorways, the other two being panelled. Over this is a series of five panels filled with sculpture representing the Annunciation, the Birth of Jesus, the Resurrection, the Ascension, and the Descent of the Holy Ghost on the Disciples. Surmounting the whole are battlements ; and a bold group of pinnacles at each end of the front over the buttresses. Each side has three three-light windows, and the east end has a large window of five lights ; all have rich Decorated tracery. A well-designed turret stands at the north-east angle, and contains the staircase which communicates with the roof and crypt. On the north, south, and east fronts is a panelled parapet, and there is a canopied niche over the east windows. There was formerly a priest's house adjoining, but the last vestiges of it were removed in 1866. . . . The windows on the south and east are filled with stained glass. The interior is in good repair, and is fitted up for service." * And service also is held there.†

Leland, who returned from his antiquarian tour in 1542, collected in Wakefield a good many suppositions about the origin of St. Mary's Chapel. He was happy there, because a right honest man fared well for " 2 pens a meale." On

---

* See "The Builder," November 22, 1890.

† There has been much disputation over the origin of St. Mary's Chapel, and I refer you to the following books : 1. "Remarks on Wayside Chapels," by two architects, J. C. and C. Buckler, 8vo, Oxford, 1843. This book was approved by Parker, an excellent recommendation. 2. "A Dissertation on Ancient Bridges and Bridge Chapels," by Norrison Scatcherd, 1828. 3. "The Chapel of King Edward III on Wakefield Bridge," by Norrison Scatcherd, 1843. In the earlier treatise the chapel is attributed to the reign of Edward IV. Scatcherd belongs to an old school of polemical swashbucklers, but what he says is worth attention, though difficult to follow. 4. "The Histories of York."

the east side of a fair bridge of stone, under whose nine arches the Calder flowed, Leland was charmed to see a right goodly chapel of Our Lady, with two cantuary priests founded in it, by the townsmen, as some say; but, on the other hand, the Dukes of York were taken as founders because they had obtained the mortmain. He heard someone say that Edward IV's father, or else the Earl of Rutland, brother to Edward IV, "was a great doer of it," for "a sore batell was fought in the south feeldes of this bridge," and in the flight of the Duke of York's party, either the duke himself, or his son the Earl of Rutland, was slain a little above the bars, beyond the bridge, going up into the town of Wakefield. "At this place is set up a cross in *rei memoriam.*"

Very often to-day, as in Leland's time, the Chapel of St. Mary is supposed to have been founded later than 1460, partly to commemorate the battle of Sandal Castle Field, now called the battle of Wakefield, and partly as a monument to a boy of eighteen, poor Edmund Earl of Rutland, second son of the Duke of York, who was murdered by the "black Lord Clifford," called the Butcher. Then a royal chantry seems to have been founded in St. Mary's Chapel, and endowed; but chantries were founded often in bridge chapels, as we have seen in the case of London Bridge (p. 217); and so we must not suppose that "chantry" and "chapel" mean always the same thing. Moreover, in architectural character the chapel belongs to about the time of Edward II, who died in 1327. This was proved by Buckler, and in a charter of about 1358, dated at Wakefield, Edward III settled " £10 per annum on William Kaye and William Bull and their successors for ever to perform Divine Service in a chapel of St. Mary newly built on the bridge at Wakefield."*

Still, the precise date of the foundation is unimportant. Scatcherd ascribes it to a time earlier than 1357, and dwells upon a resemblance between St. Mary's Chapel at Wakefield and Prior Crawden's Chapel at Ely, 1321–40 ; he is "almost persuaded" that they were built by the same great architect, Alan de Walsingham.†

I chose the story of this bridge chapel as an instance of the desecration thrust upon old English shrines after the Reformation had let loose the creed of self into sect-making zealotry. In the presence of fine art Puritans were often like starving dogs in the presence of raw meat. Though every mediæval bridge without exception was united to the Church by a Christian symbol, a cross or a crucifix, yet the Puritans were so thorough in their fanaticism that only a bridge here and there was allowed to keep even the stump of a smashed cross. Some broken crosses were handed on to Victoria's time, but highway boards and their parapet repairs destroyed the stumps one by one, as in the case of Ashford Bridge, Derbyshire. A few years ago the stump of a cross had not yet been stripped from one Derbyshire

* Camden's "Britannia," Ed. Gough, Vol. III, London, 1789, pp. 38–9.

† St. Mary's Chapel was illustrated by Toms, after George Fleming, 1743; by Lodge, in Thoresby's "Ducatus"; by Cawthorne, about 1800; and by "The Builder," November 22, 1890.

bridge, the Derwent packhorse bridge, but I dare not say that it still remains. At any moment the vandalism of a "restoration" may remind us that our highway boards ought to be guided and disciplined by independent committees of architects and artists. Their work is far less intelligent than that of the *Ponts et Chaussées* in France. And so, what with the ravaging hands of our roadway officials, and what with the destructive sanctity of Puritans, our old bridges and their religious adjuncts have suffered long and much and continually. Many bridge chapels have been destroyed, as at Cromford, Doncaster, Ludlow, Bideford, Richmond (Yorks), Leeds, Newcastle, Barnard Castle, Durham (on the Elvet Bridge), Catterick, Bridgenorth, Bristol, Wallingford, Bedford (St. Thomas's Chapel, Bunyan's gaol), and Droitwich, where the high road passed through the chapel, and separated the congregation from the reading-desk and from the pulpit! What a relic of old wayfaring life! Yet it was cleared away as hateful to progress.

A small oratory remains on the bridge at Bradford-on-Avon, Wiltshire. It is not quite on the same lines as the original structure, for in the seventeenth century its roofing was altered into a sort of dome built with stone. It is a "housing," a tiny place for a passing prayer, not a chapel; and this class of bridge oratory has become so uncommon that I doubt whether another exists. As Mr. Emanuel Green has said, it "is now perhaps unique," and "should be carefully preserved."* In recent times neither reverence

* "Bath Old Bridge and the Chapel Thereon," by Emanuel Green, F.S.A., F.R.S.L., p. 143, British Archæological Association.

nor care has been bestowed on this oratory. After the Reformation it was profaned, as a matter of course. For a long time it was used as a "lock-up," and in 1887 it was a powder magazine !

Its pyramidal roof is crowned with a tall finial, which in its turn carries a pretty wind vane ; and in the wind vane we find the emblem of St. Nicholas—a gudgeon. The towns-folk used to be known as Bradford gudgeon, and those of them who had been shut up in the little prison on the bridge were said to have been "under the fish and over the water."*

At St. Ives, Huntingdonshire, called Slepe in "Domesday Book," and Asleep to-day, there is another degraded oratory, a bigger one, with an apsidal termination eastward. Its original parapet has been torn down, and a brick house of two storeys adds greatly to its height. Derby also has a bridge chapel, whose history may be studied in the works of the Rev. Dr. Cox ; but I am more interested in the oratory on Rotherham Bridge, Yorkshire. Here, as at Wakefield, the chapel stands on a small island, the upper part is corbelled out on each side, and the end against the bridge is carried by a half-arch. The plan is a rectangle about 30 ft. by 14 ft., while at Wakefield the external width is 20 ft. and the total length about 45 ft. During many years Rotherham Chapel was almost as beautiful as the masterpiece at Wakefield ; and even now, after infinite ill-usage, there is charm in the embattled parapet graced with pinnacles.

* "The Builder," August 20, 1887.

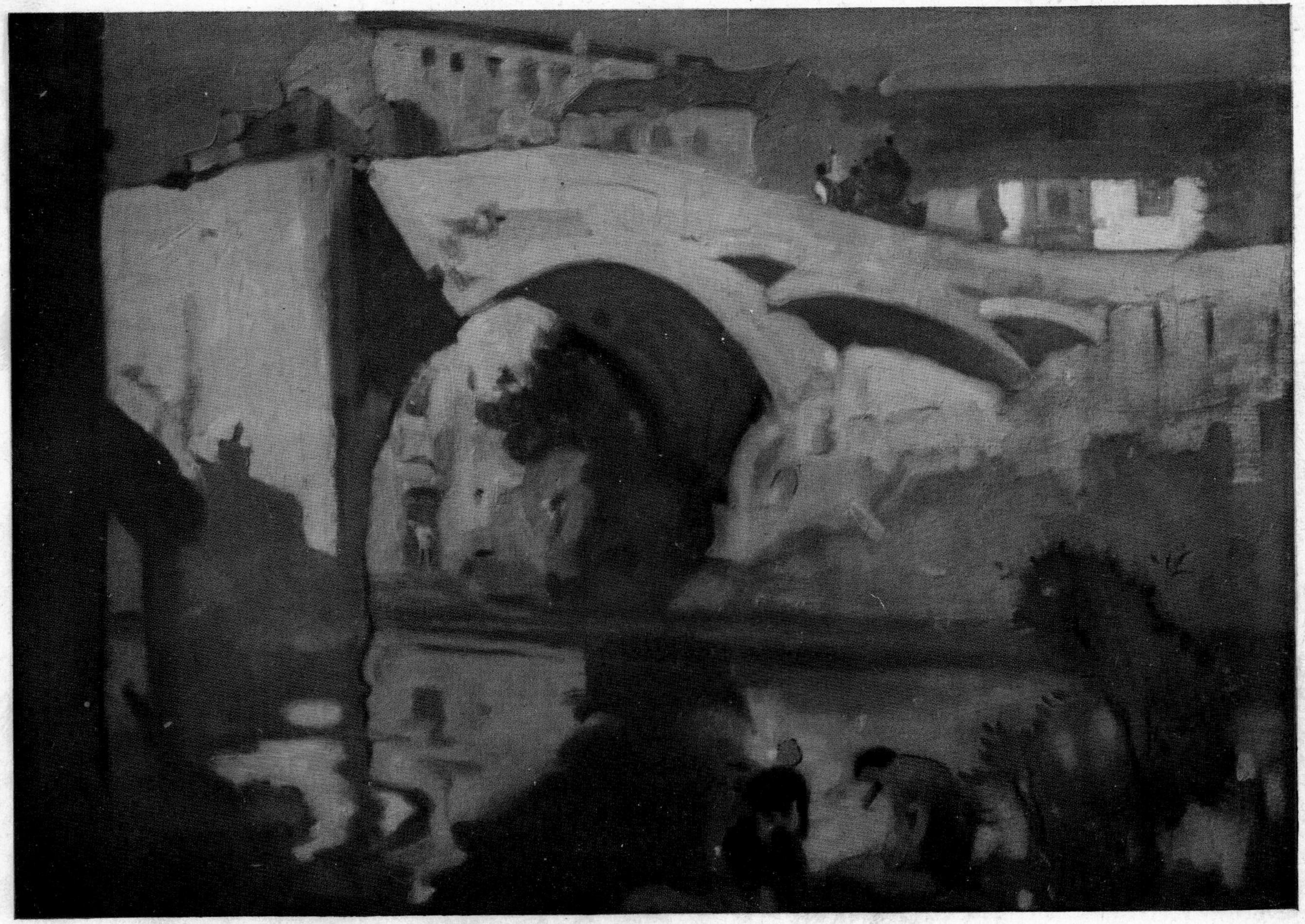

GOTHIC BRIDGE AT BARNARD CASTLE, YORKSHIRE

We hear of this chapel for the first time in the will of one John Bokyns, who in 1483 left three and fourpence " to the fabric of the chapel to be built on Rotherham Bridge." There seems to have been no endowment, as this chapel was unnamed by the Commissioners of Henry VIII. In 1681 she was turned into an almshouse, she was a prison in 1778, and also in 1831 ; but at last she became more reputable as a warehouse. May we hope that her lost window tracery will be renewed, and will she ever be restored to the service of the Church ? Her degradation has lasted far too long, certainly, but it is not easy to collect money for church restoration. If our golf fanatics took the matter in hand and made an appeal to the public, their popularity would bring in subscriptions.

From a standpoint of historic social life this irreverence to ancient bridge chapels cannot be anything less than horrible, because the earlier England owed all her best qualities to that faith which preceded Protestantism, and which passed without much injury through the terrible alembics of mediæval war and of social egotism. In Shakespeare himself we find a product of the spectacular display which the old Church had encouraged by her festivals ; and it is certain also that Shakespeare could not have been a dramatic poet if the Puritanism of his time had been a leading motive-power of public life, and not merely a writer of unpopular books. No pontist should fail to read the early Puritan scribblers, who give in a frenzy of carica-ture much valuable social history, without a knowledge of

which the sixteenth century cannot be understood. Their
language is graphic, and so violent that it takes one's
breath away ; but in all reprints, as in those of the New
Shakespeare Society, it is kept away from the general
reader by the dismal pedantry which copies the freakish
spelling of sixteenth-century books.

Let me give, with modernised spelling, an abridged
extract from an Elizabethan Puritan, Phillip Stubbes,
whose "Anatomy of Abuses" has come at last into the
history of historians. My aim is to show three things : a
spirit of fierce intolerance not yet popular enough to close
the theatres of London, but foolish enough to wreck shrines
and to take pride in a very bad system of supposed moral
teaching. It was the earlier Cromwell who appointed
Sir William Bassett, Knight, to the holy office of shrine
destroyer and image breaker ; and Bassett, whose humour
was killed by zealotry, regarded as sinful things even the
baths at Buxton, for he locked them up and sealed them,
"that none shall enter to wash . . . until your lordship's
pleasure be further known." Into this novel sanctity
Phillip Stubbes poured his abundant venom. Being at
heart a thorough Puritan, it never occurred to him that it
would be better to educate human nature than to take away
from it the discipline of temptation. As in earlier times
the better minds and characters had sneaked away from life
into nunneries and monasteries, so Phillip Stubbes wished
mankind to be a recluse, a hermit, separated by stern laws
from everything that folly could abuse. Because minstrels

and mimics sang many a lewd song, as do fools to-day, Stubbes raged against all itinerant clowns, buffoons, and singers, and demanded that they should be put down ; by no other means could men be taught to value a little decency and self-respect. His language runs thus :—

"Such drunken sockets and bawdy parasites range the country, rhyming and singing unclean, corrupt and filthy songs, in taverns, ale-houses, inns, and other public assemblies. . . . Every town, city, and country is full of these minstrels to pipe up a dance to the devil. . . . But some of them will reply, and say, 'What, sir! we have licences from justices of the peace to pipe and use our minstrelsy to our best commodity.' Cursed be those licences which license any man to get his living with the destruction of many thousands! But have you a licence from the archjustice of peace, Christ Jesus? If you have not . . . then may you, as rogues, extravagants, and stragglers from the heavenly country, be arrested of the high justice of peace, Christ Jesus, and be punished with eternal death, notwithstanding your pretended licences from earthly men. . . ."

Briefly, the people had degraded their singers, just as to-day they degrade those Sunday newspapers which have the widest circulation ; yet Stubbes believed that the people could be saved from themselves if their victims were condemned to everlasting punishment by "the high justice of peace, Christ Jesus." In like manner the people were to be improved somehow by the destruction of old votive shrines, or by the desecration of the bridge chapels in which for ages the pilgrims of England had solaced their long journeys. Henry VIII himself, in 1510, is said to have made a pilgrimage to Our Lady of Walsingham, barefooted, and carrying a rich necklace—a light but expensive gift that did not add to his fatigue. Erasmus visited the same great shrine and kissed the relics, and all at once the Virgin nodded at him, owing to the indiscretion of a priest who pulled some strings. In the fourteenth century thirty-eight shrines drew pilgrims to Norfolk; for illness rambled from place to place, feeding a superstitious piety, and praying for that relief which doctors in their wild ignorance could not give. The shrines of Europe were the only physicians that the sick dared to trust.

Many a pilgrim visited the Pont St. Bénézet at Avignon, and legend speaks also of miracles; the good friar was buried in his bridge chapel, and during his life he healed the sick and the maimed. I know not why legend should say these things, since Bénézet did quite enough good work by building his noble structure over the Rhône, a terrible river. A Roman bridge had occupied the same spot, so that Bénézet may have used some of the Roman foundations. His work, in any case, was done with unusual rapidity, being finished in eight years (1177–1185).* In Brangwyn's glorious picture of the Pont St. Bénézet one

---

* These dates I take from the catalogue of historic monuments issued by the Ministère de l'Instruction Publique et des Beaux-Arts. Some writers give the dates as 1178 and 1188.

romantic feature is the friar-architect's tomb, the venerable Chapel of St. Nicholas; and historians dwell upon the fact that never once has the chapel been injured by floods or by wars. All has been wrecked except the four arches dominated by the shrine of St. Bénézet. Pope Clement VI (1342–1352) had to rebuild four arches; in 1395, during a fierce attack on the palace of the Popes, the bridge was cut by the Catalans and Aragonese, who destroyed an arch; and this breach was not repaired with stone till the year 1418. The masonry was not good, for in 1602 the arch gave way and caused the loss of three others. Disaster followed disaster, two arches falling in 1633 and two in the winter of 1670. Turn to the Sieur Tassin's "Plans et Profils des principales Villes et Lieux considérables de France," issued in 1652, and you will find a view of Saint Bénézet's Bridge, with two arches missing on Barthelasse Island, and three on the great arm of the Rhône. As a rule such gaps were bridged with timber, because a French bridge cut in war could not be repaired until permission had been gained from the foe who had done the damage. This curious fact in mediæval history I take from Viollet-le-Duc; and it may help to explain why the masterpiece of St. Bénézet was allowed to perish.

Bénézet constructed twenty-one* arches, and the line of his bridge made an elbow pointing upstream, beyond Barthelasse Island, on the Villeneuve branch of the Rhône.

---

* According to Degrand; some other writers say nineteen. The largest spans were a little more than thirty-three metres; but even in these the size varied somewhat.

Two ideas governed this angular disposition : first, to thrust into the river a tremendous wedge of arcaded stonework to resist floods ; next to thwart an attack by cavalry and infantry ; since a bridge with a bend in it would be more difficult to storm than a level and straight footway. In Spain there are several bridges of this angular sort, notably a very long one over the Pisuerga at Torquemada ; and in Corsica also there is a fine example, but in caricature, the bridge over the Tavignano being shaped like a Z. Bénézet made another concession to tactical defence : his bridge was only 4 metres 90 wide, including the thickness of the parapets, so it was very narrow in proportion to the nine hundred metres of its length. Just a few soldiers in a line could have walked along it from end to end ; and wheeled traffic must have been hindered, for at one point— face to face with the chapel—the roadway dwindled to half its breadth. Even in times when carts and chariots were long and narrow, a journey across this bridge on a market day must have been an adventure.

This cramped road over the Rhône was the only permanent way connecting the Papal territory of Avignon and the French territory of Languedoc. Many troubles arose on this account, and France never rested till she had gained control over the Pont Saint-Bénézet and Avignon. A century after Bénézet's death the King of France put up a bullying fortress on the right bank, and closed the Villeneuve entrance whenever he liked. For about fifty years Avignon took no steps to counterbalance this attack on her liberties ;

then a Bastille was built on her side of the river, and now the Pont Saint-Bénézet was nearly as martial as the Bridge of Saintes (p. 300) or as the Pont d'Orléans, which from October 12, 1428, to the arrival of Jeanne d'Arc on April 29, 1429, aided Gaucour to baffle the earls of Salisbury and Suffolk. In the eighth year of the fifteenth century the contention between France and Avignon reached a crisis, not at all an infrequent thing in their history; but this crisis of 1408 unseated the Papacy at Avignon, and expelled Benedict XIII, bringing to an end a religious domination which had lasted in the city for ninety-nine years.

It is clear from this brief record of events that the Pont St. Bénézet, like many another great bridge of the Middle Ages, had but a poor chance of becoming social and useful. Instead of being an open road to the democratic spirit and the growth of trade, she kept watch and ward incessantly, and aided the misruling class to nourish their egotisms without any care at all for the common weal. It said very little for the half-sense of ordinary men that they in their millions were unable to defend themselves against a tiny class of despots. The people were like leaves on forest trees, that fluttered ineffectually as soon as a gale began to blow. For the ounces of brain in each human skull have never been of any real worth until genius has taken control of them, for good or for ill. More than one insect has had a brain more fertile than that of the average man. Thus the cerebral ganglia of the ant, though not so large as a quarter of a small pin's head, have evolved a marvellous routine of life, which includes the making of bridges and the boring of tunnels under running water. Ants were civil engineers long before men had constructed their first tunnels and drains. Have you ever tried to imagine what would have happened in the world of primitive men if every atom in every ounce of human brain had been as fertile as the cerebral ganglia of the ant? A civilization no worse than our own might have been evolved by the year 100,000 B.C., if not earlier.

From time to time, however, amid the congealed blood that lay so thick over the mediæval history of France, some true social justice did shine out, here and there. A few French nobles built communal bridges, and set the Law to keep them for ever from the tyrannies of a superior class that found in ordinary men neither the intelligence of ants nor the discipline that united wolves into formidable packs. The people being too silly to defend their own rights, these few good nobles tried to foresee all dangers, but their legal documents were rarely strong enough to resist their incessant foes, the stupidity of the mob and the gradual encroachments of military leaders. When Eudes, Count of Chartres, built a bridge at Tours, as an act of piety that would benefit his soul, he decreed that its public value for all time was to be as free from all restraints as a church. At an earlier time, in a deed of 998, William the Great, Duke of Aquitaine, went so far as to forbid *pour toujours* a collection of tolls on the Pont Royal. He did not realise

OLD BRIDGE OVER THE BORNE AT ESPALY, NEAR LE PUY IN FRANCE;
BEHIND THE CROIX DE LA PAILLE, A ROCK OF VOLCANIC BRECCIA,
WITH HOUSES, AND WITH RUINS OF A THIRTEENTH-CENTURY CASTLE

that his populace would cease to value the bridge as soon as they got the freedom of it for nothing. Again, in France during the Middle Ages no bridge could be fortified without permission from its founder or founders. This was a rule or law, and yet it must have been broken hundreds of times, for what bridge of any importance did not become a fortified work, a genuine stronghold?

One form or custom of the Middle Ages tried to encompass bloodshed with the glamour of religious fervour. After the battle of Towton, for example, a chapel was built on the stricken field by the Yorkists as a memorial to the souls of their dead. And a famous chapel on the Ouse Bridge at York is said to have been erected after a stiff fight between the citizens and a Scotchman named John Comyn. The fray happened on the bridge itself, in 1168, or thereabouts, and John Comyn lost several of his followers. Then came some negotiations, in the course of which it was agreed that the city should erect a chapel on the spot, and find priests to celebrate mass for the souls of the dead. Another story relates that in 1153, when Saint William was restored to the See of York, a vast crowd assembled on a timber bridge that crossed the Ouse, so eager were the citizens to welcome their prelate, who in 1147 had been deprived of office after a reign of three years. In the hustle and excitement of the home-coming, the bridge gave way, and many persons fell into the river, but no one perished because William prayed and his prayer was answered. To commemorate this miracle a chapel was built on the new

R

bridge. This legend may have some truth in it, for the chapel was dedicated to Saint William; and perhaps the other legend about John Comyn is not entirely mythical.

One thing is certain: that in Norman times a stone bridge was built at York and graced with a fine chapel. Between 1215 and 1256 it was reconstructed by Archbishop Walter de Gray, who preserved some portions of the Norman chapel. More than three centuries later, in 1564, two arches were destroyed by a flood, with twelve houses that stood upon them; and for nearly two years the bridge remained in a ruined state. Then the broken arches were rebuilt in the thirteenth-century style. Among the contributors to this work was Lady Jane Hall, whose donation was recorded on a brass plate on the north side of the bridge. The inscription was quaint :—

William Watson, Lord Mayor, An. Dom. 1566.
Lady Jane Hall lo: here the works of faith doth shew;
By giving a hundred pounds this bridge to renew.

On the west side of Ouse Bridge there were several houses, which flanked the Chapel of Saint William. At the Reformation the chapel contained several chantries, the original grants of which are still among the records of the city. After the Reformation, of course, these pious endowments were confiscated, and the beautiful little building was turned into an exchange where the York Society of Hamburg Merchants assembled every morning to transact business. At last, in 1810, the chapel was removed. Some parts of it were excellent work in the Early English style, while the porch and a stone screen were enriched with cable and chevron ornaments, characteristic of Norman work. A few etchings of these charming details were published in Cave's "Antiquities of York" (1813).

At the east side of Ouse Bridge stood the old gaol for debtors, built in the sixteenth century. It lasted till 1724, when it was purchased by the city and the ainstey, and a better place was built, by assessment, as a free prison. The old bridge was condemned as dangerous in 1808, and on December 10, 1810, the foundation-stone of a new bridge was laid.*

Among my thousands of notes and papers I have a good article on ancient bridge chapels written in 1882 by the late S. Wayland Kershaw, F.S.A., of Lambeth Palace Library. Mr. Kershaw made a study of old Rochester Bridge and its chapel, which stood on the main road to the Continent, close to the great cathedral, whose main architects were Bishops Ernulph and Gundulph. These bishops favoured the bridge, partly because it brought pilgrims to the shrine

* See Allen's "History of the County of York," 1832. P. Atkinson was the architect of the new bridge, and his work went on till March, 1810. As for the old Ouse Bridge, good views of it will be found in the "Antiquarian Itinerary," Vol. I, 1815; the "Antiquarian Cabinet," Vol. III, 1817; and the "Encyclopædia Britannica," ninth edition. Let us take a glance at one of the pictures. On the west end of the bridge is a tall building carried by two pointed arches and crowned with a small steeple. It is the great Council Chamber, with a prison for felons beneath it, according to the "Antiquarian Cabinet." We cross the river and find at the other side the gaol which was rebuilt in 1724. Two small arches on this side of the bridge balance those that arcade the Council Chamber, and in the middle is a graceful pointed arch with a span of 81 feet. The spandrils are relieved by a well-marked string-course, he parapets are fringed with railings and graced in the centre with two finials, which displace the mediæval cross.

at Rochester, and partly because it was a kindness to all wayfarers. "The Crusader on his way to the East, the stately cardinal and foreign prince, the wayworn pilgrim, and the merchant-voyager would form but a few of the passengers . . . who would say a passing prayer at the Bridge Chapel of All Souls."* Rochester Bridge in mediæval times was closely linked to the history of the cathedral. The first bridge was constructed of wood, and, according to Prior Ernulph's testimony, it existed before 1215. In Vol. VII of "Archæologia," the Society of Antiquaries published a plan of this ancient timber bridge, with a most valuable description. At the east end there was a tower of wood, with strong defensive gates, which may have resembled the timber fortifications with which the Romans barred their wooden bridges. In 1281, according to Kilburne's "Survey of Kent," the earliest bridge at Rochester was borne down by the Medway after a severe winter; and there is no mention of another bridge till the year 1387, when Sir John Cobham and Sir R. Knolles put up "a fair bridge of stone." Such was the slack and lethargic citizenship of Rochester. About 1800 years after the Pons Sublicius was thrown across the Tiber, a common timber bridge was carried over the Medway in an effort of progress. As for the belated stone bridge, the charter of its foundation is preserved in the Bishops' Registers, and a transcript of it is given in Thorpe's "Custumale Roffense." Philipott, in his "Kent Surveyed," 1659, says that the

* See Mr. Kershaw's article, "The Builder," April 29, 1882, p. 531.

chapel on Rochester Bridge was founded in 1399 by John de Cobham, and dedicated to the Holy Trinity, but called at its first institution All Souls' Chapel, because prayers and orisons were to be offered up there for the health of all Christian souls.   Two earlier writers—Fabyan in 1406, and Grafton in 1409—attribute the finishing of the chapel to Sir R. Knolles, Knight.*   Another chapel, a small one, was built on the stone quay at the Strood end of the bridge, its founder being Gilbert de Glanville, Bishop of Rochester (1185-1215).   "We learn that Queen Isabella, when she came to Strood in 1357, entered the Chapel of St. Mary, and offered an oblation of six and eightpence in honour of the eleven thousand virgins."   Gracious! This army of fair saints inspired a very wee act of devotional charity.   There is reason to believe that the larger chapel was not closed by legal dissolution, but passed out of use when pilgrims became afraid to anger their Protestant neighbours ; for in the nineteenth year of Elizabeth's reign Thorpe wrote as follows in his "Custumale Roffense":—

"The Queen's Attorney-General sued the wardens of the bridge for £513, being the amount of £18 per annum for twenty-eight years and a half, the last past, which sum was at that time presumed to be forfeited and due to the Queen by virtue of the Act 1, Ed. VI, for dissolving charities.   It not appearing to the jury that any service had been performed here, nor a stipend paid to any chaplain or chantry

* In Vol. X of the "Archæologia Cantiana" an inventory is given of the possessions of the chapel in the year 1549.

priest for officiating here, for five years next before the passing that Act, a verdict was given for the Wardens."

In 1882, when Mr. Kershaw wrote his paper, the Chapel of All Souls was roofless, and nearly hidden by new buildings. Its width was about fifteen feet, and its length about forty feet. Windows were pierced in the north and south walls, and two of them were filled with brickwork or with masonry. In the south wall were traces of a piscina, and some ornamental details had been saved from the general wreckage.

Much more might be written on bridge chapels and crosses, but this monograph is only a brief introduction to a vast subject, and we must pass on to the other topics after noting two points more. Both concern the sanctification of bridges by means of religious emblems. It seems quite certain that the fourteenth and fifteenth centuries were most favourable to wayside crosses. By then very popular saints had been added to the old shrines, and the custom of making pilgrimages was tormented by fewer dangers, as a rule. Many a cross was a simple thing of wood fixed in a stone base, and sometimes it carried at top a small wind vane or weathercock. Many crosses were raised to commemorate historical events, while others were put up by sinners who wished to announce their repentance. Here and there a beautiful cross became celebrated. For example, the Belle Croix on the old bridge at Orléans was a nobly modelled crucifix of bronze that stood up high from the buttress of the middle pier ; its pedestal was ornamented with low-reliefs representing the Holy Virgin, St. Peter, St. Paul, St. James, St. Stephen, and the bishops St. Aignan and St. Euverte. As we have seen (p. 230), the centre of a mediæval bridge was marked invariably by a cross. To-day, on the Continent, this old religious custom gives grace to a few bridges, and I value a large photograph of Trier Bridge over the Moselle, where the Virgin is enriched above the middle buttress, and where a crucifix, flanked by two columns, rises above the parapet.

Yet we must not rush to the conclusion that this old sacred custom had its original source in the Christian religion. At first it may have belonged to a faith in evil spirits, whose power for mischief may have seemed to be increased by every roadway that enabled them to pass over running water. I have by my side the photograph of a steep bridge in Western China, at Shih-Chuan, and here below the middle of the parapet is a small image of stone representing a tutelary god! To me it is a curious little bit of rude sculpture, all head and stomach and truncated thighs. Its position on the bridge corresponds with that of the cross on mediæval parapets—a fact of great interest.* Brangwyn depicts, in a very brilliant pen-drawing, a Chinese bridge larger and finer than the one at Shih-Chuan,

* The photograph belongs to the London Missionary Society. The bridge itself has points of interest quite apart from the idol. There is a single arch of a horseshoe form with long and narrow archstones. The shelving parapets are decorated with small knobs of stone, and they do not rise to a gable point, like those in the Spanish variety of gabled bridge; there is a flat space at the summit, and below the middle of it the small idol is placed.

but there is no image, so I set great store by the evidence of idolatry in the smaller bridge.

Again, the province of Sichuan (pronounced Sit-you-on), in Western China, preserves another ancient custom.

STAIRCASE BRIDGE IN CHINA

When a flood threatens to overwhelm a bridge, and particularly a bamboo suspension bridge, which is a common thing in the mountains, "the local official and the people throw a living pig into the river, to stay the rising water: the pig disappears, and the flood goes on." *

* From information sent to me by the Rev. O. M. Jackson, who for more than twenty years has worked as a missionary in Western China.

This dire superstition is far more primitive than the idol fastened below the parapet of a Chinese bridge; and so, perhaps, we find in these things a parent emotion and its improved offspring. Perhaps: for Superstition rests on dark foundations; we know not precisely where it fades into a belief that is genuinely kinder.

III

WE pass on to some important topics that worry a writer because they cannot be arranged in a neat scheme. Some of them are technical, but everybody will be able to understand their bearing on the main subject. We have seen that fords gave place to bridges very slowly, even in some neighbourhoods where the Church was exceedingly active, as at Rochester.* Can you explain why? There were a good many reasons, and among them is the fact that it was a long time before bridges won a good reputation among the people. Wood being abundant everywhere, they were timber bridges at first, and rudely built; many of them were carried away by storms, as Matthew Paris related in the thirteenth century. So people set their hearts on the greater safety of stone bridges; but money was difficult to collect, and stonework cost a great deal more than timber; and no bridge could be built until permission had been gained from the King, often after tedious negotiations. Further, the lands through which rivers flowed were owned at times by rival noblemen,

* Take the dates of a few important bridges in Lancashire. Time of King John, Lancaster Bridge; 1225, Preston; 1305, Warrington; 1365, Salford; 1372, Stockport; and 1490, Garstang Bridge. The first Lancashire bridges were but narrow structures for foot and horse. Some had very high single arches, and those with from four to six spans were steep and lofty; they seemed to fly away from spates.

who put a veto on the project, either in a spirit of perverse antagonism or because a stone bridge might benefit one landlord more than another. And it was easy for the stronger man to explain his antagonism in a reasonable manner, for he could say that the cofferdams used in grounding piers diverted rivers from their channels, causing inundations. This objection seems to have been raised pretty often, as many piers were grounded in a very primitive fashion, just by throwing down stones and cement till a bed of masonry rose above water-level.

In the Ballad of Abingdon Bridge, written by Richard Fannande Iremonger in the thirty-sixth year of Henry VI (1458), we find most of the difficulties that attended mediæval bridge-building. Till the fourth year of Henry V (1417) the townsfolk of Abingdon and Culham had nothing but a ford, which could not be passed after a storm of rain or after a thaw. Yet Abingdon lived under the shadow of a great monastery, and roads were constructed from her streets to the ancient or Roman highways. Not even a timber bridge preceded the charming stone one that charity built in 1417, the very year in which Henry V sailed from England with 16,000 men and ravaged Normandy. But in the Middle Ages most people regarded bridges as we in our ignorance regard hospitals, as useful and necessary things to be supported by charitable doles, and not by district rates. To beg is a degradation, no matter what the cause may be, and many a small town could have built for itself a bridge but for the ruling custom that taught it to be a mendicant. Culham and Abingdon waited a very long time before almsgiving got rid of their dangerous ford. The Abbot gave his aid, and Geoffrey Barber paid a thousand marks to the workmen, and Sir Peris Besillis, Knight, provided the stone, and "the gode lorde of Abendon left of his londe, for the breed [breadth] of the bridge, twenty-four fote large" :—

> It was a greet socour of erthe and of sonde,
> And yet he abated the rent of the barge.
> An C. Pownde, and xv^{li}, was truly payed
> By the hondes of John Huchyns and Banbery also,
> For the waye and the barge, thus it must be sayed.

But I am happy to add that "the Commons of Abendon" had to do something for themselves. It was "set all in one assent that all the brekynges of the brige the town bere schulde." In other words, charity had produced a free town bridge, leaving the inhabitants to pay for its upkeep.

During the building of this pretty structure an unsuccessful attempt was made to ground the piers while eleven men baled water from the river. Then a dam was built, and trenches were dug to prevent the water from overflowing the dam. This I gather from the ballad, but the wording is not at all graphic in any technical matter.*

* On the other hand, there is a good social picture, showing that workmen in those days fed very well, though they could not afford to subscribe to the building of a bridge :—

> Wives went out to wite [know] how they wrought ;
> Five score in a flock, it was a fayre syght.
> In broad clothes bright white bread they brought,
> Cheese and chickens clerelych a dyght [prepared].

We are not told why cofferdams * were not tried. In the Middle Ages cofferdams were known as brandryths or brandereths; by this name they are mentioned in the Contract Deed for the building of Catterick Bridge over the Swale, A.D. 1421; and they were large enough to obstruct most rivers, for they had to surround enormous piers, and the thickness of their sides was never less than from four to six feet. It is interesting to note, in this connection, that during the construction of Old London Bridge, between 1176 and 1209, the Thames "was turned another way about by a trench," which, according to Stow, began east near "Rotherhithe, as is supposed, and ended in the west about Patricksey, now termed Battersea." In those days no embankments controlled the Thames at London; wide shores, littered with the odds and ends of a waterside life, were playgrounds for the ebb and flow of the tidal waters; and the main purpose of the "trench" or canal was to lessen the risk of floods while the huge piers were being founded. Stow's words give us to understand that *all* the

* Cofferdams are embankments which surround the site so as to exclude water from it. "They are formed in general by driving two rows of piles round the site so as to enclose between them a watertight wall of clay puddle; in depths of less than three or four feet, where there is little current, a simple clay dam may be used. In greater depths, the timber walls consist of guide piles at intervals, with some form of sheet piling between them; in extreme depths the timber walls may be composed of stout piles driven in side by side all round. The dam must be sufficiently strong to bear the pressure of the water against the outside when the space enclosed has been pumped dry. . . . The 'Cours de Ponts,' at the School of the Ponts et Chaussées, states that a cofferdam need never be made of greater thickness than from four to six feet, as the interior can always be sufficiently stayed inside. This method of founding is now seldom practised; it is costly and causes great obstruction in the stream."— Professor Fleeming Jenkin.

water in the Thames "was turned another way about"; a very important feat of civil engineering. Perhaps the purpose of the canal was not so thorough; perhaps it drew from the river sufficient water to lower its normal level by several feet and to diminish the force of the tidal current. In any case, however, Stow's evidence has great interest.

One of Brangwyn's animated drawings, the Pont des Consuls at Montauban, comes in here to illustrate the many troubles of mediæval bridge-building. In 1144, when Montauban passed from an unknown village into a known town, its patron or founder, Alphonse Jourdain, Count of Toulouse, commanded that a bridge should be made at once, and that the little township should keep it in repair; but, somehow, for many generations, nothing was done. Sometimes poverty was pleaded as an excuse, and sometimes the Albigeois wars were blamed; but at last, in 1264, the good men of Montauban ventured on a little action. Indeed, they stretched themselves yawningly, and said that a bridge over the Tarn would be a boon indeed. Their ferry was a slow nuisance, we may presume, and their trade ought to be increased by better communications. For twenty-seven years they repeated these truisms; then, in 1291, they bought the island of Castillons or of Pissotte to serve as a foundation for several piers. Tired by this unwonted exertion, Montauban wished to take a long holiday, but Philip the Fair came forward and asserted himself as a king. A bridge over the Tarn must be built! It should have three fortified towers, one at each end, the other in the middle; and these towers were to be garrisoned by royal troops, so that no harm should happen to the king's authority. In order to collect money for the bridge-building a tax was to be levied on all visitors to Montauban, and two consuls were to overseer the work. His Majesty chose Mathieu de Verdun, a citizen, and Étienne de Ferrières, who was keeper of the town. They seemed to be honest men, but funds collected for the bridge were used for other purposes, and I know not if this action was justified. It was in 1304 that Philip the Fair gave his instructions, and the bridge was not finished till 1335. Still, the dilatory township had achieved a very fine work of art, noble in design and very well constructed.

It is a brick bridge, 250 m.* 50 cm. in length. The bricks are excellent in quality, and measure 50 centimetres in thickness, 40 centimetres in length, and 28 centimetres in width. The roadway is nearly flat, and its height above the level of the Tarn is 18 metres. There are seven pointed arches with an average span of 22 metres; and the six piers armed with cutwaters at both sides are 8 m. 55 cm. in thickness. Note how the spandrils are pierced with high arched bays to facilitate the passage of water during floods. These relief arches were copied from Roman models. As for the defensive towers they exist no longer, but the strongest one kept watch and ward over the entrance across the river; it was square in shape, and its summit was a crenellated platform fringed with machicolations. The other end tower—

* A metre = 1·093633 yards, or 39·37079 inches; a centimetre = 0·39371 inch.

the one on the town side—was also square in form, while the central defence was triangular. It stood on the middle buttress on the side looking downstream, and the lower part of it was used as a chapel dedicated to St. Catherine. A flight of winding steps went down to a postern, cut through the buttress a little above water-level ; and at the other side of the pier, just below the arched bay, was an instrument of torture, a see-saw that carried an iron cage in which blasphemers were ducked in the river.

The Pont des Consuls has one quality that Englishmen ought to study with the greatest care ; it is in scale with a great river. To build a vast bridge for a little township was in part a just tribute to the beauty of a noble site, and in part a prophetic compliment paid to the future history of Montauban. How differently we have acted in our London bridges ! We have disgraced the Thames with the Railway Viaduct from Charing Cross, for instance, and neither Waterloo nor London Bridge does justice to the size of our Nation-City. There are three or four good bridges on the Thames, notably those at Maidenhead and Richmond, but they are nothing more than delicate works of refined engineering. Not one is inspired by awe, the only feeling that can bring home to our minds the wondrous grey antiquity of the Thames and the immensity of London. So we have feared to be great in the historic symbolism of bridge-building, unlike the citizens of Montauban, who were lifted far above their indolence by a brave inspiration as ample as was the Tarn after a flood.

LE PONT DES CONSULS OVER THE TARN AT
MONTAUBAN IN FRANCE, FOURTEENTH CENTURY

In 1823-4, when George Rennie designed New London Bridge, London was probably two hundred times as big as was Montauban in the fourteenth century; and certainly the Thames was not inferior to the Tarn as a historic inspiration. Yet Rennie failed to understand the importance of being large in scale. In less than fifty years his work was "insufficiently wide for the traffic";* and since then, on a good many occasions, we have been asked to disfigure London Bridge with overhanging footpaths. "London can well afford to pay for new bridges, but can by no means afford to part with a single object of real beauty."* For Rennie's bridge, despite all errors of scale, has points of charming interest. Her roadway has a graceful curvature that delights the eye, her arches have an excellent shape, and the variation in their size could not well be bettered.† Later we shall see (p. 325) that much money was ill-spent on hammer-dressing the whole external face of the masonry; but an engineer with a very weak feeling for scale was afraid to use either scabbled stone or stone with a rough-axed facing. Rennie learnt all that he could learn by studying fine models of style, such as the Roman bridge at Rimini, but his own equipment as an artist was terrene.

Would that we had in England an old bridge equal to

---

* Professor Fleeming Jenkin, Ninth Edition of the "Encyclopædia Britannica."

† The centre arch has a span of 152 ft., and rises 29 ft. 6 in. above Trinity high-water mark; the arches on each side of the centre have a span of 140 ft., and the abutment arches 130 ft. Total length, 1005 ft.; width from outside to outside, 56 ft.; height above low water, 60 ft. Centre piers, 24 ft. thick. Materials: the exterior stones are granite, the interior, half Bramley Fall and half from Painshaw, Derbyshire.

S

the Pont des Consuls! Would that old London Bridge had been delivered down to our sixpences and shillings! Yet I suppose we must consider ourselves lucky in the fact that historic bridges in Great Britain, though much inferior to those on the Continent, are fairly numerous in districts where there has been but little increase of traffic. We possess three bridges with defensive gateways (Stirling, Warkworth, and the Monnow Bridge at Monmouth); five with chapels, or with relics of chapels (St. Ives in Huntingdonshire, Derby, Bradford-on-Avon in Wiltshire, Wakefield, Rotherham); and many good specimens exist of bridges with angular recesses built out from parapets and forming part of the piers.* These recesses were designed not only as shelter places for wayfarers, but because they lessened the cost of production, inasmuch as they gave width to narrow footways; and so their value in an old bridge is very similar to that of bay-windows in cottage rooms.

Very often the modern engineer has misunderstood their origin, and, regarding them as decorations, he has used safety recesses to ornament his wide bridges, just as he has put battlements on iron parapets and stuck machicolations on defenceless gateways. Brangwyn has drawn for us three or four big Gothic bridges with safety recesses. Among them is a fine structure over the Main at Würzburg,

---

* For example, King John's Bridge at Tewkesbury; Barden Bridge and Burnsal Bridge in Wharfedale; the Old Dee Bridge at Chester; Huntingdon, Bridgenorth, Baslow, Froggall, Brecon, and Llangollen. There are many others.

in Bavaria; there are eight arches, and the length is 650 ft. This bridge dates from the year 1474, but his adornment with statues of saints belongs to later times. Indeed, the architecture and decoration take us from the end of the

THE BRIDGE OVER THE MAIN AT WÜRZBURG IN BAVARIA (1474-1607)

Middle Ages to the year 1607, when the spirit of the Renaissance was active and generative.

Here is an old defensive bridge that does not resemble a common man-at-arms: in him there is a fine courtesy, as of a knight long used to the etiquette of tournaments; but yet the technical inspiration is rather inferior to that in his great

rival, the Moselle Bridge at Coblentz, built in 1344, by the
Elector Baudouin, and charmed with a mellow grace that
imparts a rare distinction to the vigour of fourteen bold
arches.　The Moselle Bridge is 1100 ft. long, or ninety-five
longer than London Bridge.　There is but one fault, and
this one fault belongs to the Middle Ages : the ten piers
obstruct the river too much, and two or three of them might
have been omitted without harm to any strategic consideration.

In the Middle Ages almost everything was looked at
from the standpoints of attack and defence.　Bridges as
well as soldiers needed armour, so their gateways and
towers were built in a military fashion, and at times curious
traps were devised along the footways.　For example, con-
sult the " Pacata Hibernia," and you will find an engraving
of Askeaton Bridge,* with a sort of hangman's trapdoor at
each end of the footway.　In 1586, or thereabouts, Askeaton
Bridge had another peculiarity : a castle stood close to it on
an island in the river; and between the castle and the bridge
was a fortified platform with two gateways.

It happened often, in mediæval times, that one arch was
a drawbridge.　Take Old London Bridge as an example.
One of her twenty arches—the thirteenth from the City end
—was a toll-gate for merchant shipping, and a drawbridge
to gap off enemies from the town.　It served this latter

---

* This valuable reference was brought to my notice by Mr. H. T. Crofton, an
able pontist, who sent me his notes on bridges, asking me to cull from them whatever
information my own research had missed.　A hobby is the only altruism.

purpose in 1553, when Sir Thomas Wyatt and his insurgents tried to enter London. Everybody knew which was the movable arch, because it was connected in all popular talk with the tower that rose beside it, a terrible and gruesome tower, for on its summit executioners displayed the heads of decapitated persons, who ranged from common bandits to the great Sir Thomas More.

Some defensive bridges in Old England had an important look as late as the reign of George III. This applies to the Welsh Bridge at Shrewsbury, which had a noble tower at the entrance that looked towards Wales. Perhaps it belonged to the reign of Edward I, as a statue of Llewellyn was placed over one of the arches. At the present time our fortified bridges are minor specimens. The "auld brig" over the Forth at Stirling, once "the key of the Highlands," is the most interesting architecturally. He still retains a defensive gateway at each end, and his four arches, now closed to traffic, have a bold and pleasant rhythm. They date from the last years of the fourteenth century. From this century also Warkworth Bridge comes to us; it is a smaller structure, with a triangular recess at each side, projecting from the parapet into the central pier. The gate-tower is at some little distance from the abutment; it has a low and narrow archway under which carters swear unhopefully, believing that their wagons will stick fast. A person who was present on the occasion told M. J. J. Jusserand that a gipsy's caravan, not long ago, was stopped at the tower on Warkworth Bridge, and waited there while the pavement was being hollowed out to make the passage deep enough for a safe journey.

The pier midstream is triangular, and almost as sharp as an arrow-head. This shape is very common in mediæval cutwaters, but it belongs to a technical routine which cannot be regarded as practical. Floods cannot eddy around the flat surfaces of a triangle; they are cut into waves that soon break with an increasing force against the piers and spandrils. On the other hand, when a cutwater is shaped like a Gothic drop arch, or like a tierce-point arch, it meets the current with a much bolder wedge of stone, whose curved sides are better playgrounds for water in spate. Cutwaters of this improved sort are uncommon in mediæval bridges, but some are to be found in French work of the Limousin.

Viollet-le-Duc was the first critic who called attention to this technical matter, and no pontist should fail to note how cutwaters are designed. For example, in a bird's-eye view of the bridge at Avignon the buttressed piers jut out on each side beyond the narrow footway, looking like boats that support a long line of planks; and I have no doubt that Saint Bénézet had in mind this figure of boats when he planned his roadway over "the arrowy Rhône." It is far from my wish to compare the little Warkworth Bridge with this French masterpiece, but let us note in its cutwaters a similar character.

Again, when you remember that Warkworth Bridge belongs to the fourteenth century, do you not expect to find in it the pointed vault, whose lighter grace is among the most beautiful things both in Eastern and in mediæval architecture? Yet the two ribbed arches are segments of circles. For many a generation Northern England has been famed for three things—a long-headed thrift, a discontent that is said to be a Radical in politics, and a stubborn hatred for any new knowledge that attacks the dull mimicry of customs. It is to Lancashire, for instance, that you must go if you wish to study in old packhorse bridges the retention of Romanesque forms. A considerable number are described popularly as Roman bridges, probably because they are found on the old pilgrim ways, which, after the Reformation, were scorned as Roman Catholic.

For some reason or other Northern England welcomed in bridges the bluff economy of ribbed arches, while neglecting the more gracious thrift of Early English or pointed vaults. These are easier to build because they need lighter centres or arched scaffolds, and their thrust being less powerful than that of round-headed arches, they require less bulk in the piers. Some writers say that pointed arches interfere with sailing-boats, but this depends on the size of their spans. At Montauban there is room enough for ordinary boat traffic under the Pont des Consuls.

The Pont Valentré at Cahors has ogivale arches, and in one fine drawing Brangwyn studies the technique of their construction. For instance, the embattled piers are triangular, and each of them is pierced transversely by a bay or passage, which is put on a level with the springing of every arch. Below this bay are three holes; and another line of holes runs across the under surface of the arch beneath the springing.* Now, these holes and the bays have a great technical interest, they remind us how the Pont Valentré was built in the thirteenth century. With their help simple scaffolds were erected. The first step was to thrust fir saplings through the holes in a pier till they jutted out on each side; then they were covered with planks and used as footbridges by the workmen, and also as resting-places for barrow-loads of dressed stone, which were lifted up by movable cranes. The service of the masons was effected through the bay in a pier, and the centring of every arch was fixed in those other holes which Brangwyn has represented in his vivacious water-colour.

Not more than two arches were built at the same time. At any moment, in those rude, warfaring periods, work might be interrupted by strife, and its progress was so very slow that it took from ten to thirty years to bring a bridge to completion, usually after a continuous fight against money troubles. Many a hint on economy was borrowed from the Romans, whose enterprise was far in advance of their current cash. Piers that look marvels of solid masonry may be nothing more than shells filled with beaten earth and gravel; and those passages through the piers at Cahors have one thing in common with the relief arches that pierce

* *Springing.* The plane of demarcation between the ring and the abutment is called the "springing" of an arch. A "ring" is the compressed arc of materials known as archstones or voussoirs; and the "springing" marks the place where a ring starts out on its upward curve from a pier or from an abutment.

PONT VALENTRÉ AT CAHORS-SUR-LOT
A FORTIFIED BRIDGE, THIRTEENTH CENTURY

the spandrils of the Pont des Consuls at Montauban : they enabled the builders to be thrifty.

In a Persian bridge (on the way between Resht, on the Caspian Sea, and Teheran, the capital) thrift hollowed the spandrils into chambers, some of which were used by travellers. This bridge carried a rough highway over the Kâredj River, which runs down from the Elburz Mountains between Kasvîn and Teheran, and disappears in a gravelly plain. In 1874 the Kâredj Bridge was studied in measured drawings by J. Romilly Allen, and eighteen years later (November 19, 1892) the drawings were published in " The Builder," with a most valuable description. Let us linger for a few minutes over Romilly Allen's research, as the technique of old Persian bridge-builders has points in common both with Gothic methods and with modern practice also. Some mediæval spandrils are hollow, for example ; and a very noted French architect of the eighteenth century, Perronet, not only left empty spaces behind the haunches* of an arch, but made tunnels in piers, after the manner used by Pope Sextus IV in the Ponte Sisto. And the bridge of Glasgow over the Clyde has tunnelled piers, so this technical detail has a long and entertaining history.

In the Kâredj Bridge, then, the builders had to solve three or four difficulties that strained the usual penury of Persian finance. The river itself must have been a constant trouble while the bridge was being constructed. A rapid

---

* The *haunches* of an arch are those parts that lie midway between the springing and the crown : the crown being the summit of a ring.

mountain torrent with precipitous rocky banks, it pours through a gorge of rock, and at one spot only it forms a good foundation for a wide pier ; but this spot has a situation that divides the bridge into inharmonious parts, making symmetry impossible. Allen's drawing shows both arches, one with a span of 23 ft., the other with a span of 72 ft. 9 in. ; and between them is a vast pier not less than 31 ft. 9 in. wide. Forty-six feet separate the highest point of the parapet from water-level ; and from water-level to the peak of the big pointed vault is thirty-seven feet. In width the bridge measures thirty feet across the outside of its parapets, and twenty-six feet across the roadway, so there is room for a great deal more wheeled traffic than Persia has yet developed along her dusty trade routes.

From this description it is evident that the builders had a stiff job. Timber for centring has ever been scarce in Persia* ; so in Persian bridge-building the usual plan is to set up a light scaffold just strong enough to bear its own weight and a few rings of brickwork. After a single rib of bricks has been made, other bricks are dabbed against the first set, more being added at the abutment ends than in the centre of an arch ; and so, as the work goes on, the arch grows to be self-supporting, like a cantilever bridge. When the middle part of the span has been covered over, the remaining courses at each side are completed with bricks set at right angles to the others. In looking upward at the under surface of a Persian vault a pontist sees that the courses of brick go in two directions, one parallel to the central axis of the bridge and another at right angles. Such is the Persian method of building a brick arch; its main object is to evade, without too much risk, the cost of heavy centring, timber being so difficult to get and so expensive to carry about.*

In the four bridges that Romilly Allen studied, between Resht and Teheran, the building was brickwork, and the bricks were rather like Roman tiles; they measured 10 in. by 10 in. by 2½ in. At Kâredj the mortar joints were about ¾ in. thick, so that twenty-four courses of bricks with their mortar joints built a wall about 6 ft. 2 in. high. At the thinnest part of the big arch there were only three bricks, giving a thickness of 2 ft. 6 in.; further on there were five bricks, and two more were added at the abutments, where the walls were 7 ft. 6 in. thick. Here is much economy, for thick joints of mortar are not praiseworthy (p. 175); and thrift is very noticeable in other details of the workmanship. Beneath the roadway were two chambers with pointed barrel vaults, which were built partly to relieve the haunches of the big arch, and partly to save materials. On one side of the arch the chamber was about 12 ft. high; its length, varying with the curve of the voussoirs, and extending across the abutment, ranged from 27 ft. to 49 ft. On the pier side of the big arch the chamber was not so long, but its height was 12 ft.; and the pier itself was chambered in its upper part and pierced below with a Tudor-like arch about 14 ft. wide and 11 ft. 6 in. high. The chamber above

* "The Builder," November 19, 1892, p. 394.

had a cone-shaped roof, and at each side of it were three square-headed windows that measured 3 ft. 6 in. wide by 6 ft. high. I am speaking in the past tense, for I know not whether this bridge is still in use; but now we will return to the present tense in a short quotation from Romilly Allen :—

"This chamber appears to be . . . a temporary living-room for travellers. It . . . communicates with the cells above the haunches of the arch by an opening 4 ft. 6 in. high. The inner room is probably intended to afford sleeping accommodation. The living-room is approached by a stair-case in the thickness of the wall leading up from the top of the pier. The Persian name for an upper chamber of this kind is 'bala-khana,' literally 'a house up above.'"*

Perhaps the finest bridge in Persia is the far-famed Ali Verdi Khan at Isfahan.

Ali Verdi Khan was the general of Shah Abbas, and his bridge, if not the greatest in the world, has no rival that excels it in stateliness. As Lord Curzon has said, it alone is worth a visit to Isfahan to see. I know it in photographs only, and in written descriptions, but I feel its beauty and magnificence. In many respects it resembles the Pul-i-Khaju (p. 213), but it is a great deal longer, and no pavilions rise above its tiers of arches. To my mind the pavilions of the Pul-i-Khaju have an architectural value that cannot be rated at too high a level. So I miss their grace in the Ali

* "The Builder," November 19, 1892, p. 394.

Verdi Khan, though this noble structure ought not to be criticised—except in an ashamed whisper.

There is a gateway at the north end, so we must place the Ali Verdi Khan among the minor defensive bridges. A paved ramp or causeway leads from a great avenue to the

THE BRIDGE OF ALI VERDI KHAN OVER THE ZENDEH RUD AT ISFAHAN, PERSIA

gateway; and then a visitor has 388 yards to walk before he reaches the far end. The main road is paved, and its width is thirty feet. Upon each side is a gallery, or covered arcade, two and a half feet wide, which is pierced through the outer wall of the bridge from one end to the other; it communicates with the main road by frequent arches, it opens by similar arches—over ninety in number —on to the river view, and here and there it expands into large chambers, as we see in Brangwyn's pen-drawing. The chambers used to be decorated with "not too proper paintings," done in the time of Abbas II. At both entrances the Ali Verdi Khan is flanked by round towers, and staircases in the towers go up to a fine platform which in earlier times was a favourite promenade; but now it is disfigured by telegraph poles, the modern spirit everywhere having an unrivalled vulgarity.* "Similar staircases, cut in the basements of the towers, and also at regular intervals in the main piers, conduct from the road level to a lower storey, where, but little elevated above the bed of the river, a vaulted passage runs along the entire length of the bridge, through arches pierced in the central piers, crossing the channel of the river by huge stepping-stones planted in its bed. Colonel Johnson gives the dimensions of these transverse arches as ten feet span and nine feet high; and of the main arches (thirty-three in number) which they bisect, as twenty feet span and fifteen feet high, separated by piers eleven feet thick. There is thus a triple promenade on this remarkable bridge—the vaulted passage below, the roadway and lateral galleries above, and the open footpath at the top of all. I should add that the upper part of the bridge is of brick, the piers and towers are of stone."†

* If Cæsar's bones were found they would be sold at Christie's to a tradesman millionaire.

† Lord Curzon's "Persia and the Persian Question," 1892, Vol. II, pp. 45–6.

There is no European structure akin to this, but for a long time Rothenburg on the Tauber has been famous for a two-storeyed bridge; also we know that some modern commercial bridges have an upper road and a lower one, like the High Level Bridge at Newcastle. In every case the idea was suggested by the Roman practice of building aqueducts in tiers.

IV

AND now let us give all our attention to the more military bridges. Brangwyn has studied them with the utmost care and interest; there are but few variations of the war-bridge that his art has not yet represented. Let us see, then, what his research has found.

1. This bridge from Bhutan has the same technique as the cantilever bridges of Kurdistan (p. 74); but the gateway towers mark an advance. They are militant works, partly because they control the traffic, and partly because they are open below the eaves for archery and for other defensive warfare. Brangwyn suggests that gateway towers of this kind may have been brought to India by Darius Hystaspes (512 B.C.) or by Alexander the Great (327 B.C.). On this point there is no evidence. On the other hand, there seems to be no doubt that the timber gateways on Roman bridges in England, as in Gaul, were prepared for defence, though their main use was to limit the freedom of a public thoroughfare, invariably after sunset, and during the day in times of unrest. This was the first aim of defensive bridges, so the gateway towers in Bhutan are suggestive things to study. They are too light in structure to give us an idea of the bold and stern gateways built by the Romans with newly-felled trees; but yet they help us

to realise vaguely what every young civilization must have done when it learnt from a free use of bridges that foes as well as friends were eager to pass without danger across rivers.

PRIMITIVE TIMBER BRIDGE IN BHUTAN, INDIA

Again, the earliest defensive bridges had another point in common with the primitive carpentry of Bhutan: they were made with tree-trunks resting on supports, and, when necessary, a part of their footways could be removed. Diodorus Siculus wrote a flaming account of a great bridge built by Semiramis over the Euphrates, rather more than

T

two thousand years before the birth of Christ. After making due allowance for the frolicsome legends with which ancient history is enlivened, there are things worth noting in the enthusiasm of Diodorus. Herodotus attributed the same bridge not to Semiramis but to Nitocris, so evidence can be drawn from two authors. Pontists gather from the evidence that stone piers were connected by planks, which were taken up at night, just as the central part of a bridge in Bhutan could be removed as a military precaution. Diodorus draws entertaining pictures, and tries to prove that bridge-building was far advanced twenty centuries before our era began. If Semiramis collected architects and craftsmen from all the known civilizations, until at last she had at her beck and call a great host of capable servants, it is not surprising that she was able to build a fine bridge as well as to enlarge Babylon. The piers were grounded in deep water; their ends were protected by triangular buttresses; their stones were clamped together with thick bars of iron, which were soldered into the stones with molten lead. As for the superstructure, it was thirty feet wide, and all of wood—cedar, and cypress, and palm tree. In all this, probably, there is some exaggeration, but a famous bridge did exist at Babylon, and a combination of timber with stone piers was the most logical development from the simplest natural bridges— the fallen tree and the bridge of stepping-stones. Also it is likely enough that metal clamps were employed; iron was in vogue, and by using it in stonework under water an architect would feel less mistrustful of his cement and less anxious about the risks of floods. Further, it is quite probable that the entrance at each side was protected by a sort of drawbridge, because the times were lawless. Semiramis herself was put to death by her son Ninyas, and Ninyas in his turn was murdered.*

An important timber bridge with stone piers belongs to a handicraft more advanced than that in the bridges of Bhutan; it comes between the primitive inspiration of the Bhutan carpenters and the simplest arched bridges with plain gateway towers. It has not yet vanished from Europe, for a Gothic example exists at Thouars, in Deux-Sèvres, France, according to a photograph sold by Neurdein, of Paris. Another example crosses the Guadalaviar above Albarracin, in Aragon; and let us remember also that the tree bridge resting on stone piers has influenced some metal viaducts, such as Runcorn Bridge, near Liverpool, dating from 1868. In principle the construction is the same, timber being displaced by metal. At the end of its approach arches, where the metalwork begins, Runcorn Bridge has two gateways, each with twin turrets, and a great display of battlements and of machicolations. Although this make-believe of war has a farcical bad taste, like the assumed erudition that keeps dummy books in a

* According to some writers, the earliest known arches of handicraft—pointed, and round, and even elliptical—are Babylonian, but I do not care to be so dogmatic. Dates very often are as elusive as dreams. But the influence of Babylon was, doubtless, very great on the traditions of the building arts; perhaps we find it even in the elliptic vault of Chosroes' great hall at Selucia-Ctesiphon. This vault, dating from the sixth century A.D., was a forerunner of St. Bénézet's elliptic arch (p. 81).

library, yet Runcorn Bridge has a well-defined interest : it mimics a phase of military architecture which was evolved from such carpentry as to-day we find in Bhutan.

DEFENSIVE BRIDGE AT SOSPEL

2. Gateway Bridge at Sospel, in the Italy of France. This drawing illustrates very well the transition from the primitive bridges of Bhutan to a simple arched bridge guarded by a gatehouse of control. It is a poor little house, its architecture being less intelligent than that in the Bhutan gateway towers. In these there is cleverness enough to prove that the bridge represents a stale old

custom which has lagged behind the advance of handicraft,
whereas the bridge at Sospel is far in advance of the tawdry
little gatehouse.   A span separates the gatehouse from the
town, and the roadway is not on the same level above both
arches.

AT NARNI IN ITALY: THIRTEENTH CENTURY

3. A Broken War-Bridge of the Thirteenth Century,
Repaired with Timber.

A very valuable illustration, and for several reasons.
The gatehouse with its pointed archway is unusually tall;

and the machicolated box below the slightly gabled roof is unique in my experience. The holes above this defensive work are partly for ventilation and partly for crossbowmen, whose fire would "puncture" an attack on the right entrance of the bridge, There is but one arrow-hole on the first storey, and I should not care to shoot through it while molten lead or boiling oil came sizzling down in two streams from that machicolated box. I do not know why the gate-tower was made so very high, but suppose that its engineer wished to build a place of vantage from which the movements of an attack could be seen afar off, beyond the entrance gates. In any case it failed to save four of the arches from gunpowder wars; and note the restoration! Could anything speak to us more clearly of the primitive bridge with stone piers united by rough timbering?

4. The War-Bridge at Orthez.

In the wizard country of the French Pyrenees there are some very notable bridges, such as the Pont Napoléon, near Saint-Sauveur, the Pont d'Espagne, beyond Cauterets, and the Vieux Pont at Orthez. To study these three works, side by side, is to learn that modern bridge-building has achieved in stone a few great works as daring as any that the Middle Ages produced. The Pont d'Orthez has a graceful distinction, and for nearly six hundred years it has borne the formidable spates of the Gav-de-Pau. In the tierce-point arches, and particularly in the largest one, there is good drawing; the spandrils are relieved from dullness in a simple and effective manner that gives support to the base of the parapet; perhaps the roadway dips too much on the left-hand side, and the fortified tower is too slim to be in scale with the broad pier from which it ascends. Add

WAR-BRIDGE OVER THE GAV-DE-PAU AT ORTHEZ IN FRANCE

twelve inches of width to the side face, and see how different the tower looks! In fact, Brangwyn has done this instinctively, as I find by comparing his vigorous pen-sketch from nature with my photographs. The tower has but one machicolation, it guards the base of the pier from boat attacks and scaling ladders; but the spy-holes below the roof served many purposes, including those for which machicolations were invented. A vaulted passage conducts the road through the tower; it is lighted on the far side by an opening called the Priests' Window, because the priests and monks of Orthez jumped through it into the river, driven to this act by the orders of Gabriel de Montgomery. Such is the legend, and there's not a word of history in its drama. For the rest, Orthez has seen no war since the great combat of February 27, 1814, when Wellington prepared the way for the battle of Toulouse by defeating the French, under Soult.

But this old bridge, with all its charm and interest, is eclipsed as a work of art by the Pont Napoléon, whose gigantic arch, in a very noble curve, spans the rocky and precipitous gorge of the Pas de l'Échelle, along which the furious Gave de Gavarnie pursues a foam-bubbled race against time, sixty-seven metres below the bridge. Here is a masterpiece that rivals the Puente Nuevo at Ronda, thrown across the tremendous chasm of the Guadalvia.*

5. The Monnow Bridge at Monmouth.

* Brangwyn has drawn for the édition de luxe the bridge at Ronda, which dates from 1761. Its architect, José Martin Aldeguela, was even more unfortunate than were Peter Colechurch and the good Saint Bénézet; these masters died before their work was complete, while poor Aldeguela fell from his bridge and was dashed to pieces. Two other bridges, one Moorish and one Roman, cross the chasm at Ronda, but at the upper end where the depth is less prodigious; so their architects had easier problems to solve, and yet they did not equal in any respect the heroic inspiration of Aldeguela. Mr. Edgar Wigram has said that although Ronda Bridge owes much of its effect to its extraordinary site, yet an extraordinary piece of architecture is necessary to command the site; it is the triumph of genius over nature that we feel both at Ronda and in the Pont Napoléon.

This bluff old gate-tower is a bolder specimen of mediæval work than the smaller one at Warkworth. We are lucky indeed to possess a war-bridge which has suffered so little from time and trade and highway officials. If you compare

WAR-BRIDGE AT MONMOUTH

it with the Brangwyn water-colour of Parthenay Bridge, over the Thouet, you will be better able to put the Monnow Bridge in its proper place as a work of defensive art. The French tower is far and away superior: it has scale and dignity: it is a work of architecture as well as an instrument of war. At Monmouth, how different is the technical inspiration ! Not a trace of good design saves the gate-tower from being no more than a weapon for ruthless men. A Peace Society could publish the Monnow Bridge as a fact to prove that slaughtering wars have been more vulgar even than the cruel battles of finance. It is the undefensive parts of this bridge that I admire. The ribbed arches are good (p. 93), and in them a slight tentative effort has been made to free the ring of voussoirs from the oscillation sent down through the spandrils when a great weight passes along the footway. "A slight tentative effort," I repeat, because the archstones have not been made independent from the spandrils.

6. To find arches of this kind we must return to the Pont Valentré at Cahors, which dates from the middle of the thirteenth century. In this noble bridge the voussoirs of all the arches look isolated from the spandrils, as they are rimmed and "extra-dossed." It was the Romans who invented the "extra-dossed" arch, and they proved that by separating archstones from the spandrils a bridge was relieved from much wear and tear. On the other hand, when archstones are unequal, when they are thicker in their haunches than at the crown, oscillation goes along the full length of a bridge, fatiguing the piers, and causing at times a noticeable shiver, as in the Llanrwst Bridge, designed by Inigo Jones.* Even Perronet forgot this effect of reper-

---

* The middle arch of 58 ft. span, 17 ft. rise, and 14 ft. in width across the soffit, has archstones which are only 18 ins. deep, and they vary in thickness from 5 to 16 ins. : many of them are 8 and 9 ins. Sometimes there are two headers to answer a

cussion when he built his bridge in the Place de la Concorde at Paris; and ever afterwards he clamped the headers with iron to the interior archstones, as if iron fastened into stone could never become a destructive agent.

The architect of Valentré Bridge was wiser than Perronet, every arch in his work being an elastic bow that moves between two piers without conveying its oscillation beyond these supports. To our modern eyes, no doubt, there are too many arches across the River Lot at Cahors, but this defect seemed necessary in the Middle Ages, and for two reasons. It was regarded as a defensive precaution, because narrow arches were easier to protect from the roadway when an enemy tried to assemble boats under a bridge; and since in the frequent wars of those days a bridge had often to be cut as a final resource against defeat, it was essential that the destruction of one arch should not upset another by the withdrawal of a counterbalancing thrust from one side of a pier. Many piers of a large size were looked upon as particularly needful when the greater lateral thrust of round arches had to be considered in its relation to a bridge cut

course of common archstones; and sometimes two courses of archstones answer one header. The piers are 10 ft. thick, and the middle arch springs about 3 ft. above the river's bed. A steep road over the bridge diminishes the weight upon the side arches; but Telford believed that if the spandrils had been hollowed the road could have been made with an easy gradient of 1 in 24. The workmanship is very light, and it appears to be stable, though a shivering bridge inspires no more confidence than a stammering man. In 1803, owing to a defect in the foundation of the western abutment, one of the side arches fell, yet the others remained uninjured while the broken one was being rebuilt. So the bridge in the proportion of all its parts must have been very well balanced, despite its quivering alertness and lightness.

in a single place. Also, as we have seen (p. 264), bridges
in the Middle Ages were built very slowly, and as war at
any moment might stop the masons, piers were regarded
as abutments and made very strong.

This much is known, but none can say why piers were
built unreasonably large. Frequent inundations from obstructed rivers were as evidently harmful as weak piers that
floods overthrew; and the genius that solved so many
problems in church architecture ought to have shown in
bridges a riper discretion. Often piers and arches were
of the same width—a waste of labour and material, as well
as of space in the waterway. Even the Romans, though
their piers were less bulky, impeded the current of rivers
with too much stone; and to save their work from the
floods which they provoked, they built relief bays for spate
water above that part of their piers where adequate resistance
had been obtained against the lateral thrust of heavy arches.

In the Valentré at Cahors the architect scorned the aid
of relief bays, and grew five vast piers from the river-bed;
not a courteous thing to do, seeing that the word river in
French is a lady-word, " La rivière "—the very sound of it
is a sweet compliment to the youthful waywardness of
running water. Yet French bridge-masters have sinned
against rivers as frequently as we English. If the Valentré
had one pier less, how ample and noble the design would
be! Even now the design is so virile, so masculine, that
we ought to speak of this bridge as we do of a great soldier.
The feeble word " it " does not belong to the Pont Valentré.

THE ALCÁNTARA AT TOLEDO, SHOWING THE MOORISH
GATEWAY TOWER AT THE TOWN END OF THE BRIDGE

"He" and "him" and "his" are the right pronouns. According to many writers he is the finest military bridge in the world, but comparisons are difficult and risky: they are affected too much by a writer's moods. One thing is certain—that the Valentré has no superior in his own line. His most celebrated rivals, two bridges at Toledo, in Spain, have a feminine grace; they are too courtly to be typical soldiers. There is another Spanish bridge that ranks high as a fortified work: it dates from the fourteenth century, and, in sixteen pointed arches, crosses the Duero at Zamora. Brangwyn prefers the Toledo bridges, the Alcántara and the Puente de San Martin, because they are lofty as well as spacious, while Zamora Bridge is long and low, like a good many Spanish bridges, both Roman and mediæval.*

7. The Alcántara at Toledo. From every point of view this bridge makes a good picture, but I like her best when she is seen from a level only a little below the footway. Then I look down at the upward flight of her architecture, and watch how a luminous patterning of shadow enriches the suave yet austere masonry. Somehow I think of a courtly abbess whose half-smile is a discipline feared by everybody. In no other way can I describe the technical inspiration that makes this bridge very uncommon. Looking down again, I see that the Spanish masons—or shall we call them Hispano-Moresque?—were as thrifty as the

---

* Roman examples: the two bridges at Mérida, and the bridge of Salamanca. Mediæval examples: Tudela, Tordesillas, Talavera, Zaragoza, Castro Gonzalo, and El Burgo, near Coruña, the scene of a good fight in Drake's expedition of 1589.

Frenchmen at Cahors; across the breadth of the bigger
arch, and below the springing, there are seven holes, from
which the centring was scaffolded.   Technically the arches
are inferior to those of the Pont Valentré, because their
rings are not sufficiently rimmed and extra-dossed, so they
lie too close into the body of the spandrils.   The pier is
designed very well, it has a distinction of its own and forms
on each side of the roadway a narrowing shelter-place with
four angles.   Lower down, near the Moorish adaptation
from a Roman triumphal arch, a long recess carried by five
brackets varies the line of each parapet, in which there is
no pretension, no swagger, no balustraded bombast.   On
the town side the bridge is guarded by a Moorish gate-
tower, while across the river is a gateway dating from the
time of Charles the Fifth.

A Roman bridge crossed the Tagus at this great spot,
and was repaired in 687 by the Visigoths, but in 871 it disappeared, I know not how or why.   Then a bridge was built
by Halaf, son of Mahomet Alameri, Alcalde of Toledo,
but Halaf obeyed a command from Almansor Aboaarmir
Mahomet, son of Abihamir, Alquazil of Amir Almomenin
Hixem.   I hope you like these names and titles?   They are
given by George Edmund Street,* who quotes from Cean
Bermudez; and so with confidence we may add Halaf
Alameri to the few early bridge-masters who are known to
us by name.

For 340 years no accident seems to have happened to

* "Gothic Architecture in Spain," 1865, p. 211.

Alameri's work. Then in 1211 a part of the bridge fell into the river; and six years later, during its restoration, Enrique I had a gate-tower set up by Matheo Paradiso, a military architect with too angelic a name. Forty-one years passed, and then the bridge was renewed once more, this time by the King D. Alonso, who put the following inscription on a piece of marble above the point of the arch : "In the year 1258 from the Incarnation of our Lord Jesus Christ was the great deluge of water, that began before the month of August, and lasted until Thursday the 26th of December; and in most lands the fall of rain did much damage, especially in Spain, where most of the bridges fell ; and among them was demolished a great part of that bridge of Toledo which Halaf, son of Mahomet Alameri, ... had made . . . . in the time of the Moors, 387 years before this time ; and now the King D. Alonso, son of the noble King D. Ferrando, and of the Queen Doña Beatriz, who reigned in Castile, has had it repaired and renovated ; and it was finished in the eighth year of his reign, in the year of the Incarnation 1258."

Even then some of Alameri's work remained, but I fear that it all vanished in 1380, when Archbishop Pedro Tenorio, a kinsman of Don Juan, and a great pontist, became patron of the Toledo bridges and gave to the Alcántara the appearance that we know, apart from the fortified gateways, which were either altered or built by Andres Manrique, A.D. 1484.

8. Brangwyn has sketched the other great bridge at Toledo, the Puente de San Martin, a better work of art

than the Alcántara. Here the style is far more masculine, and there is no wide expanse of barren wall such as we find in the Alcántara below the bracketed recesses. The five arches vary much in size, no doubt, but yet they harmonise very well, and the most important one is heroic in scale, being not less than 140 Spanish ft. wide and 95 ft. high. As for the piers, each has a character of its own : they have but one thing in common—bulk enough not only to resist floods, but to be in keeping with a defile of rocks. There are two gateways, and one of them has Moorish ornament and a Moorish battlement.

The Puente de San Martin seems to date from the year 1212. In 1368 he met with an accident that destroyed the big arch. Shortly afterwards, about 1380, Archbishop Tenorio began the restoration, aided by a careless architect. One day, in fact, the architect perceived that his new arch would fall down as soon as the centring was removed. Panic-stricken, he went home and consulted his wife, who happened to be a forerunner of the Suffragettes. What could be done to save her husband's reputation ? She could set fire to the scaffolding; and when the arch fell Toledo was quite awed by the accident. All the usual things were said about the terrible destruction that flames could do in a brilliant hour; and then the architect was asked to renew what the fire had ruined. This time he did his work admirably, and his wife was too much elated by his complete success, for she gave discretion to the winds and told the tale of her incendiarism. If Pedro Tenorio had punished

A SPANISH WAR-BRIDGE—THE BRIDGE OF ST. MARTIN, TOLEDO. ITS HISTORY SEEMS TO DATE FROM 1212, BUT IN THE XIV CENTURY IT WAS REBUILT BY ARCHBISHOP PEDRO TENORIO

her by claiming payment for the new work from her husband, Toledo would have been amused, perhaps ; but the good Archbishop had learnt too much in confessionals to expect very much from human nature. He seems to have done

THE RABOT AT GHENT : A FORTIFIED LOCK

nothing more than congratulate his architect on the wife's devotion.*

9. Defensive Bridges in Flemish Towns. They represent the manly, swaggering burghers who were not clever

* See George Edmund Street, whose valuable book on Spain ought to be studied side by side with those by Ford and Edgar Wigram.

U

enough to keep their liberties. The Pont des Trous at Tournai, for instance, guarded at each end by a huge round tower, has more to say to us about the turbulent old Flemish pride than have many chapters written by good historians. It is a bridge enlivened by art, yet blinded by an excess of warlike caution. There are three good pointed vaults, each with a double ring of moulded voussoirs; and there are two piers equally well designed; but the parapet rises into a high rampart pierced with nine arrow slits, and the ungainly towers have such flat summits that they appear to be roofless.* At Courtrai, on the other hand, we find the Pont de Broel, whose tall round towers have conical roofs lighted in a playful way by dormer windows, and graced with long weather-vanes. The Pont de Broel is a small bridge with three round arches, it looks very trivial between its formidable guardians. Both towers are encircled by machicolations, whose snarling teeth make an unpleasant girdle almost a third way down the walls. Between them and the roof are many small openings, defensive windows let us call them; and beneath the machicolations some other windows keep watch, with a proper respect of scaling ladders. We pass on to Ghent, where fifty-eight bridges span the canals, and connect the thirteen islands into which the brave old city is divided. In 1488, after Frederick III, Emperor of Germany, with

* I am reading my proof sheets on the 10th September, 1914, so it is necessary to add that the Pont des Trous at Tournai has renewed its military value, aiding the Belgians in their heroic efforts against that avalanche of inhumanity, the German Army.

his son Maximilian, had raised the siege of Ghent, the victorious burghers began at once to build the famous Rabot Forts, which included a defended lock. Brangwyn represents the Rabot lock and its bold defensive towers. These have two points of interest. They do justice to the character of mediæval Ghent, being bluff, stern, fanciful, ambitious, but short-sighted; and they seem to be copied from the Holsten Gate at Lübeck, built by this Hanseatic and republican city as a protection against frequent attacks from Denmark.

10. Covered Defensive Bridges of Timber. In these the protection has been of three sorts: against the weather, against riots, and against primitive weapons. Thus the covered bridges of Sumatra, made with bamboo and boards, are sunshades in bridge-building; and this applies to the roofed timber bridges in Western China. Some of these are carried over important rivers on stone piers, their roofing is decorative, and even to-day they would be useful in a time of unrest, especially to women and children. As for the Swiss variety of covered timber bridge, it seems to date from the period of lake-dwellings. But, whatever its lineage may have been, it is very ancient. Throughout the Middle Ages it was valued in war as well as in winter, when its footway was always free from snow. Often there was but a narrow space for light and air between the over-hanging roof and the balustrade of heavy planks. It is not surprising that Swiss timber bridges were to mediæval archers and crossbowman what Hougomont was to

Napoleon's troops.   On the other hand, it is surprising
that these primitive structures are still as popular among
the Swiss as they ever were.   The most remarkable
specimens are at Lucerne.   In Brangwyn's vivid pen-

TODENTANZBRUCKE AT LUCERNE IN SWITZERLAND

drawing we see the Todentanzbrucke, which is decorated
with thirty pictures of the Dance of the Dead, by
Meglinger.

As for the Kapellbrucke, also at Lucerne, it dates from
1303, and its length is 324 metres.   It crosses the mouth of
the river Reuss, that flows impetuously under it in a limpid

torrent. The timbers that support the roof are ornamented with 254 scenes from the history of Switzerland.

11. Pont Saint-Esprit, over the Rhône, below the confluence of the Ardèche. This bridge, like the Pont Valentré, is a masculine structure, so we must speak not

PONT SAINT-ESPRIT

of "it" but of "him." Always there is a point of sex to be considered in architectural inspiration. Some bridges are women, either high-born or low-born; others are common soldiers; a few are great men of action, like the Roman Alcántara in Cáceres; while many have no distinctive sex, and we need pronouns with which to describe

their character.   If we speak of a neutral bridge as "it" we
say nothing at all; but if we could refer to it as "itshe" or
"ithe," then we could show in one word which sexual
qualities predominate.   In old English bridges it is the
neutral type that holds the field, very often in the "itshe"
class.   We have nothing to place side by side with the
Pont Valentré and the Pont Saint-Esprit.   Even Old
London Bridge was a heroine, not a hero.   A certain weakness germinated in the past of England, and influenced
several phases of art and architecture.   It is from this
weakness, which seems to be racial, that modern England
has grown by the score feeble artists limp with sentiment,
and feebler faddists troubled with "nerves."   Whenever I
see one of our little old ballad bridges—an "itshe" or an
"ithe"—I say to myself, "Here is modern England in
embryo; here is the beginning of a weak sentiment which
in course of time will sap the vigour of our race."

So the Pont Saint-Esprit is to my mind something
more than a noble achievement in manly bridge-building;
he marks for me also a startling difference between the
undergrowth of the French character and the undergrowth
of the English genius.   We are beginning to realise in our
own sports and games, as in boxing and in football, a truth
which has long been known to students of French art,
namely, that although the surface of the French character
has boiled swiftly, like scum over jam, yet no other people
have had in equal measure the self-belief that triumphs over
frequent disaster, and the intrepid hope that gives ample

pinions to the imagination. Study the churches of France in their historical sequence from their Romanesque period to the last phases of Gothic; contrast their varied charm with the almost incessant wars that devastated the country; and then lift your hat to the greatness attained by the French genius in times, not of crisis only, but often of catastrophe. We have reason to be very proud of our own churches, but they do not equal the French when they are studied side by side from large photographs. The unhappier country was the more adventurous builder, notwithstanding the virile influence brought to England by French Cistercian monks and by such bridgemasters as Isembert. This fact is galling to our patriotism, but yet it helps us to appreciate those Englishmen of genius who have risen far above the many littlenesses which English public opinion has been overapt to approve both in art and in architecture.

Again, there are three geographical reasons why the Pont Saint-Esprit is very notable: he crosses the Rhône, one of the most treacherous rivers in Europe; he belongs to the Department of Gard, where historical bridges have been famed since the times of the Romans; and he is in the district of Uzès, where we find the Pont Saint-Nicolas, on the road to Nîmes, a lofty bridge of the thirteenth century, with a beautiful distinction, built by the Priory of Saint-Nicolas-Campagnac.

Now these two bridges, so different in technical inspiration, yet so alike in thorough scholarship, mark a very important time of transition in French architecture. The Pont Saint-Esprit was designed and built by the *Frères pontifes*, or Pontist Brothers, but already the good example set by these friars was followed with enthusiasm by a great many laymen, whose guilds were competing against the religious corporations. Sooner or later, inevitably, civil work of every sort would have to pass under the sway of laic schools and masters; but the people of France were superstitious in their fondness for the Pontist Brothers, whose ferry-boats had saved a great many lives, whose bridges were famous everywhere, whose hospitals lodged and fed pilgrims, and whose white dress was in harmony with their good work and their good conduct. So the public was very far from pleased when a bridge of importance was built without help from the Pontist Brothers. For this reason, and no other, the Pont Saint-Cloud was called *un pont maudit*, and its construction was attributed to the Devil. Still, the Pontist Brothers had to go. During the thirteenth century their public value as bridge-builders grew weaker and weaker, until at last their competition against the trade guilds could be regarded no longer as a political offence.* It says much for them that their last undertaking, the Pont Saint-Esprit, was in most respects

* The religious order of Pontist Brothers came to France from Italy. It was called the order of Saint-Jacques-du-Haut-Pas, and its chief resided at Lucca. From about the year 1286 the French brothers had a great hospice in Paris, built on the site now occupied by the church of Saint-Jacques-du-Haut-Pas and the deaf and dumb asylum. In the fourteenth century the order confined its attention to the care of pilgrims, and at last—in 1459—it was suppressed by Pope Pius II.

THE PONTE NOMENTANO, A MEDIÆVAL WAR-BRIDGE IN THE
CAMPAGNA, THREE MILES FROM ROME. IT SPANS THE
WILLOW-FRINGED ANIO, A SACRED RIVER IN ITALIAN LEGEND

their best achievement : a fact which time itself has recognised by keeping this bridge in use to the present day.

The Pont Saint-Esprit was commissioned by the Abbey of Cluny, and in 1265 the Pontist Brothers began to found the piers, after discussing their plans with Jean de Tessanges, Abbot of Cluny. Now, an earlier work of the Pontist Brothers, the Pont Saint-Bénézet at Avignon, was eighty years old in 1265, and his behaviour in the Rhône must have been a subject of interest to the successors of Bénézet. I conclude, then, that the Pont Saint-Esprit may be looked upon as a technical criticism of the earlier bridge, and it approves in all respects the work of St. Bénézet. Both bridges have relief arches for spate water, and when they are examined in bird's-eye views, both have an elbow opposed to the current of the Rhône, and each suggests the image of a bridge of boats to which already I have drawn attention (p. 262). This image is rather more pronounced in the case of the earlier bridge, for the length of Bénézet's piers, in the direction of the current, is enormous, being not less than thirty metres.

For the rest, the Pont Saint-Esprit seems to have an enchanted size, his most confident historians giving neither the same dimensions nor the same number of arches. Men with tape measures have grown tired of their job, seemingly; and even in photographs some arches are omitted while others are blurred by distance. On my table is an excellent photograph : it takes in just a bit of the metal arch which, about fifty years ago, displaced two of the old arches and made a passage for boats. From this point to the elbow upstream, there are eleven arches; beyond the elbow there are six more, and the bridge is not complete. This is all the camera can do. According to Viollet-le-Duc, there are twenty-two arches in a length of about 1000 metres; the roadway is five metres wide. Larousse tells me, on the other hand, that the length is 738 metres, the width 5 metres 40, the number of arches twenty-six; and another great work of reference, published also by Larousse, gives 919 metres for the length, and says that among the twenty-five arches there are nineteen ancient ones. We ought to admire the variegated self-confidence of historians.

But the main point is evident enough: the Pont Saint-Esprit is one of the longest stone bridges in the world. And the construction is truly marvellous. This was proved when a pier was pulled up to make room for the iron arch. The labour required was astounding, so excellent was the cemented masonry. But, of course, the bridge has passed through a good many changes to keep him in touch with the increase of traffic. In the seventeenth century he was still closed at both ends by strong gateways, while on the town side was a quite important defence of the fourteenth century, afterwards embodied in the citadel by which the river was guarded above-bridge. These defensive works have all gone, but their effect can be studied in "La Topographie de la Gaule," where an engraving gives a good idea of their appearance.

12. Ponte Nomentano in the Campagna, three miles

from Rome. This, no doubt, is the most romantic of all the fortified bridges that Brangwyn has painted. Both bridge and castle are mediæval, but they rise over the willow-frilled Anio, a river haunted by myths which to the ancients were sacred truths. It was in the Anio that Rhea Silvia passed from the brief hours of her mortality into the life of a goddess; and to this river Silvia confided her two children, Romulus and Remus, the twin Moses of Roman story, who were carried in their cradle to the Tiber, where other waters bore them on and on till at last they came to land under the fig tree at the foot of the Palatine hill. What a delightful legend to be whispered by the current of the prattling Anio below the uncouth stones of the Nomentano! What other war-bridge has been united to such a gracious myth?

And history as well as legend has been busy on the banks of the Anio. Into this river the ashes of Marius were thrown by the adherents of Sulla; and beyond the bridge, on the right bank, west of the Via Nomentana, is a very famous hillside, the Mons Sacer, to which the plebeians retreated, as to a fortified place, when they asserted their right to tame the patricians. Their first great strike, or secession, occupied four months in the year 549 B.C., when four thousand of them encamped on the friendly hill, leaving the crops unharvested, and the city without a garrison. Mount Sacer became sacred to the People of Rome, and to the historic sense it is the Hill of Liberty, sanctified by the first brave ideals of a democratic justice. Yet in recent times vulgarians have taken hold of Mount Sacer, and have carted it away by the ton to be used as building material.

As for the Ponte Nomentano, he is nothing more than a burly soldier, a common man-at-arms. The mediæval engineer was uninspired by an enchanted site, and gave the whole of his attention to the pronged battlements. He had no feeling for proportion, and no liking for a stern eloquence of line such as we find in the noble castle of Chenonceaux, a masterpiece of the French Renaissance, whose long wing is carried by a bridge of five round arches, and whose turreted portion is pierced by a single arcade.

13. The bridges of Laroque, near Cahors, on the river Lot. In this rapid sketch Brangwyn represents a riverside Gibraltar upon which an ancient village stands, partly on bridges. Its value in "the good old times" as a stronghold fortified by Nature is patent, and the watch-towers have an unsleeping alertness that looks out upon the world through one eye or window. I should like to know who built the first bridge at Laroque. There is a Romanesque form in the arch drawn by Brangwyn, and the Romans were active in the neighbourhood. Over the Lot at Divona, now called Cahors, they built a bridge, which perished some years ago in a local storm of party feeling. To imagine Rome with a Gibraltar on the Lot is a great pleasure.

Before we pass on from the defensive bridges, I should like to give you a picture of the famous old bridge at Saintes, in France, that lasted to the year 1843, when it

LAROQUE ON THE RIVER LOT, NEAR CAHORS, A SORT OF
INLAND GIBRALTAR; A PART OF THE VILLAGE IS BUILT
ON BRIDGES THROWN ACROSS CHASMS IN THE ROCKS

was destroyed. I know not why I use the silly word "it," for the bridge of Saintes was an exceedingly martial structure that united all the main phases of military art—the primitive, the Roman, and the mediæval. Let me give an abridged description from Viollet-le-Duc's "Dictionnaire raisonnée d'Architecture" :—

"The first gate appeared on the right shore of the Charente, on the side of the Faubourg des Dames; next came the Roman arch,* the upper part of which was crenellated during the Middle Ages; next on the side of the town stood a tower of oval plan, through which the road lay; the town gates with flanking towers closed the end of the bridge. From the first gate to the Roman arch the bridge was of wood, as was also the case between the great tower and the town gates, so that by the removal of this part of the roadway all communication could be cut off between the town and the tower, as well as between the bridge and the Faubourg; moreover, the parapets were crenellated, so that the garrison of the town at any moment could stop all navigation."

* The triumphal arch of Germanicus, dating from the time of Tiberius. It is extant at Saintes; but when it was reconstructed after its removal from the bridge it suffered much from a mixture of new stones with the old. It is an arch with two passages 38 ft. high.

V

A BRIEF introduction to the history of bridges has so many difficulties that I creep through my work, a few hundred words in a long day. To try to plant an oak tree in a thimble would be more difficult, I suppose, but gleaning here and there over vast fields brings trouble enough to any writer. I go through scores of photographs, and turn over great piles of notes, and seek for a topic that is not too technical for the general reader, but that touches a really important phase in the evolution of bridge-building. There is a species of bridge to which the arches at Laroque belong; it may be called either freakish or very exceptional. Let me give a few examples.

There is one at Crowland, a curious three-branched structure which for many a year stood at the confluence of the Catwater drain and two streamlets, the Welland and the Nyne. To-day no water flows under this bridge, and common little modern houses do not make pretty pictures when they are framed by the arches. There are three pointed arches, with their abutments at the angles of an equilateral triangle; they meet in the middle, and form three roadways and three watercourses. They have three stone ribs apiece, and the nine ribs meet in the centre.

I note, too, that these arches were built not by a bridgeman, but by a mason skilled in church work, for their rings are moulded elaborately as in Gothic windows and doorways. As for the style of architecture, it is not older than the beginning of the fourteenth century ; but a much earlier bridge at Crowland, probably of wood, was famed for its triangular shape, and mentioned in a charter of the year 943, when Edmund was King.

At the south-west entrance of Crowland Bridge, beyond the five steps, there is a rough-hewn statue that represents a crowned and bearded figure seated up high against the parapet walls, in an attitude of sorrow, with arms folded (and perhaps they may be bound together) over a long robe. Time has frayed and scarred this uncouth sculpture, but not without leaving some mellow lines and planes. The archæology of guesswork has called this effigy by various names, such as Ethelbald, and Saint Guthlac, and Henry II, but I prefer to look upon it as a simple Pietà chiselled by a mason who had been trained to do enniched figures for church decoration—work without detail, to make at a distance a broad effect. This conjecture is in accord with the ecclesiastical moulding of the archstones, and with the mediæval custom that united bridges to Christianity by means of sacred emblems. Crowland Abbey ruled over the district, so one of the Abbots may have built the bridge ; and perhaps the pointed arches, three in number, with their triple ribs, and their three pathways, and the three streams of water, may have been intended as symbols of the Trinity.

If so,—and there is nothing in this view to clash with the spirit of the Mediæval Church,—then a Pietà turned toward the west would be the most beautiful symbol of that Light which went down with the sun, and then rose again through the dark into the dusk, and through the dusk into a dawn where faith for ever dwells.   On the other hand, if the crowned figure represents a mere earthly king, I know not why Ethelbald should be chosen, for his reign of two years was not a creative time and he died in 860, just eighty-three years before Crowland's triangular bridge was alluded to in the charter of the year 943.   Alfred, Edward the Elder, and Athelstan—these kings in succession were nearer to the charter, and their longer reigns were more notable than the short hours of Ethelbald.   Alfred we should prefer, of course, but he has been passed over by the busy minds that have weaved around Crowland Bridge so many cobwebs of the study and so much haze of idle conjecture.   My own views are conjectures also, but they are taken partly from the bridge itself and partly from the care and affection that the Church during the Middle Ages bestowed on bridge-building.

And now a technical matter ought to be considered in its bearing on the arches of Crowland Bridge.   At a time when bridges were protected by the Church, their arches were affected by changes of style in ecclesiastical windows and doorways; but, of course, whatever shape was given to them, they were treated differently from doorways and windows, for these had to bear only a downward thrust, while bridges had to withstand five trials: their own "spring," the vibration caused by wheeled traffic, the lateral pressure of flowing water, the disturbance of gravity by immersion, and blows from drifting ice and timber. With these problems to be solved, bridgemen set no store by moulded archstones, a kickshaw of style. Sometimes they built the ring of an arch with two or three sets of voussoirs,* but their aim was practical, not ornamental; they wished to give greater resistance to their work, and not merely to spend time and money on a decorative effect. So when we find in the arches of Crowland Bridge such moulded handicraft as was used in church decoration, we may surmise that the architect and his masons were not bridge-builders, and that they worked only for the light foot-traffic of a village.

It is worth noting that in the year 1752 a French architect named Beffara took a hint from Crowland Bridge, and then achieved fame with a daring structure built near Ardres, in the Pas-de-Calais. There are four branches to

---

* There are many old arches with two or three sets of voussoirs. Over the Loire, at Brives-Charensac, there is a Roman specimen with two rings, now a ruined bridge. Some English examples: the Jolly Miller's Bridge over the Dee, Chester; Bradford-on-Avon, Wilts, the round arches; Bideford, Devon, twenty arches, built in the fourteenth century with help from indulgences sanctioned by Grandison, Bishop of Exeter; Lostwithiel, Llangollen, Fountains Abbey, Bishop's Bridge at Norwich, West Rasen, Lincolnshire; Eamont Bridge, Penrith, a triple ring of archstones; Higherford Bridge, near Colne, reputed to be Roman, a wrong attribution, I believe; St. Neots, the most important arch is very interesting; and the Abbot's Bridge at Bury St. Edmunds. This one is Early English, and its three remarkable arches give us a parallel to the ecclesiastical workmanship in the arches at Crowland. The piers also and the buttresses are unsecular.

x

this bridge, and they carry roads over two canals that intersect at right angles. One canal goes from Saint-Ouen to Calais and the other from Ardres to Gravelines. Beffara's work is placed by Larousse among the fifty-four most notable bridges in the world, and this honour it seems to merit; but Frenchmen in their vanity have tried to make it into a pretentious bridge by giving to it a braggart name—*Le Sans-Pareil*. Gracious! It is fit for a café or for a battleship, in whose nomenclature bravado and bombast rule as customs. Poor Beffara! "Le Sans-Pareil," like "Titanic" or like "Dreadnought," defies the powers of Nature, inviting them to do their worst; and what good omen can there be in such bantam cockiness?

For a long time the old bridge at Bâle, over the Rhine, remarkable for its length and for its beautiful site, was not only freakish but exceedingly insolent. At one end, on the side of greater Bâle, was a tower decorated with a grotesque head called Laellenkoenig, which, in answer to the working of a clock, put out its tongue and rolled insulting eyes at the opposite bank. Eight or ten times an hour this abusive pantomime was repeated, and it never failed to anger little Bâle, which had the pugnacious vanity of a small organism. I do not know how many duels were fought, but at last a touch of Rabelaisian humour suggested a mechanical revenge, far more regular in its action than were fights and punctured bodies. A tall post was set up by the inhabitants of Bâle junior, and on the top of it stood a hateful statue that affected to turn its back on the enemy with a shameless movement.

It is risky at the present time to say that a bridge has certain old characters : change is so rapid that no pontist can keep in touch with its vagaries ; but I believe the old bridge at Bâle is alive, and that it keeps in use the Gothic tower, a triangular defence of red sandstone erected on the middle pier, and devoted now to a thermometer, a barometer, and a table of weights and measures. Lællenkœnig has gone, of course, and Bâle junior has grown much bigger and less techy.

The Bridge of Sighs, at Venice, must be included among the exceptional bridges, being equally celebrated in history and in art. Who can say how many times she has been etched and painted and engraved ? She is not very important as a work of architecture, yet artists are drawn towards her invariably, and seldom do they fail to make her impressive. Brangwyn loves the Bridge of Sighs, and does her much more than justice in one of his finest etchings. There is something trivial in her Renaissance ornament, and her proportions are not great, being only two metres wide and six high ; on the other hand, her abutments are famous buildings, the ducal palace and the State prison. It is from the second storey of the palace that we enter the gloom of her covered passage, concerning which a Frenchman writes as follows : "*On pourrait presque le comparer, en agrandissant les proportions, à nos fourgons d'armée.*"

It is said that only a prisoner here and there went over

this bridge more than once—in his compulsory walk from a dungeon in the prison to the Council of the Ten. Those who awaited their trial in the dungeons were looked upon as already condemned; their appearance before the Ten was a formality, at least in public opinion; and for this reason the dark corridor across the canal was called the Bridge of Sighs.

Among the bridges of the fourteenth century there are two that history has set down as very exceptional. One of them is a covered bridge over the Ticino at Pavia, erected under the care of Gian Galeazzo Visconti. Professor Fleeming Jenkin says of it: "This bridge, which still exists, has seven pointed brick arches, each 70 ft. in span and 64 ft. in height; the depth of the arch ring at the crown is 5 ft. 6 in. The tympanum is pierced; the bricks used in the arches are formed to suit their position, and are hollow in the middle to diminish the weight. The roof of the roadway is carried by a hundred rough granite columns."

This neat description is accurate, but in it the bridge is not visualised. Would that we had a Brangwyn sketch! I have by my side an engraving of the bridge, and the effect of the design is that of an open-work frieze. Each gracefully pointed arch is a repetition of the other six; the piers also are uniform and graceful, being all 16 ft. 3 in. wide; and all the spandrils are pierced in the same triangular fashion. The point of each triangle is turned downwards, its sides are the inner surfaces of two arch rings, and its base, turned upwards, and gracefully arched with seventeen long bricks, helps to support the parapet. On this parapet at equal intervals rise the hundred granite columns by which the covered roadway is carried. So the design is a clever feat not merely of repetitive decoration, but of repeating solids and voids that oppose each other in a harmony of contrasts ; for the empty spandrils in their form oppose the leaf-shaped openings made by the arches, and all the curved solids of the bridge are foiled in a rugged manner by the upright columns, as well as by the long horizontal lines of the covered roadway. In the contrast between cold granite and warm brick there is colour also, and it suits the pulsating light and heat of Italy.

As for the second bridge of the fourteenth century, which architects regard as very uncommon, it exists in drawings only, for it was destroyed by Carmagnola. Its founder was a duke of Milan, Bernabò Visconti, and it crossed the Adda at Trezzo. According to Hann and Hosking, it had "a single arch of granite, very well constructed of stones in two courses, the innermost $3\frac{1}{4}$ ft. thick in the direction of the radius, the outermost 9 in., the span at low water 251 ft. ; the river rises sometimes 13 ft." The radius of the arch was 133 ft. A span of 251 ft. in a stone bridge was a noble achievement. It is the largest that I remember. The Grosvenor Bridge at Chester has a span of 200 ft., just thirty yards wider than the central arch of Trajan's Bridge over the Tagus. New London Bridge in her finest arch attains a span of 152 ft., beating Waterloo

Bridge by nearly eleven yards. Two French bridges of the eighteenth century—the Pont de Lavaur and the Pont de Gignac—have spans of 160 ft.; and let me refer you also to the Pont de Neuilly-sur-Seine (p. 338).

Many uncommon bridges have been attributed to the Chinese, and I know not what to say about some of them. Let me quote from Marco Polo, giving also the excellent notes written by his editor Colonel Yule. In the twenty-seventh chapter of his travels Marco Polo speaks " of the river named Pulisangan, and of the bridge over it." This river, whose name is written variously, is believed to be the Hoen-ho of the Jesuits' map, which, uniting with another stream from the north-west, forms the Pe-ho or White River. When Marco Polo comes to the Pulisangan* he finds "a very handsome bridge of stone, perhaps un-equalled by another in the world." " Its length is three hundred paces, and its width eight paces; so that ten men can ride abreast without inconvenience.† It has twenty-four arches, supported by twenty-five piers erected in the water, all of serpentine stone, and built with great skill.

* It may be remarked that in the Persian language the words *pul-y-sangi* signify the "stone bridge," and it is not improbable that the western people in the service of the Emperor may have given this appellation to the place where a bridge of great celebrity was thrown over the river, which is here applied to the river itself. It will be found to occur in Elphinstone's "Account of Caubul," p. 429, and in Ouseley's " Ibn Haukul," p. 277.—Colonel Yule.

† Ten horsemen could not draw up abreast in a space less than thirty feet, and might probably require forty when in motion. The paces here spoken of must there-fore be geometric; and upon this calculation the bridge would be five hundred yards in length.—Colonel Yule.

On each side, and from one extremity to the other, there is a handsome parapet, formed of marble slabs and pillars arranged in a masterly style. At the commencement of the ascent the bridge is something wider than at the summit, but from the part where the ascent terminates, the sides run in straight lines and parallel to each other.* Upon the upper level there is a massive and lofty column, resting upon a tortoise of marble, and having near its base a large figure of a lion, with a lion also on the top.† Towards the slope of the bridge there is another handsome column or pillar, with its lion, at the distance of a pace and a half from the former ; and all the spaces between one pillar and another, throughout the whole length of the bridge, are filled up with slabs of marble, curiously sculptured, and mortised into the next adjoining pillars, which are, in like manner, a pace and a half asunder, and equally surmounted with lions,‡ forming altogether a beautiful spectacle. These

* By P. Magalhanes, who particularly notices this description, our author is understood to speak here of the perfect level of the surface, and not of the straightness of the sides : " Aux deux extremités," he translates, " il est plus large qu'au haut de la montée : mais quand on a achevé de monter, on le trouve plat et de niveau comme s'il avoit esté tiré à la linge " (" Nouv. Relat.," p. 14). But the words, " uguale per longo come se fosse tirato per linea," seem rather to refer to the general parallelism of the sides, although at the ends they diverged, as is the case with almost all bridges.—Colonel Yule.

† The ideas of the symbolic lion and of the tortoise are borrowed by the Chinese from the *singa* and the *Kûrma* of Hindu mythology.

‡ It is difficult to understand from the words of the text . . . the position of these larger columns with regard to other parts of the bridge ; but it seems to be meant, that in the line of the parapet or balustrade, which was formed of alternate slabs of marble and pillars, there was in the middle (or over the centre arch or pier) a column of a size much larger than the rest, having a tortoise for its base or

parapets serve to prevent accidents, that might otherwise happen to passengers. What has been said applies to the descent as well as to the ascent of the bridge." *

I do not understand why this description is considered very difficult to understand. It depicts a gabled bridge with a flat top, not an uncommon form of bridge in China, I believe. The footway ascends to the beginning of the middle arch, where it becomes flat and level ; it continues so for the full width of the arch, and then it descends toward the abutment across the river. With this picture in mind it is easy to decorate the bridge over the Pulisangan, or Hoen-ho, with the accessories described by Marco Polo. The parapets have coping stones of sculptured marble, and pillars are carefully set along the parapets at an equal distance from each other. These pillars are of two sorts. Those above the flat part of the roadway, where the parapets also are horizontal, are tall and massive. On each side, at the brow of the ascent, there is a tall pillar upon the summit of which is a

pedestal; and it may be presumed, although not so expressed, that there was a similar column in the balustrade on the opposite side. . . . One of the Jesuit missionaries who mentions a bridge which he had crossed in this part of the province, says, "Les gardefous en sont de marbre; on conte de chaque côté cent quarante-huit poteaux avec des lionceaux au-dessus . . . et aux deux bouts du pont quatre éléphans accroupis."—Colonel Yule.

* Notwithstanding any partial difficulties in the description, or seeming objections to the credibility of the account given of this magnificent bridge, there is unquestionable authority for the existence of one similar to it in all the essential circumstances, and as nearly about the situation mentioned as can be ascertained from the conciseness of the itinerary, so lately as the seventeenth century. It may well, however, be supposed that in the lapse of four hundred years material changes must have taken place, in consequence of accidents, repairs, and perhaps removals. —Colonel Yule.

stone lion ; and in the middle of each parapet, on this level part of the road, there is a taller and heavier column, whose pedestal is a marble tortoise, and whose summit carries a symbolic lion. Another lion is placed near the tortoise, perhaps on a ledge of stone corbelled out from the parapet. As for the parapets that slope up from the abutments to the point where they become level, or horizontal, they, too, have their emblematic lions carried by pillars, and these ornaments, in accordance with the logic of design, are much smaller than those on the summit of the steep bridge. For the rest, Marco Polo speaks of twenty-four arches and of twenty-five piers ; and if we give to the arches an average span of fifty-two feet, and to the piers an average width of thirteen feet, we get a bridge 1573 ft. long, or seventy-three feet longer than the five hundred yards suggested by Colonel Yule. Viewed in this way, apart from the vague glamour of enthusiastic words, there is nothing extravagant in Marco Polo's description.

Many writers have been astonished by another Chinese bridge, called the Bridge of Cho-gan, in the province of Shen-si. Its great arch is said to have had an unrivalled span. I am told that it was built with huge blocks of stone, cut into voussoirs, the joints of which converged towards a common centre, as in our own bridges. This may be true, though in photographs of Chinese bridges which I have seen the voussoirs do not resemble ours ; not only are they much longer, they are much narrower also, and recall to my memory a good description written by Barrow, whose impressions of China are invaluable to students. Barrow speaks of archstones from five to ten feet long, and says that each stone "is cut so as to form a segment of the arch." "There is no keystone" when an arch is built in this manner. Again, "ribs of wood fitted to the convexity of the arch are bolted through the stones by iron bars, fixed in the solid part of the bridge"; sometimes no wood is employed, and then "the curved stones are mortised into long transverse blocks of stone." It would be ridiculous to speak of this technical method as one that employs voussoirs, since the arch ring is built with a few segmental stones and without a keystone; and possibly the Bridge of Cho-gan was constructed in this fashion. A drawing of it is given in Kircher's "La Chine Illustrée"—or, rather, in Dalquié's translation of Kircher's book, published in 1670 at Amsterdam. It is not a geometrical drawing, and the dimensions are given in Chinese measures, which do not help us to love Kircher and Dalquié. M. Degrand is baffled by these measures;* but he admits that the Bridge of Cho-gan must have been a grandiose structure dating from a very remote time.

Gauthey speaks with admiration of the "Pont de Fo-Cheu sur le Min"—a bridge not less than 7935 metres long by 19 metres 50 wide, with a hundred arches, all semi-circular, and thirty-nine metres in their average span. The piers were nearly as broad, and their height was thirty-nine metres. Here is a bridge that Dean Swift ought to have

* Ponts en Maçonnerie."

put into his pictures of Brobdingnag. Gauthey seems to have faith in it, while M. Degrand has doubts. He says: " Even if we admit that there is no flagrant exaggeration in the documents from which the account of this bridge is taken, the workmanship in its general character, as shown in the drawing given by Gauthey, has a near resemblance to that in Roman bridges, and ought not to be assigned to a period earlier than theirs." Gauthey describes the decorative treatment. Under the parapet of white marble ran a line of consoles; the piers were surmounted by figures of lions in black marble, cut from blocks seven metres long; and above each twentieth arch the footway was guarded by a gateway, *un arc de triomphe.*

For the rest, as I wanted to learn something more about this bridge of a hundred vast arches over the Min at Fo-Cheu, I wrote to the Rev. O. M. Jackson, whose kind help I have already acknowledged (p. 248). There is a river Min in Sichuan, but no news of such a bridge has reached Mr. Jackson, though he has worked in Western China for more than twenty years, and has travelled on foot over a very wide area in the province of Sichuan. Again, Mr. Jackson does not recognise the spelling " Fo-Cheu," but refers me to the city of Fu Chow in the coast province of Fukien. One day, perhaps, research will bring me in touch with the colossal masterpiece described by Gauthey, though at present I am baffled by the variety of geographical names that travellers have given to the bridges of China. Still, the Chinese have been great bridge-builders, and some of their stone arches have been very high and very wide. Perhaps the one described by Kircher may have been as wide as Trezzo Bridge, over the Adda, with its wonderful span of 251 feet.

My favourite bridge in the class of exceptional merit is the Ponte della Trinità over the Arno at Florence, designed in 1566 by the architect of the Pitti Palace, Bartolomeo Ammanati, a devoted admirer of Michelangelo. Both in science and in art the Ponte della Trinità is complete as an original success. Its vaulting—I ought to say *his* vaulting, for in this bridge the male qualities of genius are much stronger than the female—his vaulting, then, if not the most scientific in the world, is not excelled by any other work either ancient or modern. There are three arches, and their curves are cycloids ; the rise from the springing level is only a trifle more than one-sixth of the span. How Ammanati managed to get his effect of perfect balance and symmetry is a question very hard to answer, for there is a considerable difference between the width of his arches, the central one being 96 ft. in span, and the others 86 ft. and 88 ft. This fact has been established by measured drawings, but do you notice it out of doors, in the magic of this beautiful bridge ? The piers are simple and excellent. Their width, twenty-six feet, is not too much for the spates of a freakish river, nor too heavy for the bridge as a linear composition ; on the upstream side they have stern cutwaters, good foils in a piece of architecture that blends an alert grace with a supple vigour. Another point worth noting is the gradient of a roadway that starts out from low abutments. Ammanati was bent upon being a friend to the traffic of Florence, and with the help of his cycloid arches he kept the road on a mild curve. To-day this good point attracts little attention, as most of us forget that steep bridges were in vogue till late in the eighteenth century.

A Victorian pontist, William Hosking, endeavoured to prove that Ammanati made one mistake in the Ponte della Trinità. It seemed to Hosking that the piers were too bulky, so he cut them down in a sketch and spoilt the whole bridge by altering the proportions. Architects told him so, but Hosking crowed over his little sketch and published it with pride, as you will find by turning to his "Architectural Treatise on Bridge Building"—a valuable work from other standpoints.

THE great work of Ammanati sets thought in movement on bridge decoration, and I wish to offer some hints on this subject, not for the purpose of finding rules, but in order that a public debate may be invited. Rules would be very useful if they could be formulated, but in bridge decoration national sentiment and personal feeling have been exceedingly active ; no writer, then, can do more than offer suggestions from his own point of view.

Less than twenty years ago a debate on this subject would not have been easy, for good books on the technical history of bridges were uncommon, and photographs of fine examples were far more difficult to get than they are now. English books on bridges are still formidably dull ; to read them is perhaps as troublesome as hill climbing on a foggy day ; but the fear of being " ploughed " in a stiff examination helps young men to be intrepid. In France, on the other hand, the public is served very well by literary pontists. M. Charles Béranger, for instance, from his Librairie Polytechnique in Paris, is publishing a series of thorough books on bridges, as useful to us as they are to French students. Already eight volumes have been issued. They include :—

1. "Ponts en Maçonnerie." Par E. Degrand, Inspecteur-Général des Ponts et Chaussées, et Jean Résal, Ingénieur des Ponts et Chaussées. Two volumes, illustrated ; 40 francs.

2. "Ponts Métalliques." Par M. Pascal, Ingénieur. One volume ; 15 francs ; illustrated.

3. "Croquis de Ponts Métalliques." Par Jules Gaudard, Ingénieur Civil et Professeur Honoraire de l'Université de Lausanne. Profusely illustrated ; 20 francs.

4. "Cours de Ponts Métalliques." Par Jean Résal. Vol. I, 375 illustrations ; 20 francs.

5. "Manuel Théorique et Pratique du Constructeur en Ciment Armé." Par MM. N. de Tédesco et V. Forestier. One volume, 242 illustrations ; 20 francs.

6. "Études sur les Ponts en Pierre remarquables par leur Décoration." Par F. De Dartein, Inspecteur-Général des Ponts et Chaussées en Retraite, etc. Vol. I, "Ponts Français antérieurs au Dix-Huitième Siècle"; not yet published. Vol. II, Ponts Français du Dix-Huitième Siècle—Centre"; published. Vol. III, "Ponts Français du Dix-Huitième Siècle—Languedoc"; published. Vol. IV, Bourgogne; published. Vol. V, "Ponts Étrangers antérieurs au XIX siècle—Italiens, Espagnols et Anglais"; not yet published. Price, 25 francs the volume.

For this work M. De Dartein has made exact measured drawings from sixty-eight bridges, and each example has a great historic interest. The author has taken a line of his own, dwelling on the ornament of bridges, their decoration; several of his volumes are long overdue, but in his earnest study of the eighteenth century we see what he admires in French design. M. De Dartein is thoughtful and thorough, but I wish some photographs had been added to the illustrations, because measured drawings give only the dry bones of architecture.

How to decorate a bridge is a question beset with so many problems, some practical, and others æsthetic, that it ought to be debated at an international congress of engineers and architects and artists. There are persons who think that M. De Dartein will say the last word on his important theme; but it is enough for me to believe that his material and his personal taste will be invaluable, presenting facts and provoking discussion. He lingers too often over details of trivial ornament, which increase the cost of production without doing any good at all to the architecture. In other words, M. De Dartein speaks too often as an engineer.

The qualities of a great bridge should make their appeal in stern lines, in ample proportions, in a scale that befits not the site alone but the site and its history; for all fine architecture dwells with the fugitive generations as a lasting citizen; it is an epitome of racial character alembicated by genius. Bridges cannot be fine when they are dwarfed by their environments, or when they are too big to be in harmony with the externals of their setting. This, no doubt, is a staring truism, yet it is unseen by most modern engineers, whose metal monsters are often as wrongly

THE PONT NEUF AT PARIS, BUILT IN 1604; IT HAS
BEEN MUCH ALTERED SINCE THE RENAISSANCE

placed in a gentle landscape as a giant from Brobdingnag would be at Lilliput.   On the other hand, can you explain why the Roman bridge at Alcántara is tremendous art ?   Is it not because he is in scale with the rocky gorge of the Tagus ?   This virile bridge completes a grand site, and finds in the site his own completion.

Still, it cannot be said that Roman bridges were always free from redundant ornament.   There were times when pomp exerted a bad influence ; and later ages borrowed oddments of Roman decoration that weakened in many countries the aspect of bridges.   It is from such Roman work as the Pont du Gard, where no detail was called for, and where the architect's aim was to be unpretentious, that we learn never to worry a bridge with embellishments.   To construct ornament is very often an easy accomplishment of bad taste, while to ornament construction is a very difficult problem of self-restraint in art, because judgment tells us that a great design carried out in simple and thorough masonry is in itself ornamental, if not complete.   Applied decoration is almost certain to harm it, just as a human face is disfigured by sticking-plaster.

For example, turn to Frank Brangwyn's drawing of the Pont Neuf at Paris, and note under the parapet the well-spaced brackets.   Each bracket is decorated with a mask. Why ? Simpler and shorter brackets would have been more in keeping with the architecture, as these long ones overlap the keystones—a serious blunder.   Partly to hide a ring of voussoirs is to blur the whole structural beauty of

Y

an arch.   It is like covering the eyes with blue spectacles.
And there are other mistakes of scale in the Pont Neuf.   No
fewer than six piers are crowded into the Seine, as if inundations were amusements to be liked very much.   But the
spirit of Renaissance art was overapt to be finikin.   In a
fine bridge at Chatsworth, for instance, a charming effect
is troubled by a too expensive parapet ; and statues are
lodged on pedestals above the cutwaters.   Why ?   Is the
cutwater of a bridge a convenient spot for the display of
sculpture ?   As many persons fear in talk a sudden silence
made by thought, so many architects in their revisions fear
the plain spaces left in their designs by a creative inspiration.   Then in a hurry they add some "ornament" such as
we find at Chatsworth, or in Gauthey's Pont de Navilly on
the Doubs.   In this bridge narrow spandrils are choked
with an overturned vase surrounded by an ornament of
bulrushes, and over each cutwater there is a huge stone
shaped like an egg and garlanded.   I decline to speak in
technical terms because the folly of using superfluous
"ornament" is hidden by words that look erudite.   Was
it an admiration for Moses that caused Gauthey to put
bulrushes on a bridge?   And did he suppose that they
suggested water and adventure?   As for those huge eggs of
stone, if they came from some bird five or six times as big
as an ostrich, I should like to see them in a museum of
natural history, but without their ornamental wreaths.

In brief, are you attracted by any phase of modern
bridge-building that copies the decorations of civic archi-

tecture, displaying columns, pilasters, niches, balustrades, battlements, towers, turrets, pinnacles, or any other finery that serves no organic purpose in the life of a contemporary bridge? Myself, I hate such a strumpet of a bridge as the Hoogesluis at Amsterdam, with her ornate spandrils, and her embossed masonry, and her balustraded parapet surmounted by a row of obelisks around which lamps are bracketed. Also I hate such a suspension bridge as the one at Conway Castle, where the metal rods that support the roadway pass through a brace of turrets on each of the embattled gateways. The effect is not only comic but ludicrous. No engineer with any sense would have put a metal viaduct within a few yards of Conway Castle. Or, if a metal suspension had been forced upon him by his employers, he would have made in a modern style a very simple and stern design. Instead, we have two vulgar gateways rudely copied from Conway Castle, and then lacerated by five metal rods that cut through each of the four turrets. I am reminded of an absurd railway bridge at Cologne, whose parapets are—or were—flanked by small turrets, and whose gateway has—or had—two high towers formidably armed with make-believe battlements and machicolations. Such futile pretension is a public insult; it implies that laymen have no common sense at all in their attitude to " feats of engineering."

But it is not the modern bridge alone that provokes criticism in this matter of decorative art. Some ancient and famous bridges are hard nuts to crack as soon as we pass from their structural fitness to their ornamentation. As an example I may choose the Ponte Sant' Angelo at Rome, which has been copied feebly by the Schloss Brücke at Berlin. Originally the Sant' Angelo was the Pons Ælius, built by Hadrian (A.D. 13) face to face with his mausoleum, to-day the castle of Saint Angelo. In the seventeenth century new parapets were added to the bridge, and ten colossal statues by Bernini were put up on pedestals along the parapets. Around these statues many a controversy has raged, and I am not surprised. In my photographs there is a small lamp-standard between each pair of huge figures; even the lights of Rome have to twinkle below the decorations. The bridge looks burdened rather than adorned: it is neither wide enough nor high enough to be used as a gallery for sculpture modelled on a large scale. That a great effort was made by an artist of power is evident, but the artist worked for his own ambition, and not for the Ponte Sant' Angelo. He had no conception of the fact that the bridge and its environment were so good that they could not be improved by huge "embellishments." Yet there are writers who say, "Yes, no doubt, Bernini's bouncing figures are theatrical, but, after all, their general effect is grandiose." The truth is, every great city needs a Parliament of Taste where questions of civic art could be debated publicly, with help from lantern slides. No writer can hope to do much in his defence of art. Indeed, books are studied so infrequently that they cannot draw public attention to the larger problems of architecture and decoration ; whereas free debates in a Parliament of Taste, centring always around object-lessons, might restore to art the life of a great citizen.

In this matter we owe much to Hosking, the Victorian pontist, who cried out against the blunders made in the ornamentation of bridges. As early as 1842 he told the truth boldly, declaring that the most eminent civil engineers, in their efforts to take hints from street buildings, had failed to produce anything but meanness or absurdity, or a combination of both. Hosking had faith in three simple principles :—

1. That bridges, in the combination of their leading lines, should be bold and simple ;

2. That their passage over dangerous places ought to be a secure highway ; and,

3. That in stone bridges far too much money had been wasted on the high finish of exterior surfaces. In very ponderous language Hosking said :—

"It may be fairly questioned whether Waterloo and London bridges would not have been finer objects had the masonry of their external faces been merely rough-axed, or even left scabbled, instead of being fair hammer-dressed ; and certainly many thousands of pounds might have been saved in the execution of Waterloo Bridge, and a much better result produced, by the omission of the coupled columns and their immediate accessories, and by the use of a plain parapet of a more reasonable height, instead of the high, the enormously expensive, and absurdly ugly balustraded enclosures which now aid the columns and their projected entablatures to deform a splendid structure."

This Puritan outlook appeals to me, for I believe that good bridges should be as sternly efficient as were the Ironsides of Cromwell's army. Their beauty is a thing apart from any cavalier-like finery of dressing ornament. It shows that all the parts of a bridge are co-ordinated with fine judgment, and that each part is in nice accord with its own work and with the great office which the bridge as a whole has to fulfil daily.

When the railway viaduct at Ludgate Hill was finished, there was a public outcry because of its gaunt and shabby ugliness; but Londoners were appeased as soon as some "decorative" metalwork was nailed upon the parapets. This "ornament," a trumpery makeshift, was supposed to have given merit to an imbecile design that disgraced the main road to St. Paul's Cathedral. As things of this sort are allowed to happen in the heart of our great city, who can have confidence in civic authorities? What chance is there that new projects for bridges will be considered intelligently?

In 1815, when Rennie began his bridge over the Thames at Southwark, neither the Government nor the City of London employed him; it was a Company that approved his designs, and financed the undertaking. At an expense of £800,000, three bad arches of cast-iron were put up from "elegant" stone piers and abutments; yet London was charmed by "a great feat of engineering," partly because 5780 tons of ironwork had been employed, and partly because the central arch had a span of 240 ft. From 1819 to November 8, 1864, the Company was a toll gatherer on their industrial bridge; then the toll was done away with, and the Company received from the City an industrial compensation. Here is a financial adventure which might have been undertaken to benefit a small township which had in its neighbourhood some new iron-works and collieries. Still more farcical was the public lottery that helped to collect money for the building of the first Westminster Bridge, between 1738 and 1750. Even now, after many lessons from past follies, London has made more than one muddle over the project of St. Paul's Bridge. Not even the Tower Bridge, with all its blatant defects, has enabled the City to be alert and clever as a pontist.

A more absurd structure than the Tower Bridge was never thrown across a strategic river. What would be the use of those ornate towers if the suspended roadway connecting them to the banksides were cut by a shell or by a falling bomb? And what anachronism could be sillier than that which has united the principle of metal suspension to an architecture cribbed partly from the Middle Ages, and partly from the French Renaissance? The many small windows, the peaked roofing, the absurdly impudent little turrets, the biscuit-like aspect of the meretricious masonry, the desperate effort to be "artistic" at any cost: all this, you know, is at standing odds with the contemporary parts of the unhistoric bridge, parts huge in scale, but so commercial that there is not a vestige of military forethought anywhere. It is mere perishable bulk.

THE TOWER BRIDGE, LONDON

CANAL BRIDGE IN VENICE

CHAPTER THE FIFTH
ON THE EVOLUTION OF UNFORTIFIED BRIDGES

I

BRANGWYN'S water-colour of the Pont Henri IV at Châtellerault, over the Vienne, represents a bridge built and fortified by an architect of the Renaissance, Charles Androuet du Cerceau. Here is a fact to be remembered, for Androuet du Cerceau was perhaps the latest European bridge-builder who tried to fit his work into a nation's policy of defence. From his time onward to our own no high road conducted over a river has been made in any respect a military way, safeguarded from the dangers of war, at least as much as possible.

If Androuet du Cerceau had been asked to foretell the development of bridge-building, his answer could not have been less militant than the Pont Henri IV; he would have said that bridges, like battleships and fortified places, would continue to oppose the science of military attack, because their safety would be affected by all improvements in the methods and materials employed by armies. His view of life and art, as we see it in his work, has been the view of all thoughtful craftsmen. He believed that the genius of invention, age after age, set up her home in the ablest minds, and passed through an ordered growth, till at last she attained her culmination. As long as improvements could be made in the action of aggressive war, counter improve-

ments could be made in the reaction of defence, for the art
of inventing each new weapon would suggest a means by
which its utility in war might be thwarted, and perhaps
nullified.

But I do not think that Androuet du Cerceau realised to
the full what competent bridges ought to have been to his
generation.   He was too mediæval in his attitude to strife,
and this defect was perhaps inevitable.   You see, the Pont
Henri IV was erected between the years 1564 and 1609 ;
and during these forty-five years the spirit of the times was
dead against an efficient strategy both in defence and in
attack.   Soldiers of every rank were passing through a
transition, unaided by much enthusiasm.   Indeed, new
methods were hated rather than liked, because they seemed
to be less chivalric, or what the French called less " heroic,"
than were the ancient methods, though many of these had
grown obsolescent.   Alexandre Dumas wrote several delightful books on this period in the evolution of fighting,
when gunpowder was a war-god that no brave man was at
all eager to worship before an altar of unwieldy firearms.
Soldiers liked a battle to be a duel at very close quarters, so
they were not amused when they fired through a fog of
suffocating smoke, and coughed and sneezed in a chorus,
while tears dripped from their eyes.   Here and there, of
course, while Androuet du Cerceau was engaged upon his
bastille bridge, " villainous saltpetre" had some ardent
followers.   Turn to the military writers of Queen Elizabeth's
reign, for instance, and read the long dispute that went on

PONT HENRI IV OVER THE VIENNE AT CHÂTELLERAULT IN FRANCE
BUILT BY CHARLES ANDROUET DU CERCEAU, 1564-1609.   TILL 1824
THE TWO GREAT TOWERS WERE UNITED BY A PAVILION FORM-
ING A GATEWAY.   ONE OF THE LATEST OF THE BASTILLE BRIDGES

between the old school and the new. Some experts had a firm belief in the old archery statutes, while others put their trust in ponderous firearms that went off after much coaxing and never carried straight for a hundred yards.

In those days there were two handguns, both rather old, and their improvement baffled the ingenuity of gunsmiths. One was the petronel or arquebuse, which had come into vogue in 1480; the other was the musket, which in 1521, or thereabouts, was brought into use by the Emperor Charles V, who believed in it because he had never tried to hold the "kicking demon" through a battle. For a long time petronels were discharged by a lighted match, but at the beginning of the sixteenth century a wheel-lock was invented, to be superseded at last—about the year 1692—by the flint-lock. Progress was exceedingly halt-footed; but one day a pious clergyman, the Rev. Mr. Forsythe, happened to be startled by a very profane idea; it seemed to him that gunpowder in a musket might be ignited by a percussion cap. Good Forsythe! Being very practical as well as pious (these two qualities go together like body and soul, as a rule), he patented his mother-idea, A.D. 1807; and in less than thirty years the principle of the percussion cap was accepted by the War Office, though public opinion in England cooed over Peace, believing that henceforth mankind would be satisfied with continual wars between Capital and Labour. There is no need to sketch the equally slow improvements in the manufacture of cannon. Enough to say that among

Wellington's siege artillery in Spain there were Spanish guns dating from the Armada period.

Briefly, then, from Androuet du Cerceau's time onward to the year 1857, when the old musket *Brown Bess* was put aside for ever, the dilatory progress of attack in war gave bridge-builders every opportunity of keeping pace with it and of making their defence as thorough as possible. Yet nothing was done. Not even a single effort was made to evolve the old war-bridge into a modernised protection; and it is very far from easy to explain this quite sudden departure from a very old routine of defensive forethought. Several reasons have been given, of course, but they have no backbone and no brain. It was argued, for example, that bridges were as advantageous to an attack as to a defence, so the whole strategy of war would protect them quite enough. Even in our own time this very queer argument has been advocated, as if to prove that minds as well as eyes often suffer from astigmatism. What successful army is not hindered and harassed by guarding many hundreds of defenceless bridges? And what modern army in retreat has ever failed to leave behind t an extra rearguard of broken bridges?

Let me give but one example. Sir John Moore could never have made his terrible march from Sahagun to Coruña, but for his good fortune in the matter of rivers and bridges. When Napoleon himself got within striking reach, near Benavente, on the torrent Esla, Moore's rearguard blew up three spans of the old bridge of Castro

Gonzalo; and when the cavalry of the Imperial Guard found a deep crossing and forded the river into a wide poplared plain, Paget and the 10th Hussars galloped through their broken ranks, destroying half of them, and capturing their general Lefebvre Desnouettes. Much later, when the narrow and snowbound Pass of Piedrafita was littered with dead British troops, all killed by hunger and cold and exhaustion, Moore was befriended by the great Roman bridge of Constantino, and by the noble viaduct of Corcul between Nogales and Becerrea. Paget was left behind with the rearguard, and in brilliant actions at the bridges he checked the pursuit, while Moore marched on toward Lugo. If a French spy had blown up the bridge of Constantino and the viaduct, after hearing of Moore's approach, the British would have been brought to a standstill, and from a desperate position there would have been little chance of escape. So the viaduct and the Roman bridge stood between victory and defeat; they saved the British and baffled the French. In fact, Moore reached Lugo without much further harrying.

Not only is there a bridge of Constantino in all campaigns, but we may be sure that as no country will ever wish to be invaded the airmen scouts of the future will try to destroy all bridges beyond their own frontiers, so as to cripple the enemy's prearranged movements. Defeat in the near future may be nothing more than a paralysis of communications, caused by bridge-wrecking airships and aeroplanes. Try to imagine what we should suffer, if we lost in a single night eight or ten of the bridges that help to unite London to Edinburgh and Glasgow. To lose the Forth Bridge alone would be a bad defeat; and yet, as I have said, there are people still who argue that bridges need no protection because their utility in war is invaluable to both sides.*

This hollow argument was very active during the ferment of the Renaissance, which became to architecture what a political party spirit is to an army. In fact, it was the Renaissance that produced the disintegrating party strife of rival "styles," and soon the followers of classic forms and ceremonies were more powerful than their opponents, who believed in the native genius of Gothic art. The aim of our classic men was to renew under our Northern sky an alien inspiration born and bred in the ardent climates of Greece and of Rome. In other words, they wished to repeat, by plodding and self-conscious effort, what Rome had done in architecture with the patient and slow methods of her colonisation. In this way they appealed to everybody who tried to seem erudite, and their endeavours entered that world of educated fashion where a false quantity was a greater sin than intemperance. Just as the chatty, delightful Montaigne wanted to hide his genius among profuse

---

* It is worth noting, as an example of British apathy in home defence, that the railway from Aldershot toward Southampton is for many miles a single line only, and that it passes over a good many gimcrack bridges and between some narrow and steep embankments, as in the neighbourhood of Medstead. The line is an open trap; it could be shut up in a dozen places by a few intelligent spies, if spying did not generate an excessive caution as futile as cowardice.

gleanings from ancient writers, so most architects believed that they could do no good in life unless they tried to be Greek or Roman. Progress was no longer an organic growth, it was a copied fashion, an inconvenient mode. Not even a church could be built without help from pagan temples. Not an equestrian statue could be modelled unless a Christian of sorts, either king or warrior, put on the costume of a Cæsar, and then straddled ill at ease across the back of a reasonable horse, which alone merited the long life of bronze. Amid this ferment of comic priggishness and pedantry young men served their apprenticeship, and became artists and craftsmen. Inevitably, bridgebuilders were affected, and as prigs most of them did their work as public servants.

One remarkable thing was the fussy interest that their projects excited. During the eighteenth century, for instance, a ridiculous ado was made about bridge-building. Voluntary guidance came from mathematicians, and chatter and hesitation implied that at last, for the first time in the history of the world, a reputable bridge would be erected. As for the results of all this flutter and fuss, they were usually out of joint with the public interests that bridges ought to have served efficiently. No attention was paid to military defence, and some famous men blundered like amateurs. Perronet was regarded as the most expert bridgebuilder of his time; his knowledge was prodigious, and yet he made astounding mistakes, which would have shamed such mediæval masters as Bénézet and Isembert. As an

z

example I will mention his Pont de Neuilly-sur-Seine, which was finished in 1772.* The delicate operation of striking the centres, by freeing the arches from their supports, was begun only eighteen days after the keystones were put in their places, when the mortar was not yet hard enough to resist new pressure. In one great arch the crown sank twenty-three inches—truly a historic mishap, and for several reasons. The upper part of this arch in Perronet's plan was an arc of a circle 320 ft. in diameter; after the mishap it became an arc of a circle whose diameter would be 518 ft., hence a stone arch of this size—518 ft. on the chord line—might be constructed! No wonder that writers have been astounded by the Pont de Neuilly-sur-Seine, for it passed safely through a most dangerous experience. Perronet was saved, not by his good design, nor by his mathematical calculations, but by a rare stroke of good luck. Indeed, there are a good many technical faults in his work at Neuilly. The piers are only fourteen feet broad, too small to be in scale with the wide arches, and all lateral pressure travels along the bridge to the abutments. If one arch were cut the others would be endangered. In later years Perronet became wise, and told the French Government that two or three arches in every long bridge should have abutment piers, as a safeguard against mishaps in war.†

* This bridge is 250 metres long, and the five arches have equal spans of 40 metres. Perronet died in 1791, at the age of eighty-three, and we study his best work at Mantes, Orléans, Nogent-sur-Seine, Pont-Saint-Maxence, Château-Thierry, and Neuilly-sur-Seine.

† His words run as follows: "I think that it may be prudent, when designing bridges for rivers of great width, to introduce some strong piers, which in case of need

Several famous engineers had to learn by experience, like Perronet, that a self-conscious desire to be "scientific" had dangers of its own in bridge-building. Smeaton's bridge over the Tyne at Hexham was a tragic failure; Labelye produced a very perishable bridge on the Thames at Westminster; and learned engineering did not save the Tay Bridge from catastrophe, though science welcomed it with a din of confident approval.

The Tay Bridge was a railway track to connect the town of Dundee and the North British Railway System in Fife; it crossed the Firth of Tay about a mile and a half to the West of Dundee. Its length exceeded two miles, and journalists with rapture bragged about it as the longest iron bridge in the world. Even the responsible engineers, Thomas Bouch and A. D. Stewart, did not keep their heads while their work was being done, for they published in the "Encyclopædia Britannica" a long article on their unfinished bridge—a fine example of modern vanity. Soon afterwards, on February 4th, 1877, the building work was badly injured by a gale, yet in a few months—on September 25th, in fact—the over-confident engineers had the bridge

---

may serve as abutments, putting them at distances of three or four arches apart. Moreover, this arrangement will enable us to construct long bridges in different parts successively, and each part may be considered as a complete bridge, having its own independent abutments; but strict care should be taken not to contract the beds of rivers by using too many thick piers." One of Perronet's immediate predecessors, the engineer Gabriel, built a bridge of this sort, over the Loire at Blois. He spaced his plan into eleven fine arches, and erected two abutment piers, placing them at four bays from each bankside, and leaving three bays between them. By this means his bridge was divided into three independent parts.

tested from end to end, and on the 31st of May, 1878, it was opened to train service.

Thomas Bouch became Sir Thomas.   No one suspected that a "scientific bridge" might be a trap for railway carriages. The structure was superlatively modern: huge, ugly, vulgar, meretricious, mechanical, and charmed also with a small cost of production, which included twenty human lives and £350,000.   At this price, you will understand, the longest metal bridge in the world seemed very cheap and fascinating.   Newspapers were overjoyed, of course, and declared that the Tay Bridge was admirably fitted for the rushing enterprise of a commercial time.   Yet every part of it was ill with the cancer of cheapness, and in 1879 the disaster came, on a Sunday evening, three days after Christmas.   At about seven o'clock a terrific gale struck the eighty-four spans of the bridge, making a gap of about three thousand feet: and a few minutes later a North British mail-train drew near.   Into the gap carriage after carriage dived: about eighty passengers perished, down below in the raging waters.   It was a lofty bridge, in some places 92 ft. above high tide, so the falling carriages turned more than one somersault before they plunged into the Firth of Tay.

The Board of Trade held an enquiry and issued a report, affirming "that the bridge had been badly designed, badly constructed, and badly maintained."   True: but the verdict was without pity.   Some excuse should have been made for the engineers' modernity.   The Tay Bridge was no worse than the popular spirit that liked screaming newspapers, and fevered excitements, and wild adventures in the quicksands of jerried workmanship. The Board of Trade published its report on the 3rd of July, 1880 ; and a few months later, on October 30th, Sir Thomas Bouch died of a broken heart. Perhaps the most humbling trial in his adversity was the foolish article written by his second in command, Mr. A. D. Stewart, who wanted to be quite contemporary with the flying minutes. The " Encyclopædia Britannica" deleted the article from its next edition, and printed . . . some tame remarks on the disaster. . . .

No public calamity has much effect on the modern mind. Tay Bridges and Titanics are like strong acts in a tragic play, whose influence we forget very soon. It is a thousand pities, for the next war may teach us, by frequent disasters, that machine-worship has been a mad gambler everywhere. Bridges suffered much from the priggishness of the Renaissance, but they have suffered infinitely more from the obsessions that ruined Sir Thomas Bouch. Poor Bouch! Not only did he wish to astonish the world by constructing an unparalleled bridge, wonderfully long, curved at both ends, and with a varying gradient. He desired also to prove to his employers that he could be a pattern of unusual economy. Worse still, he was so wrapped up in his calculations that he looked upon Nature with little respect. In other words, he tried to achieve " a great feat of engineering "—not often a fortunate enterprise.

From the founding of his piers he ought to have learnt

that his work would be endangered partly by the repercussion
of railway traffic, and partly by the varied way in which the
piers would feel the scour of tidal waters during bad weather.
Fourteen piers on the southern side were built on rock, then
for six piers the bed was a layer of hard material resting on
silt, and from the twenty-second pier northward there was
sand, with occasional beds of gravel mixed with boulders.
Here was a site to inspire as much awed patience and care
as the Bridge Friars gave untiringly to the Pont Saint-
Esprit over the Rhône. Yet in Mr. Stewart's description
there is but one emotion—a quiet self-confidence, as if the
forces of Nature were as easy to manage as well-trained
poodle dogs.

II

TO be brief, it is evident that the bridge-building of modern times—from the Renaissance to our own day—has been nothing more than a long series of experiments from which a good many important matters have been excluded. High artistic qualities were divorced from military forethought by the earlier pontists of the Renaissance; * then came the delicate swagger of a fidgety dilettantism, like that which built the Palladian Bridge in Prior Park, about A.D. 1750; afterwards, by degrees, the industrial spirit began to assert itself; and in 1779 the first metal bridge was built in Europe. How different the history would have been, how much saner and finer, if bridge-builders had taken for their guide the all-sufficient principle that their work must be self-protective, not vulnerable and defenceless. From this principle the most wonderful varied work could have been evolved, generation after generation. By this time there would have been as much difference between an Elizabethan bridge and a modern stone bridge, as between Drake's "Golden Hind" and a super-Dreadnought. But the sedulous ape has been active everywhere; and Europe to this day is proud when she builds in stone a few bridges

* Examples: See the index under the headings "Trezzo," "Ticino," "Pavia," and "Ammanati's Trinità at Florence."

that seem to be as good as their classic foreparents, though they break away from the classic principle of self-defence.

It is in metal bridges alone that we find a virile growth, a genuine evolution ; not often artistic, and as sensitive to bombs as card castles are to a touch from your finger ; but yet a great evolution because it represents modern times. If we could summon to earth the spirits of the greatest bridge - builders—Caius Julius Lacer, Apollodorus of Damascus, Isembert, Bénézet, Ammanati, and several others—they would learn nothing much from our stonework, whereas a metal bridge here and there could not fail to strike awe into these spiritual beholders. Even Lacer would be awed by the colossal newness of the Forth Bridge, whose technical inspiration might have come from Vulcan, the god of furnaces, after his annual festival on the 23rd of August. And cannot you imagine what Bénézet and Isembert would say to each other, in swift, excited French, when they gazed up and up at the airy film of road suspended over the wide Menai Straits ? This would be enough to convince them that a few recent bridge-builders had forsaken ancient forms in order to give expression to generative ideas.

The concept of metal bridges may have come to Europe from China. In the seventeenth century Kircher saw and described a Chinese bridge which seems to have been a genuine suspension bridge of metal, a true forerunner of the Pont de la Caille, over the Pass of Usses, and of the immense Pont de Beaucaire, which in four spans unites

PONT DE TOURS—A FAMOUS BRIDGE OF THE XVIII CENTURY.
IT IS IN KEEPING WITH THE SPIRIT OF WATTEAU

Beaucaire to Tarascon, covering a distance of more than
438 metres.* Who can explain why backward China has
hit upon many fertile ideas before the more enterprising
nations? Why has she not learnt to rule the world? Perhaps her body has been too numerous for her brain. On my
table lies the photograph of a bridge which may be similar
to the one admired by Athanase Kircher. It is an iron
swing bridge in Western China, near Auhsien. There are
three piers, two of stone, and the other a makeshift of two
timber piles joined together at top by a log upon which the
footway rests. The carpentry of the footway is primitive :
across the long bearing beams, which are not at all thick or
heavy, a great many slim laths lie unevenly; and up the
middle of the bridge, from end to end, is a narrow path
made with long and flat planks which rest upon the trans-

---

* See Degrand's "Ponts en Maçonnerie," Tom. 2, p. 24, note 3. See also
Dalquié's translation of Kircher's book, published at Amsterdam in 1670. There is
a reference to iron in a bridge on p. 288, but Degrand's information must be taken
from the following passage : " L'on voit un pont dans la Province de Junnan, qu'on a
basti sur un torrent, lequel roule ses flots impetueux dans le panchant d'une profonde
vallée. C'est un commun sentiment qu'il fût basti en l'an 65 après la naissance de
Jesus Christ par l'ordre de l'Empereur Mingus, sorti de la famille Hame ; il n'est pas
fait de brique ny de pierre ; mais on a attaché de grosses chaisnes [chaînes] à ces deux
montagnes qui vont d'une extremité à l'autre, au dessus desquelles on a mis des ais
pour faciliter le passage des voyageurs. Ce pont, qui a vingt chaisnes, a 20 perches
de long qui font 140 pieds : l'on dit que quand beaucoup de personnes passent
dessus, ou qu'il y a quelque grand fardeau, il branle si fort qu'il fait peur à ceux qui
y sont " (p. 289). This description is vivid, and M. Degrand regards the chains as
chains of iron. He says : " Kircher mentionne l'existence . . . d'un pont composé
de chaînes de fer supportant, en travers d'une vallée profonde, un tablier en charpente
d'une grande longueur, c'est-à-dire un véritable pont suspendu, ayant précédé sans
doute de plusieurs siècles les ponts du même genre construits à l'époque moderne en
Europe et aux États-Unis."

verse timbering. As for the iron suspension, it is a chain of thick and short rods which are linked firmly together. These rods, thus looped at each end and interlocked, run in two lines from abutment to abutment, making a sort of parapet at each side of the bridge. Bamboo rods suspend the footway to the iron chains, which pass over the abutments to be fastened securely on the ground.

There are four abutments, but my photograph shows only one; and it omits also the main thing of all—the means by which the metal chains are anchored. Still, the abutment is entertaining. It is a stone pillar about five feet high, perhaps a little more or less; it seems to be old, and from two holes pierced through it we learn that several experiments were made before the right leverage was obtained. The first hole was too low down, so another was drilled about 12 inches above it, and through this second hole the chain was passed, then tugged down to its anchorage. Even then the suspension was not effective, the hole or "saddle" being still not high enough above the footway, and the builders knew not what to do. Not only was there insufficient space for a third hole, but very few makers of suspension bridges have been reasonable enough to pass their metal chains *over the summits* of stone pillars and towers. The Chinese workmen at Auhsien were not more foolish than many European engineers have been, for their perforated pillars are not a bit worse than the perforated towers through which suspension chains pass at Clifton and at Budapest, not to mention many other familiar examples.

So determined were the Chinese to overcome their difficulties without using the summit of their pillar, that they cut away the stone until they came to the second hole or saddle, and then they thrust a lump of iron under the taut chain. Next, to increase the tension still more, they put up a smaller pillar perhaps a yard from the first one, forcing it under the iron rods, which at this point strain downward to their anchorage. Curiously enough, the lesser pillar—a sort of understudy—is used as an architect would employ it : along the top a groove is hollowed, and the chain rests in the groove and then dips down at a sharp angle. Perhaps, then, the smaller pillar is fairly new, while the larger one is old.

The Rev. O. M. Jackson* knows this bridge very well ; he lived for five years at Auhsien, and on one occasion the whole bridge was washed away by a spate. For months the iron chains lay here and there on the river-bed ; and as floods are frequent, and the bridge is not a high one, very little of the workmanship has had a chance of growing hoar. The pillars have the best chance ; and I suppose the iron chains are worth saving from the river whenever the bridge is reconstructed.

I have lingered over Auhsien Suspension Bridge not because of its craftsmanship, but because it marks a primitive phase in the evolution of metal bridges. Perhaps the example seen by Kircher was less rude ; and perhaps the principle of its construction may have been precisely like

* See Index for other references to Mr. Jackson.

that in the bamboo swing bridges of Western China. In these there are four huge cables of twisted bamboo*: two of them carry the footway, while the upper ones serve a double purpose: a strong netting on each side braces them to the lower cables, giving another support to the footway, and forming a sort of hammock a good deal taller than an average man. It is within this deep hammock that everybody walks across a bamboo swing bridge, which in a high wind is as enjoyable as a rowing-boat. At each abutment there is a gabled entrance gate, where the four cables are screwed up.† Displace the bamboo cables for iron chains, and we get at once, perhaps, an idea of the bridge that Kircher regarded as "merveilleux."

As Kircher's book was published in 1670, an iron bridge ought to have been built in Europe before the middle of the eighteenth century. An attempt to build one was made in 1755 at Lyons, but it failed. An arch was put together in a builder's yard and then the project was abandoned as too costly! But the idea was handed on somehow to an English ironmaster, Abraham Darby, of Coalbrookdale, who in 1779 won a great success by bridging the Severn with a very useful arch of cast-iron, having a rise of 50 feet, and a span of 100 ft. 6 ins. The cost of it is not known, but the weight

---

* Marco Polo describes very well how the bamboo in China is twisted or plaited into cordage. He says: "They have canes of the length of fifteen paces, which they split, in their whole length, into very thin pieces, and these, by twisting them together, they form into ropes three hundred paces long. So skilfully are they manufactured, that they are equal in strength to cordage made of hemp."

† I take this description from two photographs belonging to the Church Missionary Society.

of metal employed was 378½ tons. The design is bold, and the arch handsome. Every pontist should get a photograph of Coalbrookdale Bridge. Already it is out of date, and its value as history will not save it from destruction.

A few years later, in 1796, Rowland Burdon followed the example set by Abraham Darby, but not as a mere copyist, his Wearmouth Bridge being an arch of open cast-iron panels, which act as voussoirs. The span is 236 feet, with a rise of 34 feet; the springings are 95 feet above the river-bed; at first the footway was rather narrow, but in 1858 it was widened by Robert Stephenson. Rowland Burdon used 260 tons of iron, and his work cost only £27,000.

Soon afterwards, in a great cast-iron arch thrown over the Spey, Telford made new experiments, and, as Professor Fleeming Jenkin has said, his bridge at Craigellachie marked "a great advance in the conception of what was the safest form in which to apply cast-iron to an arch." But more than this was expected from an engineer of Telford's reputation, and nothing more came from him, unfortunately. In fact, Telford divorced his work from the good sense of good design, which Darby and Burdon had endeavoured to respect. At each abutment he put up a silly tower pierced with arrow-slits and armed with battlements, advertising a farce of warlike make-believe which scores of foolish engineers would copy and adapt, while leaving their bridges entirely unfortified.

A bridge here and there is supposed to be all right.

Take, for instance, the Forth Bridge, with his 51,000 tons of steel, and his amazing cost, about £3,000,000; he is looked upon as a "safe" bridge, and safe he is if we forget what bombs and shells can do in a few seconds. At each end of this bridge the railway is carried by trivial columns forming the approach viaducts, and these a naval gun would blow to smithereens. A bomb falling upon them from an airship might put the whole bridge out of action. Further, the columns are comically out of scale with those gigantic pyramids of steel bars which counterbalance the centre girders, and yet seem to play at leapfrog in two bounds of 1710 ft. each, and in two lesser jumps of 680 ft. each. Yes, the Forth Bridge looks formidably alive and active; he is to modern engineering what the Ichthyosaurus became to our knowledge of prehistoric animals: a semi-marine colossus, fit to be kept for ever as a tremendous danger happily extinct.

Several years ago, in the "Builder," I drew attention to the defenceless character of this huge viaduct over a strategic waterway, and now I return to this topic at the beginning of a war that may well be the most terrible in all history. To-day is the 3rd of August, 1914; and the world knows that Germany has occupied Luxemburg, a neutral State, has poured her troops into Belgium, the naval key of Great Britain, and has violated the French frontier without declaring war. Here is the swift "morality" of lightning. In the strategy of war, non-moral Powers may gain over us a horrible advantage. England talks so much about peace and honour that felon Germany is able to plan at her ease great military movements of surprise as fateful as victories on stricken fields. Before this little book is published " the black bullets of Destiny " will have been cast in several countries; and not a battle will be won, nor a skirmish fought, without either help or hindrance from those soldiers unprepared that we call viaducts and bridges. Already many have been blown up in Belgium and in Servia; and by night and day, throughout Europe, men are trying to guard every bridge of vital importance to the concentration of troops. Here in England this protection is not always as alert and thorough as it ought to be. I am writing in Hampshire, near by the main line from Aldershot; within a walk of three minutes there is a high railway bridge over a road, and a few hours ago it was unguarded from the road. Yesterday evening, after dark, a German spy could have destroyed it, for I passed under its vault and found no one keeping watch and ward.* Instead, I encountered that supine national folly which has withheld our young men from national service, because of the rich liberty which we are supposed to get somehow from cooing claptrap, and Norman Angells, and the future pacification of mankind.

Whatever this fateful war may bring to us and to others, the defenceless bridge will have to be reconsidered; and for this reason its evolution attracts me even now, despite the darkling uncertainty that encompasses every hour of the day. The Forth Bridge, all shatterable bulk and no beauty

* On the 4th of August this important bridge was guarded by Territorials.

and grace, does full justice to our industrialism, but yet he belongs, not to the public spirit of Great Britain, but to the spirit of the age everywhere; for in other lands he has a great many rivals not a whit less huge and vulnerable. As an example, we will take the Illinois and St. Louis Bridge, really a fine work of his kind, dating from 1873. He crosses the Mississippi, which at St. Louis flows in a single channel 534 yards wide and 8 feet deep at extreme low water. The greatest range between high and low water is 41 feet. There are three ribbed arches of cast steel, the middle one with a span of 520 feet, while the others are 18 feet narrower. If it was worth while for the sake of public convenience to erect this great highway above a wide and dangerous river, it was also worth while for the sake of public convenience that the width of the arches should be determined by the probable dangers to which the bridge would be exposed in commercial strikes and in other wars. Human gunpowder is not a rare thing in the United States of America. The black race there has a population that increases rapidly, and some day it may breed a great soldier, a dark Napoleon, who will find it no difficult task to organise a widespread society of bridge-wreckers. No truisms are more common than unexpected events. Let us then ask whether it would be possible swiftly to repair a metal arch having a span of 520 feet. If not, why build a huge and costly structure with steel-ribbed arches which are much too wide? What if one of them was destroyed at a time when the double railway track over the river, and the wide road-

ON THE TARN AT MILLAU IN SOUTHERN FRANCE. THIS DRAWING, A COMPANION PICTURE TO GIRTIN'S "BRIDGNORTH," REPRESENTS THE BROKEN END OF AN OLD BRIDGE WITH A MILL BUILT ON IT; BEHIND IS AN ARCH OF THE NEW BRIDGE

way above for other traffic, were necessary to bring reinforcements to a stricken army?

These questions were too unmercantile to be considered by the chief engineer, Captain James B. Eads, a very scientific person, who was entirely of a piece with our European pontists. Not a scrap of attention did he pay to military matters. Every account of Captain Eads and his bridge bombards us with technical details. We are expected to gape with admiration because £60 per ton of 2000 lbs. was the price paid for 2500 tons of cast-steel. Wrought-iron in a ton of 2000 lbs. cost £40, and 500 tons at this price were used. Rolled-iron in a ton of 2000 lbs. cost £28, and 1000 tons at this price were employed, together with 200 tons of cast-iron at £16 per ton, the ton in this case being 2240 lbs. Here indeed is a golden target for bombs and for modern artillery!

Every bridge in the United States of America is a target of this sort in one form or another. There are bonfire timber bridges, for example, exceedingly deft and excessively high; sometimes their piers are nothing more than large wooden frames piled one on top of another, up and up and up, till at last they are tall enough to be known as great sky-ticklers. One example is 234 feet high. It is the great Portage Bridge spanning the Genesee River, in the State of New York, on a railroad between New York and Buffalo. It looks like a miracle of carpentry, this wonderful bridge of frames; its length is 240 metres, and the piers—sixteen romantic scaffoldings—form immense triangles with flat-

tened summits upon which a double gallery rests as a firm
support for the railway. Each scaffolding rises from a pile
of masonry nine metres higher than water-level, so that
floods do not break their force against the timber frames.
Good heavens above, how this bridge would burn! But it
has a quite modern fascination: its cost of production was
cheap!—cheap in comparison with the estimated price of a
stone bridge with the same length and aviated height. This
wooden structure cost about £36,000, for the pride of trade
likes to pay as little as possible for the largest amount
of very perishable insecurity.

Then, of course, there are sky-tickling metal bridges, and
these spindle-shanked devotees of peace are popular also in
Canada. All this work is nothing but industrial engineering, like the mighty bridges at New York, though these do
try to look somewhat architectural. One specimen, indeed,
a vast structure called the New Manhattan Bridge, has
marvellously long suspension cables which do *not* go *through*
a tower or gateway; they actually pass *over* their supports
in a logical manner. What a blessing! On the other hand,
Brooklyn Bridge at New York has the same mistake as
our suspension bridge at Clifton (p. 346); and the pierced
towers, each with two lancet-shaped openings, are affected
and trivial. Brooklyn Bridge has a total length of nearly
1141 yards, and between the two towers there is a span of
1595 feet. The roadway is upheld by four galvanised steel
cables not less than sixteen inches in diameter. Think of
that! Try to imagine a span 1595 feet wide! Suppose an

airship crippled it with some large bombs, how in the world could repairs be made?

Briefly, then, modern bridges everywhere are anti-social. When war is afoot, they imperil the best-made plans of strategists; and even in strikes they have to be guarded by soldiers, as if they were convents where dethroned queens lived unhappily with suffragette princesses. Though we have lived for many years on the brink of war, every highway in Europe as in America is at the mercy of bridge-wreckers. Is it not dumbfounding that no respect has been paid anywhere to the social guardianship that bridges and roads ought to perform? Why has this all-important matter been forgotten? It has been made memorable a great many times in history, ever since Horatius Cocles and his two companions held the Pons Sublicius against the whole Etruscan Army under Porsena,—a lesson never forgotten by Roman citizens.

When Lord Surrey, before the battle of Flodden Field, outwitted the Scotch by throwing his army across the Till by the beautiful old Twizel Bridge; or when Charles the Second, routed at Worcester, fled by Old Pershore Bridge into the Bredon Hills, England received one of many warnings that a secure passage over rivers might be to her at any moment as valuable as an army corps. Why has she failed to take this lesson to heart? No railway is protected by two or three branch lines over an important river, so that two or three bridges—not near together, but separated by a mile or two—would have to be destroyed before the river would be closed to the passage of troops and of food supplies. Understudy lines and bridges would be invaluable to defensive strategy.

More than a century has gone over since Perronet warned France that bridges across great rivers ought to be of a kind which would facilitate makeshift repairs after mishaps in war. He spoke earnestly, but in vain ; for the conception of trade as war had not yet been forced upon the world by modernised industrialism, with its civil strikes and its international competitions. If Perronet had been able to add his foresight to the great traditions of the *Ponts et Chaussées*, his countrymen, probably, would have been loyal to his excellent advice, because the French have a Roman logic and they love their roads and bridges. But in France, as in other countries, a craze for engineering feats took possession of the public mind, excluding many other considerations. I know not how many perishable bridges exist at this moment in France, but I can give the figures for 1873. In that year there were one thousand nine hundred and eighty-two. Their total length was 106 kilometres, and their total cost was 286,507,761 francs. Here are some of the more expensive examples :—

(1) Pont de Bordeaux, 501 metres ; 6,850,000 francs.

(2) Pont de Roanne, 232 metres ; 6,438,561 francs.

(3) Paris, Pont d'Jéna, 6,135,105 francs.

(4) Pont Saint-Esprit, on the Rhône, 4,500,000 francs.

(5) Pont de Libourne, on the Dordogne, 4,236,248 francs.

(6) Tours, on the Loire, 434 metres ; 4,224,639 francs.

(7) Paris, Pont Neuf, 231 metres ; 4,000,000 francs.

Compare these figures with those of some British bridges :—

(1) The hideous Britannia Bridge over the Menai Straits, 1511 feet long, cost £601,865.

(2) Westminister Bridge, London, 1160 feet; £235,000, or £202 per foot run.

(3) Boyne, 550 feet ; £140,000, about £254 per foot run.

(4) Southwark Bridge, London, built in 1819, £800,000 ; it contains 5780 tons of iron.

(5) Vauxhall Bridge, London, built in 1816, £300,000.

(6) New London Bridge, 1005 feet long, £1,458,311.

(7) Forth Bridge, about £3,000,000.

We see, then, that the bridges of civilization, when viewed merely as financial investments, are valuable enough to be made self-defensive.* Yet it happens that I am the only writer who has tried to draw public attention to the ease with which any bridge in England could be crippled. And the trouble is that engineers hold the field, because the man of business finds in their work a hard routine that looks practical and mercantile. What we need is the influence of architects. For capable architects have the genius of artists, and when artists give their minds to practical affairs they show a range of common sense that men of trade rarely

---

* Not *all* bridges should be military, of course, since those near a frontier may have to be destroyed at a moment's notice in order to check the advance of a surprise attack.

equal. It is in their nature to look at a question from all sides till they see it amply and as a whole, while men of trade isolate two or three things from many, and accept them tenaciously as the only things that merit attention.

But in our social life and strife there are certain newcomers that will compel the world to reconsider its wrong attitude to bridge-building. I refer to airships and to aviation, with their threatened wars from overhead. A good many bridges over strategical waterways can be displaced by tunnels, but many others must be armoured with cone-shaped roofs. Art and science have done wonderful things for the modern battleship, and now—now they must invent and perfect a new battle-bridge, fit to protect arterial highways from " progress."

* * * * * * * *

It is the morning of the 4th of August, and I have just read the latest war news. The whole life of Europe is a note of interrogation, infinitely sinister and tragic. What is destined to happen? Which nations are doomed to perish? What navy will go down into the deep? Which airmen will make the most successful attacks on those bridges that govern the distribution of food supplies? Will the equity of Europe triumph, or will German felony succeed?

* * * * * * * *

Three months have passed, and I add a few lines to my page proofs. Many events have illustrated and confirmed the main arguments of this monograph. Everywhere defenceless bridges have been the cause of much anxiety, and dozens have been destroyed because they could not be turned into rearguard defences. Wellington said that his sappers in five minutes could blow up a modern bridge. In the present campaign sappers have done this work under fire, mining strategic highways being a simple job. How ludicrously tragic is the contrast between the building of a modern bridge and its easy demolition! A little common sense would have flanked each entrance with a Brialmont fort, and would have given to the bridge itself an armoured efficiency. Every bridge between the French frontiers and Paris ought to have been as effective as a super-Dreadnought. So the use of battleship steel in bridge-building is one thing that engineers must consider with the utmost care after Germany has been overthrown. If they do no more than follow their foolish old routine, then their work will be a crime against patriotism.

In other respects the Great War has been a wondrous varied surprise, bringing weakness to the strong and power to the weak. Germany has been humbled both by little Belgium and by the little British army; her prestige has dwindled so much that fighting mechanisms are regarded no longer as superior to fighting men. In true discipline there is an art of humane pride, and Germany has crushed it out of her automatic battalions, preferring an organised cruelty as insensitive as a railway accident, and a system of lying that rivals Munchausen's. Even her learned professors fill current history with explosive lies, just as her seamen before the declaration of hostilities dropped mines in the North Sea from trawlers that flew the British flag. If victory could be won by vile misdeeds, Germany would be unconquerable. Never before has a powerful nation been so corrupted by forty years of unscrupulous vainglory. Her ambition is to Europe what cancer is to a human body—a ravaging disease which may break out again after the best surgeons have finished their work. Already she has tried to postpone the operation by making overtures to stop the necessary bloodshed. Germany wants to give in before the British Empire can put a million troops in the field, because she knows not only that Allies often quarrel during the negotiations that rearrange maps, but that such quarrels occur most often when a great country has a little army in absolute antagonism with widespread interests of a vital sort. And this, moreover, is not the only peril. In the British Isles many thousands of peace-fanatics bide their time; some of them are active already as pro-Germans; many others declare that they have no wish to humble the German people, who now approve every act of a Hunnish despotism elaborated by their Government; and when our British sentimentalists, aided by several Radical newspapers, begin a campaign of shrieking claptrap, a just resentment will be felt by France and Russia. So the warfare of diplomacy may be more dangerous to the Allies than the warfare of stricken fields. We must wait and see. But the present position confirms another argument in this monograph : namely, that those who decline to see the perpetual strife that reigns in all human affairs, and who babble in a routine of fixed ideas about the illusion called peace, are quite as perilous to a country as were the creeds of bloodshed which many German writers advertised, taking liberties with the in- genuous pacifism coddled by British Governments.

Let us delete from every dictionary the lying word peace ; and let us believe firmly in the simple truth that strife everywhere is the historian of life. The strife in all its phases ought to be well trained and chivalric, of course ; and it needs vast improvements in the campaigns of business warfare. Every slum, for example, is very much worse than the longest battle with firearms, because it endures for ages ; and what chivalry in the wars of trade is as noble as that which grants to young men the privilege of defending the old age of their country from danger and dishonour ?

RAIN

APPENDICES

APPENDIX I

CHINESE GABLED BRIDGES

MARCO POLO found them in several places, particularly in Hang-cheu, the ancient capital of Southern China. This noble city has on one side the Si-hu, or western lake, and on the other is the vast river Tsien-tang-kiang, which at high tide is nearly four miles in width. Its waters are distributed by canals through every quarter of Hang-cheu, so that many bridges are necessary. Towards the end of the thirteenth century, when Marco Polo made visits to Hang-cheu (which he described as Kin-sai, or the "celestial city"), bridges over the canals were so frequent that popular opinion, glad to show off an Oriental exaggeration, declared their number to be twelve thousand, though a census had not been taken. "Those which are thrown over the principal canals," says Polo, "and are connected with the main streets, have arches so high, and built with so much skill, that vessels with their masts can pass under them, whilst, at the same time, carts and horses are passing over their heads,—so well is the slope from the streets adapted to the height of the arch." And another early traveller, P. Le Comte, with graphic brevity, writes as follows of the grand canal : "Outre ces digues, on a basti une infinité de ponts pour la communication des terres : ils sont de trois, de cinq, et de sept arches ; celle du milieu est extraordinairement haute, afin que les barques en passant ne soient pas obligées d'abaisser leurs masts " ("Nouv. Mém. de la Chine," Tom. 1, p. 161). There is also a description written by Barrow, who visited Hang-cheu before 1830, and

365

whose testimony confirms that of much earlier travellers.   Barrow
was impressed by "a great variety of bridges" that spanned most
of the canals.   Some had "piers of such an extraordinary height,
that the largest vessels, of two hundred tons, sailed under them
without striking their masts."   Last of all, in recent photographs
the stone bridges of China are steep whenever they are built with
arches, so we can follow the Chinese gabled bridge from our own
time to the thirteenth century.   They came into use partly because
they were convenient to shipping, and partly because they could be
erected from low embankments.

APPENDIX II

STEEP ROMAN BRIDGES

YOUNG pontists are always eager to know whether the Romans built gabled bridges, setting an example both to the East and to the West. On this topic there is little evidence, for most of the Roman bridges were built of timber. At Rimini, in the famous bridge of Augustus, there is an ascent at each end over the abutment, and at Alcantarilla, near Utrera, in Andalusia, the Roman bridge may be described as hog-backed. It crosses the Salado, a tributary of the Guadalquivir. Recently Mr. Edgar Wigram visited Alcantarilla, and he writes to me as follows :—

" The Roman bridge there is most interesting, almost untouched by restoration, yet it remains serviceable. It is a hog-backed structure of two arches, each about thirty-five feet in span ; the width between the parapets may be fifteen feet, but a swarm of bees happened to be merry on the bridge, so I did not try to take accurate measurements. The voussoirs and spandrils are of stone with hammer-dressed faces, while the soffits are formed with wedge-shaped blocks of concrete, and a certain amount of brick is found in the piers. Along the river on one side are remains of an embankment. A tower stands at one end of the bridge, placed centrally to it, so the road has to make a double turn to pass. One wall of the tower is destroyed, but the other three are still about half their original height. The lower courses are of big stone blocks, while the upper part of the faces are filled in with 'tapia' concrete ; the angles (or at least the two which still remain intact) are grooved with a queer circular recess some twelve inches in diameter. What purpose these grooves can have served I do not know. They look as if they may have been intended to accommodate the hinge-posts of gates; but a gate hung in them would hardly swing through ninety degrees. If a second tower ever existed, its foundations do not appear above ground-level. At Córdova there is only one tower, and it stands in a very similar position. By analogy, then, we may suppose that a second tower was not built at Alcantarilla; yet the grooved angles seem to require a corresponding tower with corresponding grooves, if gates were ever swung from them. Perhaps the grooves formed pivots for some sort of defensive engine, such as the 'iron hand' of Archimedes, which seems to have been some sort of great grappling crane. The angles of a tower would be fit places to plant a weapon of this description; but we need help from an expert in ancient military engineering."

INDEX AND GLOSSARY

INDEX AND GLOSSARY

of stone or brick. They differ from metal and from wooden arches, inasmuch as the compressed arc of materials called the *ring* is built of a number of separate pieces having little or no cohesion. Each separate stone used in building the *ring* has received the name of *voussoir*, or archstone. The lower surface of the ring is called the *soffit* of the arch. The *joints*, or bed-joints, are the surfaces separating the voussoirs, and are normal to the soffit. A brick arch is usually built in numerous rings, so that it cannot be conceived as built of voussoirs with plane joints passing straight through the ring. The bed-joints of a brick arch may be considered as stepped and interlocked. This interlocking will affect the stability of the arch only in those cases where one voussoir tends to slip along its neighbour. The *ring* springs from a course of stones in the abutments, called *quoins*. The plane of demarcation between the ring and the abutment is called the *springing* of the arch. The *crown* of an arch is the summit of the ring. The voussoirs at the crown are called *keystones*. The *haunches* of an arch are the parts midway between the springing and the crown. The upper surface of the ring is sometimes improperly called the extrados, and the lower surface is more properly called the intrados. These terms, when properly employed, have reference to a mathematical theory of the arch little used by engineers. The walls which rest upon the ring along the arch, and rise either to the parapet or to the roadway, are called *spandrils*. There are necessarily two outer spandrils forming the faces of a bridge ; there may be one or more inner spandrils. The *backing* of an arch is the masonry above the haunches of the ring ; it is carried back between the spandrils to the pier or to the abutment. If the backing is not carried up to the roadway, as is seldom the case, the rough material employed between the backing and the roadway is called the *filling*. The *parapet* rests on the outer *spandrils*."

2 D